Grade 6

Home-School Connection

Macmillan
McGraw-Hill

Credits: pages 475, 476

A

The *McGraw·Hill* Companies

 **Macmillan
McGraw-Hill**

Published by Macmillan/McGraw-Hill, of McGraw-Hill Education, a division of The McGraw-Hill
Companies, Inc., Two Penn Plaza, New York, New York 10121-2298.

Printed in the United States of America

2 3 4 5 6 7 8 9 079 10 09 08 07 06

Contents

Beginning of the Year Letter
in English and Spanish

● On-Level Books

● On-Level Books

Dear Family Member:

You can help your child practice reading skills taught at school. Working together you and your child can become partners in learning.

Each week your child will bring home:

- A **letter** that tells you about the book the class is reading that week

- Three **homework activities** that will improve reading skills and offer practice with words your child is learning

- A **story** for the two of you to read together

Your interest, praise, and encouragement are sure to lead to your child's success.

Queridos familiares:

Con su ayuda, su niño/a puede practicar las destrezas de lectura aprendidas en la escuela. Este trabajo conjunto les permitirá ser compañeros de aprendizaje.

Cada semana, su niño/a va a llevar a casa lo siguiente:

- Una **carta** contándole acerca lo que ha leído en clase durante esa semana.

- Tres **actividades de tareas para el hogar** para mejorar las destrezas de lectura y practicar las palabras que está aprendiendo.

- También llevará a casa un **cuento** para que lo lean juntos.

Su interés, apoyo y estímulo guiarán a su niño/a al éxito.

Word Workout

WORDS TO KNOW

abruptly	anxiety	cascade	conscious
engulf	intersection	procedure	souvenir

Don't Say a Word Let's take turns choosing a word. When I choose a word, I will give you one-word clues, but I won't say the word itself. Can you guess my secret word? How many clues will you need?

SPELLING WORDS

gram	clash	dense	dread	prank
strict	drill	swan	prod	shrunk
scuff	clutch	threat	dwell	fund
text	rank	brink	mock	plaid

Sort and Spell Read each word that has an **a** in it and I will spell the word. I'll make mistakes now and then. You can correct me when I'm wrong. Repeat for the other vowels **e, i, o,** and **u.** There are three list words that have two vowels. Make sure I spell these tricky words correctly.

© Macmillan/McGraw-Hill

·····(fold here)·····

Home-School Connection

Dear Family Member:

This week we are reading part of the novel *The Summer of the Swans*. It tells how a brother and sister work together to find their little brother Charlie when he gets lost in a forest. It is a tense search that challenges their persistence and faith. We learn a lot about the sister's personality during the search. The author uses the elements of fiction to create a thrilling and satisfying plot.

This Week's Skills

Comprehension: character, setting, and plot

Vocabulary: words with more than one meaning

Spelling/phonics: vowels

Name _____

Story Charts

We can use the charts to tell our own quick stories.

Directions

- Choose a character, setting, and problem from each box.
- Then try to tell a story that tells what happens.
- Your story can be believable or ridiculous.

Character
sixth grader
singer
baseball player
movie director
veterinarian
politician

Setting
swimming pool
doctor's office
sports field
car stuck in traffic
rainy day in the woods
shopping mall

Problem
dangerous weather
something is lost
fight with a friend
caught lying
a promise is broken
afraid to do something

What happens in your story? What are the main events?

How will your character solve the problem?

Is your story realistic or ridiculous? Is it believable or outrageous?

Ejercicio de palabras

PALABRAS DE VOCABULARIO

abruptly   anxiety   cascade   conscious

engulf   intersection procedure   souvenir

No digas nada Vamos a turnarnos para escoger una palabra. Cuando yo escoja una palabra, te daré pistas de una sola palabra. ¿Puedes adivinar mi palabra secreta? ¿Cuántas pistas necesitarás?

PALABRAS DE ORTOGRAFÍA

gram   clash   dense   dread   prank

strict   drill   swan   prod   shrunk

scuff   clutch   threat   dwell   fund

text   rank   brink   mock   plaid

Clasifica y deletrea Lee cada palabra que tenga una a; y yo las deletrearé. De vez en cuando voy a cometer algún error. Tú debes corregirme. Vamos a hacer lo mismo con el resto de las vocales: **e, i, o** y **u**. En la lista hay tres palabras que tienen dos vocales. Asegúrate de que yo las deletree bien.

(fold here)

Conexión con el hogar

Queridos familiares:

Esta semana estamos leyendo parte de la novela *The Summer of the Swans.* Cuenta cómo un hermano y una hermana colaboran para encontrar a su hermano pequeño, Charlie, que se pierde en el bosque. Es una tensa búsqueda que desafía la perseverancia y la lealtad de los hermanos. Aprendemos mucho de la personalidad de la hermana durante la búsqueda. La autora usa los elementos de la ficción para crear un argumento vívido y convincente.

Destrezas de la semana

Comprensión: personajes, ambiente y argumento

Vocabulario: palabras con más de un significado

Ortografía/Fonética: vocales

Nombre_____

Tablas de cuentos

Podemos usar las tablas siguientes para crear nuestros propios cuentos.

- Escoge un personaje, un ambiente y un problema de cada tabla.
- Trata de contar un cuento para narrar qué pasa.
- Tu cuento puede ser creíble o totalmente absurdo.

Character
sixth grader
singer
baseball player
movie director
veterinarian
politician

Setting
swimming pool
doctor's office
sports field
car stuck in traffic
rainy day in the woods
shopping mall

Problem
dangerous weather
something is lost
fight with a friend
caught lying
a promise is broken
afraid to do something

What happens in your story? What are the main events?

How will your character solve the problem?

Is your story realistic or ridiculous? Is it believable or outrageous?

Comprehension Check

Summarize

Use the Plot Chart to help you retell *Rachel's Choice.* Explain how the purple flower helped Rachel find Claude.

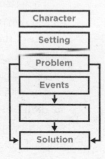

Character

Setting

Problem

Events

↓

↓

Solution

Think and Compare

1. In Chapter 1, Rachel is enjoying her ride with Lucky. What happens to change the mood of the story? *(Analyze Character, Plot, Setting)*

2. Rachel decided to search for Claude on her own. Do you think she made the right decision? What would you have done in her place? *(Evaluate)*

3. How did Rachel work as part of a team as well as independently? *(Analyze)*

© 2007 Macmillan/McGraw-Hill

Rachel's Choice

by Sarah Glasscock

illustrated by Dan Krovatin

Table of Contents

CHAPTER 1

Oil And Dogs Don't Mix

Lucky sidestepped impatiently once the saddle was cinched tightly. Using the wooden fence as a ladder, Rachel swung into the saddle. She twitched the reins, and Lucky trotted across the pasture. The grass was so tall that it swept Rachel's boots as she rode.

Rachel couldn't believe how quickly the summer had passed. School would be starting in another week. Soon, instead of taking afternoon rides in the California hills, she'd be learning French and algebra. Rachel remembered the beginning of the last school year. Just walking by the geometry classroom had filled her with anxiety. It was easy now to laugh about how worried she'd been.

Luckily, her friend Abra had been in the same geometry class. She'd helped Rachel really understand lines and angles.

They struggled to the top of the embankment and looked down into the pond. In the moonlight, the surface of the water had a strange shine. Whining, Scratch ran around the pond. Rachel followed his movements and saw a shape in the water.

The water in the pond was up to Claude's chin. He didn't answer when they called and didn't stir when they splashed into the water. Only when Tom touched his neck did Claude open his eyes. "I was afraid I was dreaming," he said, "Dreaming about being rescued. I'd have gotten out of here myself, but I think my leg's broken." Sheriff Claxton told Claude that help was on the way. After the ambulance arrived and took Claude away, Rachel finally relaxed.

A week later, Rachel watched workers from the oil company continue to clean up the oil spill. It was hard to imagine that a small hole in the pipe had created such a huge mess. The hole had been repaired, but the pond was being drained and the soil carted away.

The sun glinted off an oil-soaked rock. Rachel picked it up for a souvenir. She wanted something to remind her of what had happened to the pond. Rachel tore a sheet of paper out of her small notebook that she now carried everywhere and carefully wrapped up the stained rock. Claude's leg was healing. She and Abra were grounded for two weeks, but they were still best friends. They were still a team.

Sheriff Claxton and Vicky followed the pipeline to the west. Rachel, Abra, and Tom headed east. They all took turns calling for Claude and Scratch. Hoot owls answered them, and coyotes called to them.

Rachel suddenly felt tired and discouraged. When they approached the steep side of a pond, she didn't think she'd be able to climb it. Dirt began to cascade down the slope toward them. The beam of Tom's flashlight caught Scratch. The dog's frantic movements were sending dirt and rocks down the slope.

Yesterday Abra had confessed that she was nervous about taking biology. Rachel hoped she could return the favor and help Abra in biology.

Lucky stopped abruptly. Her head rose as she smelled the air. Rachel had learned to pay attention to Lucky's sudden stops. If she didn't, she'd be sure to miss something important.

With her ears twitching, Lucky neighed as if she were responding to a voice. Then, in the distance, Rachel heard a dog barking. "Scratch—come here, boy!" Rachel called.

Riding toward the sound, Rachel whistled loudly for Scratch. She kept expecting him to come bounding out of the grass at any moment. Of all the neighbors' dogs, Scratch was the friendliest. When his tail wagged in greeting, the rest of his body seemed to wag, too.

The barking grew louder as Rachel and Lucky approached the creek. Rachel hoped that Scratch's owner, Claude Atherton, wasn't trying to fish. Scratch's barking sounded like a broken record. But Rachel couldn't hear Claude telling Scratch to be quiet. Rachel thought that was a little peculiar as Claude and Scratch were inseparable.

There was a loud splash upstream, and a startled blue heron flew out of the creek. Then a muddy shape that Rachel barely recognized bounded up the bank. She didn't think she had ever seen a dirtier dog. Scratch's red-and-white coat was now black and brown. The fur stood out from his body in stiff peaks—and he smelled terrible, too.

The dog rolled over on his back and wiggled his wet body back and forth on the dirt trail. Rachel was glad that she didn't have to groom and clean the filthy dog. But before Rachel could dismount and take a look at Scratch, the dog bolted for home. Rachel frowned. Scratch knew that Rachel invariably gave him a treat so he never ran from her. Scratch was behaving very strangely.

Sheriff Claxton trained her flashlight on Rachel. "I'm sure you have a good reason for doing that and I'd like to know what it is."

The sheriff's voice was calm and steady, but Rachel could tell how upset she was. "Scratch won't take us to Claude if he's on a leash."

"Rachel's right, Mom. Claude trained Scratch to walk on a leash in the pasture. They always walk in a circle, and that's what Scratch always does if he's on a leash—no matter where he is," Abra explained. The sheriff nodded and said that they needed to work in teams.

The sheriff suggested they locate the pipeline and follow it. She studied the map, looked at her compass, and then moved. Everyone hurried after her.

A few minutes later, the sheriff's flashlight shone on a sign: BURIED PIPELINE: CAUTION WHEN DIGGING. BALLARD OIL COMPANY.

CHAPTER 4

Just in Time!

At first Rachel was sure that Scratch would take them immediately to Claude. Then she noticed an apple tree that they had passed before. One of its branches was broken, but the leaves on it were still green. Scratch was leading them in a big circle. Then Rachel realized that's what Scratch always did when Claude put à leash on him.

Rachel stopped, but she didn't want to unhook the leash. What if they couldn't keep up with Scratch when he ran off? Plus, everyone would think she was crazy. If they didn't find Claude, it would be her fault.

She shouted Claude's name as loudly as she could. Scratch joined her with a long, sad howl. But there was no response.

Quickly, before she could change her mind, Rachel unfastened the leash. Scratch bounded away. Shouting, the adults tried to keep their flashlights trained on the dog, but he disappeared into the darkness.

Her curiosity aroused, Rachel trotted through the brush after Scratch. At the Athertons' farm, she found him hiding underneath the back porch. Scratch madly pawed at his fur, desperately trying to get the mud off. Rachel picked up a damp clod of mud. It felt slick and didn't smell like creek mud.

Scratch whined, and Rachel wished she could read the dog's mind. When he continued to whine, she used a treat to lure him out. Once out, Scratch leapt into her lap and covered her jeans and T-shirt with sticky black prints. Scratch lifted his head as Claude drove in the driveway and before Rachel could stand up, Scratch had run to his master. Claude quickly bent down to examine his dog and then he looked at Rachel with a puzzled expression on his face. Rachel began to explain, but Claude held up his hand.

Claude asked Rachel to tell him where she had found Scratch, who was covered with oil as well as mud.

CHAPTER 2

Searching For The Spill

Early the next morning, Rachel helped her mother, Vicky, harvest herbs from the garden. Drops of dew covered the plants and sparkled in the sun. Rachel had learned from her mother that it was best to pick herbs in the morning when their flavor was strongest.

Rachel loved to rub the velvety sage leaves between her fingers. The smell reminded her of turkey and dressing at Thanksgiving.

Suddenly, Vicky snapped her fingers. "I forgot—your dad wants some parsley for the potatoes."

Rachel loved it when her dad, Tom, cooked hash brown potatoes with parsley and onions for breakfast. When she entered the kitchen with the bunch of parsley, her dad was talking on the telephone.

"Why don't you wait till this afternoon, Claude? I can go with you then . . . hello?"

Rachel's Choice

Rachel urged Lucky into a trot. A dark shape leaped out of the trees to their right. Lucky reared, but Rachel held on tightly. The shape began to circle them. Rachel yelled as loudly as she could. All of a sudden, she heard voices everywhere.

Circles of light surrounded Rachel, temporarily blinding her. She was conscious of someone grabbing Lucky's bridle and talking to the horse to calm him down. Rachel recognized her father's voice. "Dad, how did you find me?" Then she remembered why she was here in the first place. "Have you found Claude yet?"

"You are in so much trouble, young lady." Tom helped his daughter to the ground and gave her a hug. "No," he whispered, "we haven't found him yet."

Another pair of hands reached out to hug Rachel. Abra didn't say anything as she held on to her friend. Tom, Vicky, and Sheriff Claxton described how they'd discovered that an old oil pipeline ran across the Montoya property. And then Abra had told them about the finding the flower.

A wet nose nudged Rachel's leg, and she jumped. She felt silly when she realized it was Scratch. "If Scratch is here, then Claude must be near here," Rachel said excitedly.

Sheriff Claxton put a leash on Scratch's collar and then handed it to Rachel. When the dog pulled toward the orchard, everyone followed.

© 2007 Macmillan/McGraw-Hill

Rachel waved the parsley to get her father's attention. She wanted to speak to Claude, but Tom had already hung up the phone. Her father shook his head in exasperation and told her that Claude was determined to find the source of the oil. Her father had tried to persuade Claude to wait for others to help him, but he stubbornly refused.

The veterinarian, Dr. Winters, had examined Scratch yesterday, and Rachel knew the dog would be able to go with Claude. He wouldn't exactly be searching all by himself, but Rachel knew what her father meant. She wished she'd been able to give Claude some idea about where Scratch might have been yesterday.

Later that morning, Vicki went outside while Rachel and Tom cleaned up the kitchen. Vicky's voice came through the back door. "You'll never guess who I found in my herb garden."

"It's not Scratch, is it?" Rachel asked in alarm.

"No, silly, it's me." Abra followed Vicky into the kitchen. "I'm here to help you make pies, as we all know cooking is not your area of expertise."

Rachel followed her mother's procedure for rolling out the piecrust. First she pounded the ball of dough with the rolling pin. Then she began rolling it out, turning it every so often to form a nice circle.

Abra tossed sliced apples with flour, sugar, and spices. She wondered out loud, "We live a hundred miles from the Pacific Ocean. How can there be an oil spill around here?" She squinted at the apple mixture. "I think we're ready for the secret ingredient."

"All right, girls, stand back," Tom ordered as he sprinkled a little bit of chile powder into the mixture.

Vicky gently laid the top crust on the pie and began to crimp the edges. "Somebody could be dumping car oil, or an oil pipeline could be leaking."

Rachel clapped her hands in excitement, and flour flew into the air. She told her parents that she had the solution. All they had to do was follow the pipeline and they'd find the leak. But no one knew where the pipeline started. Then suddenly Abra suggested that they call her mother since she was the local sheriff and might know that information.

It was getting dark and riding past the abandoned farmhouse made Rachel feel uneasy. She called for Scratch and Claude, but there was no answer.

Rachel had no idea where to begin to look for Claude or a pipeline, since she and Abra had only explored the area around the old farmhouse. They hadn't gone into the apple orchard behind the house because it had looked spooky. Now Lucky danced to the side and refused to enter the orchard. Rachel decided to ride around the trees instead of going through them.

In the distance, coyotes began to howl. Rachel's heart began to beat faster. She had hoped that Abra and her mother, the sheriff, would be waiting for her at the old farmhouse. She had hoped her parents would be there, too—but she and Lucky were alone.

In between the coyotes' howls, there was another sound—a dog barking! Rachel turned Lucky in the direction of the sound. She reminded herself that she and Lucky weren't alone. Claude and Scratch were out here, too. Standing up in the saddle, Rachel called out Claude's name once again. Only the coyotes, moving closer, answered.

Halfway across the pasture, Rachel heard a noise behind her. Scratch was running at full speed to catch up.

At the intersection where Highway 129 crossed Old Bee Creek Road, Rachel waited for a few minutes. She hoped that somebody she knew might drive by, but the highway and road remained empty.

On the other side of Old Bee Creek Road, Rachel followed Scratch into the shallow creek. Lucky picked his way slowly along the rocky bottom. In a few minutes, she spotted the windmill at the old Montoya place and guided Lucky out of the creek.

© 2007 Macmillan/McGraw-Hill

An hour later, Rachel and Abra saddled Lucky and rode over to the Atherton farm.

Claude wasn't home, so Rachel used Abra's cell phone to call Claude's cell phone. She got his voice mail and left a message: "Claude, this is Rachel Huang. Come home! Sheriff Claxton's helping us figure out where the oil could be."

Abra leaned close to the phone and said loudly that they also had apple pie for him, and if he didn't return home soon, the pie would be history. Hearing a rustling noise, both girls looked up to see a dark shape running swiftly through Claude's pepper fields. Rachel quickly realized what the shape was— Scratch. And this time oil completely covered him. Scratch darted under the front porch.

CHAPTER 3

Rachel to the Rescue

Peering into the darkness under the porch, Rachel could see that Scratch was shivering. "Where's Claude, Scratch? Is he in trouble, boy?"

Scratch whined when he heard Claude's name and slowly inched toward Rachel on his stomach. She moved back gradually, and the dog followed her into the open. Abra held on to Scratch's collar and slipped him a tiny piece of pie.

Rachel carefully examined Scratch to see if he was hurt. He had no visible bruises but the long stem of a purple wildflower was stuck to his side. The oil acted almost like glue. She studied the purple flower. It looked familiar for some reason, but Rachel knew it wasn't a common wildflower.

"See that flower on Scratch's side?" Rachel asked Abra. "Does it look familiar to you? I know I've seen it somewhere, but I just can't remember where."

© 2007 Macmillan/McGraw-Hill

Abra stared at the flower until her eyes almost crossed, but she had to admit that she couldn't recognize it. Nor did she know where it might have been growing.

Rachel shook her head impatiently as she tried to remember where she had seen the flower. She was sure that Claude was near where she'd first seen this purple flower. A feeling of frustration engulfed Rachel. Why couldn't she remember? When her mother hiked, she always carried a small notebook and wrote down details about the flowers she saw. If I carried a notebook, too, Rachel thought, I'd know where to find Claude right now. She shut her eyes and took a deep breath. Where had she seen a field of those purple flowers?

Finally Abra remembered where she and Rachel had seen the flowers. They had seen them at the old Montoya place, which was a place they were not supposed to go. Excitedly, Rachel told her friend to come with her, but Abra said that they should go get help first. Rachel swung into the saddle and called out over her shoulder that she had to help Claude. Abra watched her determined, and foolish, friend ride away. Then she went for help.

Word Workout

WORDS TO KNOW

escort   interpreter   undergrowth   venomous

foretold   remote   vegetation   withstood

Leave the Word Out Make up a sentence that uses one of the words and then tell me the sentence leaving the word out. We'll see if I can guess which word you used.

SPELLING WORDS

slope	gaze	fuse	foal	cue
acute	rhyme	bleach	foe	pave
remote	keen	loan	coax	meek
bathe	tile	tote	bleak	shrine

Right Rhymes Find the two list words that rhyme. Then let's try to find rhymes for the other list words. For example, **slope** rhymes with **soap**. Notice that many rhyming words spell the same vowel sound differently.

(fold here)

© Macmillan/McGraw-Hill

Home-School Connection

Dear Family Member:

History is filled with amazing discoveries, but the discovery of the lost city Machu Picchu, in Peru, is one of the most amazing of all. We are reading the fascinating story *Lost City*, about how people from other countries learned of this secret city in 1911. The story we are reading is fiction, but it tells a story about real people and real places. I think the settings are almost more important than the characters. The story begins in the high mountains of the Andes and then travels through its mysterious jungles.

This Week's Skills

Comprehension: character, setting, and plot

Vocabulary: compound words, such as base/ball

Spelling/phonics: vowels

Name _____

One Big Change

We can learn a lot by making just one change to a story. What changes make a big difference? What changes are not such a big deal?

- Read this story with me.
- Afterward, we can take turns and tell our own versions of the story, changing the character, setting, or plot.

The Found City of Chicago

When Alex's family first moved to Chicago, all he could do was think about his home back in Ohio. He missed running in and out of the long rows of corn on his family's farm. In Chicago he could only run in and out of traffic.

There were clanging streetcars and honking cars. "I'll never like it here if I don't get used to it," Alex decided. "And I'll never get used to it if I don't take a good look around."

So Alex took his sketch pad outside. He drew his new apartment building. He even added a small self-portrait of himself peeking out of their window.

Each day Alex sketched another building. Lots of people stopped to talk to him. Many people admired his careful sketches. Some people gave him suggestions for improvements or told him what the block was like "in the old days."

Soon Alex had a complete set of buildings, and he felt comfortable on his block.

Ejercicio de palabras

PALABRAS DE VOCABULARIO

escort	interpreter	undergrowth	venomous
foretold	remote	vegetation	withstood

No la menciones Forma una oración con una de las palabras de la lista, dime luego la oración pero sin decirme la palabra. Veremos si puedo adivinar de qué palabra se trata.

PALABRAS DE ORTOGRAFÍA

slope	gaze	fuse	foal	cue
acute	rhyme	bleach	foe	pave
remote	keen	loan	coax	meek
bathe	tile	tote	bleak	shrine

Rimas y más rimas Busca en la lista dos palabras que rimen. Luego vamos a tratar de encontrar rimas para el resto de las palabras. Por ejemplo, **slope** rima con **soap**. Observa que muchas palabras que riman tienen el mismo sonido de una vocal escrito en forma diferente.

Conexión con el hogar

Queridos familiares:

La historia está llena de descubrimientos sorprendentes, y el descubrimiento de la ciudad perdida de Machu Picchu, en Perú, es uno de los más sorprendentes de todos. Estamos leyendo la fascinante historia *Lost City*, que trata de cómo personas de otros países se enteraron de la existencia de esta ciudad secreta en 1911. El relato es ficción, aunque habla de personas y lugares verdaderos. Pienso que los ambientes son casi más importantes que los personajes. La narración comienza en las altas montañas de los Andes y viaja a través de sus selvas misteriosas.

Destrezas de la semana

Comprensión: personajes, ambiente y argumento

Vocabulario: palabras compuestas, como *baseball*

Ortografía/Fonética: vocales

Nombre _____

(fold here)

Un gran cambio

Podemos aprender mucho con sólo hacer un cambio en un cuento. ¿Qué cambios hacen una gran diferencia? ¿Qué cambios no tienen demasiada importancia?

- Lee este cuento conmigo.
- Después podemos turnarnos y contar nuestras propias versiones del cuento. Para hacerlo cambiaremos el personaje, el ambiente o el argumento.

The Found City of Chicago

When Alex's family first moved to Chicago, all he could do was think about his home back in Ohio. He missed running in and out of the long rows of corn on his family's farm. In Chicago he could only run in and out of traffic.

There were clanging streetcars and honking cars. "I'll never like it here if I don't get used to it," Alex decided. "And I'll never get used to it if I don't take a good look around."

So Alex took his sketch pad outside. He drew his new apartment building. He even added a small self-portrait of himself peeking out of their window.

Each day Alex sketched another building. Lots of people stopped to talk to him. Many people admired his careful sketches. Some people gave him suggestions for improvements or told him what the block was like "in the old days."

Soon Alex had a complete set of buildings, and he felt comfortable on his block.

Comprehension Check

Summarize

Use the Character, Setting, and Plot Chart to help you summarize *Queen Pu-abi's Royal Tomb*. Then look for examples of foreshadowing in the story. Tell how the use of foreshadowing contributes to the story's overall structure.

Character	Setting	Plot

Think and Compare

1. Turn to page 5. What detail described on this page foreshadows the discovery of the Queen's tomb? *(Analyze Plot, Characters, Setting)*

2. Have you ever found something that did not belong to you? What did you decide to do with it? Why did you make this decision? *(Analyze)*

3. The discovery of the Royal Tombs at Ur took place during the 1920s and 1930s. Over time important sites are often looted. What do you think could be done to protect these sites? *(Synthesize)*

20

Queen Pu-abi's Royal Tomb

by George Capaccio
illustrated by Elizabeth Rosen

Table of Contents

Introduction

The country of Iraq was once part of a much larger area called Mesopotamia. *Mesopotamia* is a Greek word that means "between two rivers." Thousands of years ago Mesopotamia was the home of some of the oldest and most influential civilizations in the world.

One of these was the Sumerian civilization. It began about five thousand years ago. The people of **Sumer** (SOO-mur) lived in what is now southern Iraq. Today when historians and archeologists speak of "the cradle of civilization," they are referring to Sumer. Among the greatest accomplishments of Sumer were the invention of writing and the development of cities.

By far the greatest city was **Ur** (OOR). The ruins of Ur are about two hundred miles south of modern-day Baghdad. In 1922 British archeologist Sir Charles Leonard Woolley began his first excavation of these ruins. This story is based on what he found there.

⊕ This is Sir Charles Leonard Woolley.

Conclusion

The Real Discovery of Ur

Sir Charles Leonard Woolley explored the city of Ur from 1922 to 1934. He and his team uncovered streets and houses, a massive temple, and about 1,850 burial sites. Most of these sites dated to about 2600 B.C.

In 1927 Woolley discovered the tomb of Queen Shub-ad. Inside were incredibly rare and beautiful objects. These included the headdress that the Queen was buried in and the harp that her attendants played until they, too, died.

The tomb chamber belonged to a queen. But her name, archeologists now believe, was not Shub-ad. It was Pu-abi (poo-AH-bee). Whatever her name, her tomb in the Royal Cemetery at Ur is one of the greatest archeological finds of the past century.

Muthanna looked up from the darkness. "Bring torches," he shouted. "It's blacker than night down here. Already I have heard the hissing of snakes."

Abdullah joined Sheik Hamoudi, Max Mallowan, Katherine Woolley, and her husband. With lit torches, they climbed into the pit and cautiously inched their way down the shaft. Soon they found themselves facing a large underground chamber.

Woolley held up his torch. In its flickering light, he saw a woman's headdress. It was made of golden leaves and precious stones. "My friends," he said, "I believe we have discovered the burial chamber of Queen Shub-ad (shoob-AHD) herself!"

Quite unexpectedly, Woolley reached into his pocket and removed the golden beads Abdullah had given him the day before. "Things have turned out just as you foretold, Abdullah. Your gift has brought us more good luck than I ever dreamed possible."

Abdullah couldn't have agreed more.

18

3

Chapter 1

Abdullah and the Golden Beads

Abdullah (Ahb-DUL-lah) loosened his black-and-white head covering. Another grueling day of work was under way. His job was to help remove dirt from ancient tombs, or graves. Abdullah looked around the excavation site and tried to count all of the exposed graves. But he soon gave up. "There are too many of them," he thought. "Besides, if Sheik Hamoudi (Shayk hah-MOOD-ee) catches me counting graves instead of working, he will send me away." Abdullah threw himself into removing dirt, but while he worked, he secretly dreamed of discovering a hidden treasure.

Sheik Hamoudi was the foreman on the site. He had worked for the Englishman for a long time. For the past week, the Sheik had been the boss while the Englishman and his wife were away in Baghdad. He treated his workers fairly, and yet he frightened Abdullah when he yelled. Abdullah had grown up in the south of Iraq and had never been more than a few miles from his village.

© 2007 Macmillan/McGraw-Hill

Queen Pu-abi's Tomb

Abdullah could hardly sleep that night. He kept imagining what sort of surprise the Englishman had in store for him. The next morning he waited in front of the Expedition house. Promptly at six o'clock, the Englishman opened the door and welcomed him.

In his own limited Arabic, he offered the boy a chance to be more than a basket carrier. "If you agree, I will spend part of each day teaching you about the work I do. Someday you might become one of my assistants. What do you say?"

Abdullah was unsure if this was a good thing or not, but then he decided that it was. "Yes," he said at last. "You will be my teacher and I will learn."

That same morning Abdullah got his first lesson in archeology—how to clean pottery shards in a special cleaning solution. Abdullah worked hard.

"Mr. Woolley! Come, please! Muthanna has found something like nothing we have seen before," one of the workers cried excitedly.

Abdullah looked at his teacher. Woolley understood the unspoken request in the boy's eyes. "Yes, Abdullah, you can come, too."

Leonard Woolley knew he had offended the boy. "I accept your gift," he said, hoping Abdullah would forgive him. Abdullah gladly dropped the beads into the archeologist's open hand. Wooley smiled at Abdullah and said, "Tomorrow, I will have a surprise for you. Be at my door no later than six o'clock."

Sheik Hamoudi was very pleased that things had turned out so well. In a good mood once more, he reminded his men that work began at sunrise. Then he put his arm around Abdullah. "That golden dagger," he said to the boy, "can only mean one thing: Even greater treasures are waiting to be found."

Abdullah shrugged. "Nobody knows for sure," he said to the foreman. But the same thought had crossed Abdullah's mind.

16

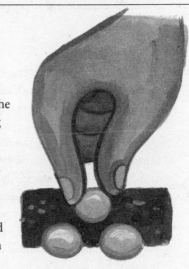

Even though the Sheik was not paying attention to Abdullah, he found himself sweating even harder under the hot desert sun. "Now is not the time to dream," Abdullah muttered to himself. He picked up his basket and balanced it on his head, and then he continued walking toward his crew's excavation area. Just as Abdullah was about to put his basket down, something caught his eye. He kneeled down a few feet from a deep, narrow trench. The boy could hardly believe his good luck. There on the ground lay three golden beads. Abdullah glanced around. When he was sure no one was watching him, he picked them up. "I wonder if I should turn them over to the Englishman," he thought.

The Englishman, Sir Charles Leonard Woolley, gave baksheesh (bahk-SHEESH), or reward, at the end of every day. He offered it to whatever crew had found something of value. Abdullah was not sure what he should do.

"What if the Englishman keeps the golden beads and gives nothing to me because I am only a boy?" Abdullah worried.

5

When it was time for the midmorning break, Abdullah left his crew's work site and climbed the steps of the old temple. This was one of his favorite places. Somehow it had withstood thousands of years of neglect. With the sun drenching the scene in golden light, the temple truly was an amazing sight. Abdullah loved climbing to the top, especially when he needed to be alone or when he had a problem to solve. From there he could see the ancient cemetery of Ur and the streets and houses where nobody had lived for centuries.

Abdullah found a comfortable place to sit. He propped his head in his hands and looked out across the vast plains that stretched out around him. Then he looked at the golden beads one more time and asked himself the question that had nagged him all morning: "Should I keep them or turn them over to the Englishman?"

© 2007 Macmillan/McGraw-Hill

The boy shook his head. Tears welled up in his eyes. In Arabic he explained his true intent. The Sheik served as the interpreter for his employer Leonard Woolley; Abdullah wondered if the Sheik would even tell the Englishman the truth. "Well," Abdullah thought to himself, "my fate is sealed."

"The boy says he found these on his own. They are not from any of the Royal Tombs. He does not want a reward. He only wants you to have the beads as a gift. He hopes they will bring you good luck. He believes there are many beautiful and wondrous things yet to be found." The Sheik bowed at the end of his speech. He glared at the boy and shook his head. The Sheik hoped that the Englishman would see that Abdullah was a mere boy and had meant well. The Sheik, however, was not so sure he could trust the boy himself.

Chapter 3

The Greatest Reward of All

Abdullah took the dinar and then removed his left hand from its hiding place. In his best English, and with the very brightest of smiles on his face, Abdullah cried out, "And this is for you, Mr. Woolley. A gift from Abdullah, your best basket boy!" The boy opened his hand.

"Three golden beads," Woolley exclaimed. "Where on earth did you find them, and why didn't you tell me earlier? You know the rules, Abdullah. Nobody takes anything from the Royal Tombs without asking me or Sheik Hamoudi."

A look of panic crossed Abdullah's face. He was not sure what he was supposed to do. But he could not run and hide, for the Sheik had observed what had happened.

He was sure Abdullah had disobeyed his orders and was trying to win an extra reward. The foreman seized Abdullah's arm. "Did you take these beads from one of the Royal Tombs?"

14

Suddenly a wild jackal howled in the distance. Pigeons fluttered up from the undergrowth. Abdullah glanced at the bushes that had hidden their nests. "Something must have startled them," Abdullah thought. Then he noticed the plume of dust from a car racing toward the site. The boy smiled when he remembered the Englishman's funny name for this car: "Tin Lizzie." It was used to escort people to and from Ur. On this particular morning, the other Englishman, Mr. Mallowan, had gone to the railway junction to pick up Mr. and Mrs. Woolley.

Abdullah made up his mind. He removed a few loose bricks from a nearby wall and prepared to stash the beads. "As soon as it is safe," he thought, "I will come back and get them. They will bring my family more money than we will ever get from the Englishman." A cloud passed over the sun and Abdullah wondered if that was an omen, or bad sign.

7

Before Abdullah had a chance to hide the beads, the old "Tin Lizzie" came to a huffing, puffing stop in front of the Expedition house. A small welcoming party gathered. As the Englishman and his wife stepped out of the car, Abdullah hid the beads in his pocket and raced down the steps of the temple to greet them. He was eager to hear about any new experiences the couple might have had in Baghdad.

Sir Leonard Woolley, the Englishman, had grown fond of the boy. He greeted Abdullah in Arabic. Abdullah was about to reply when the foreman Sheik Hamoudi cut him off. "Abdullah," he ordered, "bring Mr. Woolley's luggage into the house. Then go back to the trench. Your crew needs you." Abdullah was disappointed, but he knew better than to disobey the Sheik, especially in public and in front of the Englishman.

Sulking, Abdullah walked past the archeologist and his wife, Katherine. He dragged along two very large leather suitcases with thick straps around them.

At the end of the day, groups of dusty and tired men stored their tools and cleaned up as best they could. Those men who had found anything of value gathered in front of the Expedition house. It was time to receive baksheesh. Abdullah sat on the ground with the other men in his crew. The pick man held up the golden dagger. Leonard Woolley examined it carefully. "What do you say to 20 dinars (DEE-narz)?" he asked the crew. They discussed the amount and agreed it was fair enough.

Abdullah knew that Muthanna the pick man would get most of the money since he had found the dagger. The boy kept his left hand in his vest pocket, as if he were hiding something. In a large ledger, Katherine Woolley recorded how much each man got while her husband handed out the cash.

"This is your share, Abdullah," the archeologist said, putting a single Iraqi dinar into the boy's hand. "I wish it could be more," he said, apologetically.

Abdullah looked over the barren plains that long ago were green with vegetation. He felt a vast, unexplored world beneath his feet. "This is my land," he thought. "These are my people. This is our past we are uncovering together." Abdullah thought that maybe he did understand after all why the English dug around in the dirt here.

Then he remembered the golden beads, and knew beyond a shadow of a doubt what he must do with them.

"Sheik Hamoudi!" the pick man cried out. "Come quickly! I think I have found something." The sheik leaped from his post and climbed into the pit, only to emerge a short time later.

"Mr. Mallowan, I think you had better have a look," he said to the assistant archeologist. Mallowan dropped his sketch pad and followed the foreman into the hole.

From a distance, Abdullah watched the archeologist delicately scrape the earth from something fragile and bright. "What is it, Max?" Leonard Woolley called down.

"A dagger, sir. A golden dagger," Max answered. The day ended with great pride and happiness filling everyone at the site.

© 2007 Macmillan/McGraw-Hill

Queen Pu-abi's Tomb

As he was leaving the house, Leonard Woolley stopped him. He reached into the side pocket of his jacket and took out a small paper bag. "For you," he said to Abdullah. "A gift from Baghdad."

"More good fortune," the boy thought. He opened the bag and discovered several floured nuggets of *min simma* (men SIMMA), a chewy Iraqi dessert. The Englishman put his finger over his lips and whispered, "Sshh," as if he were saying, "This will be our little secret."

Abdullah felt a jolt of surprise. The other workers had warned him to keep his mind on his job and not have anything to do with the Englishman, but maybe he was not so bad. A big smile spread across Abdullah's face.

Chapter 2

An Amazing Discovery

Sheik Hamoudi had observed Abdullah and Woolley conversing, but he was not close enough to hear what they were saying. Nor did he see the gift Woolley had given Abdullah. Nevertheless, Hamoudi was not happy. He strode across the yard and grabbed Abdullah's arm. "Back to work!" he barked. The boy quickly and quietly obeyed. Fortunately Abdullah had artfully concealed his gift in the folds of his headscarf so Hamoudi did not take it from him.

The Sheik followed the boy as he walked down a long flight of steps to the graves where the men were working. The Sheik perched on top of a mound of earth and began giving orders to Abdullah's crew. The men were deep in a dusty pit. Basket in hand, Abdullah soon joined them.

At a signal from the Sheik, the pick man began a chant. The digger joined in. He handled his shovel as if he were paddling a boat. Meanwhile, Abdullah swung up load after load of dirt in time with the chanting.

Soon Mr. and Mrs. Woolley and their assistant, Max Mallowan, showed up. Abdullah secretly eyed them as he worked. He couldn't help but wonder what had brought these people to such a remote place. To spend your day in the dirt was not something that Abdullah wanted to do for the rest of his life.

Leonard and Katherine, seated, used small knives to scrape away at something embedded in the packed earth. Periodically Katherine blew away the loose dirt with a small bellows. Abdullah longed to see the pieces of the past that had been discovered.

Abdullah thought of his discovery and sensed a new feeling in his heart, one he never would have expected in the midst of such backbreaking labor. When he tried to find a word for this feeling, the only one that came to him was *pride*. "Today," he thought, "I am proud to work here."

Word Workout

WORDS TO KNOW

absorb	altered	concentrated
erode	innovations	

Back and Forth I'll tell you a definition and you guess the word. Then I'll choose another word and you tell me the definition.

SPELLING WORDS

reins	review	retrieve	belief	niece
freight	foreign	grieve	neither	eighty
siege	shield	sleigh	reign	wield
yield	ceiling	seize	relieve	diesel

Group and Remember Do you think there are more list words that use **ie** or **ei**? Let's use a highlighter or red pen to mark all of the words that are spelled with **ei**. Then let's take turns spelling list words.

© Macmillan/McGraw-Hill

(fold here)

Home-School Connection

Dear Family Member:

When you read a nonfiction book, you come away with two kinds of information. You learn a big idea about a topic. That's the main thing that the author wants you to know. You also learn a lot of specific details about the topic. This week we're reading "Science for All," a collection of articles about sleep, lifespans, and how product makers come up with innovations. We're learning to recognize the big ideas and details as we read these interesting articles. One of the details even tells about the weird ways that lizards, cockroaches, and spiders can help make our lives better!

This Week's Skills

Comprehension: main idea and details

Vocabulary: context clues

Spelling/Phonics: ei and ie

Name _____

Get the Idea

Articles tell more than just a random list of facts. When I read I'm learning to recognize the big ideas and the details that back them up.

There are two topics on this page, but the big ideas are mixed in with the details. Let's see if we can spot which sentences could be the main idea for an article. We'll also find some sentences that give information about the topic.

Boomerangs

Most boomerangs are made of wood.

A boomerang is a curved device that will return to the person that threw it.

Australian Aborigines have used boomerangs for thousands of years.

Today athletes compete in boomerang throwing contests.

In the world record throw, a boomerang zoomed 781 feet (238 meters) and then came back.

Hot-Air Balloons

The first hot-air balloon took off in France in 1783.

Ten years later a hot-air balloon soared in the United States for the first time.

Hot-air balloons are the oldest successful human flight technology.

They were invented by the Montgolfier Brothers.

Ejercicio de palabras

PALABRAS DE VOCABULARIO

absorb	altered	concentrated
erode	innovations	

De un lado a otro Te daré una definición y tú debes adivinar de qué palabra se trata. Luego escogeré otra palabra y tú deberás darme la definición.

PALABRAS DE ORTOGRAFÍA

reins	review	retrieve	belief	niece
freight	foreign	grieve	neither	eighty
siege	shield	sleigh	reign	wield
yield	ceiling	seize	relieve	diesel

Agrupa y recuerda ¿Hay más palabras en la lista con **ie** o con **ei**? Usa un marcador o un lápiz rojo para subrayar todas las palabras que tengan **ei**. Luego vamos a turnarnos para deletrear las palabras de la lista.

(fold here)

© Macmillan/McGraw-Hill

Conexión con el hogar

Queridos familiares:

Cuando uno lee un libro que no es de ficción recoge dos tipos de información. Se obtiene una idea importante sobre un tema, que es lo principal que el autor desea comunicar. También se obtienen muchos detalles específicos sobre el tema. Esta semana estamos leyendo *Science for All*, una serie de artículos sobre el sueño, la duración de la vida y cómo se les ocurren a los fabricantes las grandes innovaciones. ¡Uno de los detalles incluso nos da información acerca de cómo los lagartos, las cucarachas y las arañas pueden mejorar nuestras vidas!

Destrezas de la semana

Comprensión: idea principal y detalles

Vocabulario: claves de contexto

Ortografía/Fonética: palabras con **ei** y **ie**

Nombre_____

Ésa es la idea

Los artículos nos dan más que una lista casual de datos. Ahora estoy aprendiendo a reconocer las ideas importantes y los detalles que las soportan.

Aquí hay dos temas, pero las ideas importantes están mezcladas con los detalles. Vamos a ver si podemos distinguir qué oraciones son la idea principal de un artículo. También vamos a encontrar oraciones que nos dan información sobre el tema.

Boomerangs

Most boomerangs are made of wood.

A boomerang is a curved device that will return to the person that threw it.

Australian Aborigines have used boomerangs for thousands of years.

Today athletes compete in boomerang throwing contests.

In the world record throw, a boomerang zoomed 781 feet (238 meters) and then came back.

Hot-Air Balloons

The first hot-air balloon took off in France in 1783.

Ten years later a hot-air balloon soared in the United States for the first time.

Hot-air balloons are the oldest successful human flight technology.

They were invented by the Montgolfier Brothers.

Comprehension Check

Summarize

Summarize each chapter of *From Dragonflies to Helicopters: Learning from Nature* by writing a sentence telling the main idea of each chapter. Then add one or two supporting details for each chapter's main idea. How does each chapter contribute to the main idea of the selection?

Think and Compare

1. Look back at pages 8 and 9. What are these two pages about? How do they relate to the main idea of the selection? What are some of the details that support the main idea? *(Identify Main Idea and Details)*

2. Think about one of the animals you read about in this book. Which one is most interesting to you? Explain the reasons for your choice. *(Evaluate)*

3. In what ways do you think our lives would be different if humans didn't have the technology to fly? *(Apply / Synthesize)*

24

From Dragonflies to Helicopters

Learning from Nature
by Manuel Alemán

Table of Contents

Introduction

Have you ever asked yourself how birds and insects fly? Or why birds can fly, but other animals can't? Human beings have long studied nature and its mysteries. Over time they have found some amazing ways to use what they have learned.

Of course human beings can't fly. But they have reached the skies by using technology to invent flying machines. Some of these ideas for flying machines have come from animals like birds and insects.

🎧 The first flying machines were just a body and a pair of wings.

Index

Glossary

concave (kon-KAYV) a special shape that curves upward in the middle (page 4)

drag (DRAG) a force that slows an object down during flight (page 7)

echolocation (ek-oh-loh-KAY-shun) a technique using sound waves to locate objects (page 12)

flapping flight (FLAP-ing FLIGHT) a type of flight in which a bird flaps its wings (page 5)

gliding (GLIGH-ding) a type of flight in which birds use air currents to stay in the air (page 4)

lift (LIFT) a force produced when air pressure below a wing is greater than the pressure above it (page 4)

mammal (MAM-uhl) a kind of animal that is warm-blooded and has a backbone (page 12)

pollinate (POL-uh-nayt) to transfer pollen from one flower to another, fertilizing it (page 16)

radar (RAY-dahr) a device used to find and track objects (page 14)

rotor (ROH-tur) a set of large, turning blades that lift and move a helicopter or other aircraft (page 9)

stealth technology (STELTH tek-NOL-uhj-ee) a special design of modern planes that helps them avoid detection by radar (page 15)

thrust (THRUST) the force that moves an object forward in flight (page 6)

vapor (VAY-pur) small particles of mist, steam, or smoke that can be seen in the air (page 6)

From Dragonflies to Helicopters

Birds are not the only animals that humans have tried to copy. Today we are able to track a plane from takeoff to landing thanks to a system that bats and dolphins use to navigate and hunt.

There are other animals that are useful to people. Bees help people in lots of ways, providing them with many valuable products. In this book you will learn about some other ways in which humans have developed technology by imitating nature.

🎧 People track airplanes using a system borrowed from bats and dolphins.

CHAPTER ONE

Birds and Planes

A bird is an amazing animal. It can soar through the skies with what looks like little effort. However, a bird's flight is actually quite complex. One reason is the design of its wing. The shape and size of the bird's wings play a big role in how it flies. A bird's wing has a **concave**, or curved, shape, which allows air pressure to build up under it. When the air pressure under the wing is greater than the pressure above, the bird rises because of a force called **lift**.

A bird can fly by **gliding**. This is when birds ride the air currents in the sky. They can save energy this way.

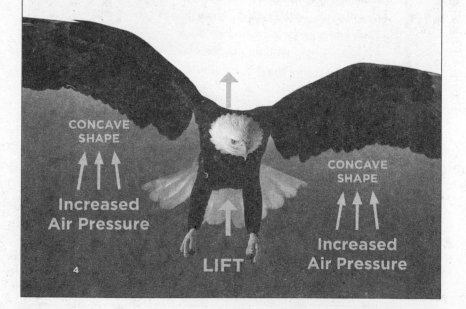

CONCAVE SHAPE

CONCAVE SHAPE

Increased Air Pressure

LIFT

Increased Air Pressure

4

From Dragonflies to Helicopters

21

Conclusion

Since the beginning of recorded history, people have tried to use nature in some way. Sometimes we have copied it, changed it, or simply used the products that nature offers. Birds and insects have given people a lot of good ideas. We have learned how to fly from them. We have made a lot of progress in conquering the skies, but we still have a long way to go. Maybe someday our flying machines will be able to do all the amazing things birds and insects can do.

People have also learned a lot by studying bats and bees. We haven't been able to copy bat echolocation exactly. But we have created a similar system that is very important. Also, scientists are still trying to find out how bees can help us treat pain.

Over the years people have studied nature to learn new ways to do things. Most of these new inventions have been good for people and our planet. But technology can also pose some problems. It can cause destruction if it isn't used in the right way. For that reason we must learn to use technology correctly and protect nature. We will then be protecting the source of many of our ideas for how to make our world a better place.

© 2007 Macmillan/McGraw-Hill

From Dragonflies to Helicopters

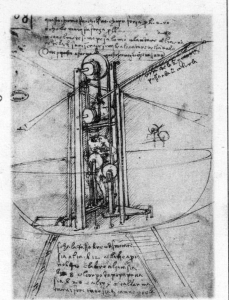

In the 1500s a famous ↻ artist and inventor, Leonardo da Vinci, made a flying machine. It never flew, but it gave people new ideas about how to fly.

A second way birds can fly is called **flapping flight**. In this type of flight, birds change the shape of their wings. They also change how they move their wings through the air. This helps them control their direction. Birds need more energy for this kind of flight. Smaller birds usually fly this way.

People have always been interested in flying. They first tried to imitate birds by attaching wings to their bodies. This always failed because the human body is not suited for flying. But people did learn some valuable lessons. They saw that birds have skinny, hollow bones, which make their bodies suitable for flying. People learned that in order to fly, the body needs to be light.

Jet Trails

The smoke trails that follow jets across the sky come from oil pumped over the engine's exhaust. This oil turns instantly into a **vapor**, or smoke, upon contact with the hot exhaust. The vapor forms the trail in the sky. The smoke is harmless, and it helps pilots spot other aircraft in the sky.

After learning more about how birds fly, people copied how birds change the shape of their wings. Just like a bird, an airplane's wings can change shape. And like a bird's tail, the tail of an airplane can change shape, too. Changing the shape of the tail helps birds and planes maneuver. Another thing that people copied is how a bird glides. For example, hang gliders ride currents of air just like some birds do.

People continued to improve the wings and bodies of their flying machines. In 1903 Wilbur and Orville Wright made the first manned flight with an engine-powered plane in Kitty Hawk, North Carolina. Since then many innovations have made flying better.

Birds and planes have some differences. A bird's wings keep it in the air and move it forward at the same time. This forward movement is called **thrust**. However, a plane's wings only keep it in the air. The thrust comes from the engine.

⌒ The muscles and venom sac attached to a stinger push it further in while injecting more poison.

For example, a person with constant knee pain would have a bee sting him or her in the knee. The knee would absorb the poison and swell up as a result. The person's body would then produce a special substance to fight the swelling. And that substance would also relieve the pain in the person's knee.

Doctors don't yet fully understand how this process works, or if it really works. Some people believe that using bee stings in this way is dangerous. But others believe they have been helped.

🔊 African honeybees were brought to Brazil in the 1950s because they produce a lot more honey than European honeybees do.

As useful as bees are, they can still be dangerous. The way a bee defends itself is by stinging whatever is bothering it. When a bee stings you, it injects venom into your body. Venom is a type of poison. The place where the bee stings you gets red and swells up. That is what your body does to fight against the bee's venom.

Bee stings can help people with health problems. People with diseases, such as arthritis, have begun to use bee sting therapy to help them feel better.

When a bird glides or rises suddenly, it changes the shape of its wings and tail. Planes do the same thing. Planes have special wing flaps. The flaps produce lift during takeoff and **drag** during landings to slow the plane down.

Planes Copy Birds

People have copied how a bird uses its wings in designing airplane wings.

Feathers spread for gliding and soaring

Flaps spread for takeoff

Feathers half spread facing down for landing

Flaps down for landing

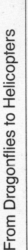

CHAPTER TWO

Dragonflies and Helicopters

People have also studied insects to better understand flight. One of the insects is the dragonfly, an insect with millions of years of experience in the air!

Dragonflies can fly forward and backward. They can move up and down and side to side. They can spin in a complete circle during flight. They can hover, or hang in the air, and turn sharply to catch prey. They can even reach speeds of 40 miles per hour! Their wings allow them to do these flying tricks. A dragonfly has two pairs of wings, which it can operate independently. It also can alter the shape of its wings as well as twist them.

In the 1940s Igor Sikorsky (ee-GOR sih-KORS-kee) copied the basic flight design of the dragonfly for his design of a helicopter. A helicopter can do much more than a plane. A helicopter can hover and fly forward, backward, and side to side; move straight up and down; and turn in a complete circle in mid-flight. But it does none of these things as well as a dragonfly can.

Since a dragonfly can control its wings so well, it can do amazing things in the air. ↻

Among other things, people use beeswax to make candles, soap, and natural cosmetic products like lipstick. Bees use wax to build their hives. The wax is formed into honeycombs, a series of connected chambers. Both honey and eggs are stored in these chambers, which are then sealed. These chambers are so strong that engineers became interested in copying them.

People make honeycombs out of metal, plastic, and other materials. These honeycombs are then turned into "sandwiches" by gluing two sheets of metal or plastic on the top and bottom. This makes the honeycomb even stronger. These honeycomb sandwiches are then used to make things like airplanes and buildings. One reason they are used in airplanes is because they are very strong and light.

How Is Honey Made?

Honey is nothing more than a concentrated form of nectar from flowers. The bees bring the nectar to the hive where it is stored. Here bees beat their wings quickly to "fan" it and evaporate the water out of the nectar. The colony then uses the honey for food.

CHAPTER FOUR

The World of Bees

Another animal that has always fascinated people is the honeybee. These amazing insects make many products that people use. The most common are honey and beeswax. The bee's honeycomb has also given people some ideas about how to make stronger structures.

Bees have always been useful to people. Bees collect pollen. As they do this, they help **pollinate** (POL-uh-nayt), or fertilize, plants. As a result more plants grow, and that is good because plant roots prevent the soil from eroding.

Bees live in large ⤴ colonies and make many useful products for people to use.

From Dragonflies to Helicopters

A helicopter has a main **rotor**, a shaft connected to the motor that has large, turning blades to lift and move it forward. It also has another small rotor in the tail. This keeps it steady in flight. If a helicopter didn't have a tail rotor, it would just spin in circles. The tail rotor works much like the dragonfly's second pair of wings. A dragonfly uses its second pair of wings to help keep it steady in flight.

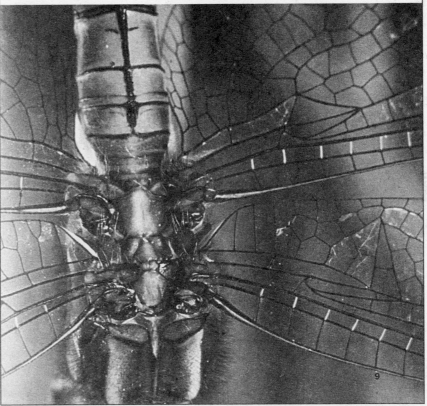

Compare the Dragonfly to a Helicopter

Dragonfly	Helicopter
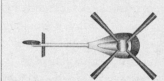	
Long body with four wings that make a cross	**Long body with four blades that make a cross**
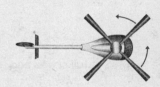	
Front and back wings move in opposite direction for hovering	**Blades spin and helicopter hovers in one place**

Back wings twist 90° on each stroke to keep dragonfly steady during flight	**Tail rotor keeps helicopter steady during flight**

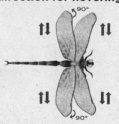

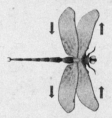

But just like the bat's echolocation, radar can also be tricked. Compare how a tiger moth escapes a bat to our modern **stealth technology** (STELTH tek-NOL-uhj-ee). Stealth technology relies on tricks just as the tiger moth does, but it does it a little differently.

Instead of sending out sounds to fool the radar, stealth technology tries to avoid it completely by becoming "invisible." Scientists have found ways to do this by designing planes with many sharp edges. The planes are also built of a special material that can absorb some of the radar signals. The sharp angles on the plane reflect the sound waves away from the source so that a signal does not come back. Much like the tiger moth, a plane with stealth technology is nearly impossible to spot with radar.

The Invisible Plane Mystery

Stealth technology is not really a new idea. It has just been a well-kept secret. In fact, it has been reported that the project to make these incredible planes started in 1974! The Air Force didn't even admit that these planes existed until 1988.

A bat's echolocation gives it a great advantage in its environment. Our modern **radar** (**ra**dio **d**etecting **a**nd **r**anging) is a great invention based on the same idea as bat echolocation. Radar uses radio waves to send signals which people cannot hear. The waves travel through the air until they hit an object, which reflects the signal back to the source.

Radar is useful in today's world. We use radar to track planes in flight and help them land. We also use radar to track storm systems.

Uses for Radar
• to track planes
• to watch for storms
• to catch speeders
• to measure the speed of a pitch
• to find enemy aircraft

Police use radar to measure the speed of motorists. You've probably even seen radar at work at a baseball game to measure the speed of a pitch.

14

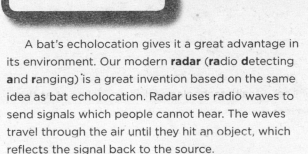

Because the helicopter can move, take off, and land easily, it has many uses. Helicopters deliver supplies to distant places, rescue people, take injured people to the hospital, and help police find criminals. But even though the helicopter is one of the most advanced flying machines, people haven't been able to build anything that can match the dragonfly.

A dragonfly is a better flier because it can fly forward at full speed and then stop suddenly. A helicopter can't do that. Also a dragonfly can make very sharp and sudden left and right 90-degree turns in flight to catch its food. A helicopter has to make these moves much more slowly than the dragonfly does.

Humans have done only a fair job of imitating the dragonfly's flight.

11

CHAPTER THREE

Bats and Radar

The bat is the only **mammal** on the planet that can fly. Bats are not as graceful in the air as birds. But bats can fly at high speeds in total darkness without running into anything. How do they do it? A bat uses **echolocation** (ek-oh-loh-CAY-shun) to find its way around and to hunt for food.

Bats send out sound waves which bounce off an object and come back as echoes. Bats send out another signal after they hear the echo, which helps them figure out the distance between themselves and the object. Bats are also able to identify the size and shape of insects by the echo they produce.

12

Echolocation at Work

The sound waves bounce off an object and return as echoes. A bat's echolocation allows it to catch insects even in the dark.

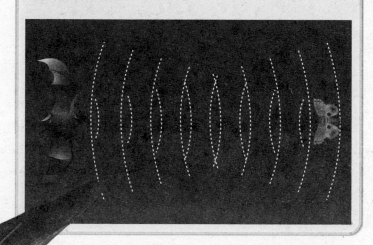

Some insects, such as moths, have developed a keen sense of hearing. They can hear the sound waves made by the bat and escape capture.

The tiger moth has developed a special way to avoid getting eaten by bats. The tiger moth moves its muscles to produce a clicking sound that bats can hear. The clicking confuses the bats. They can't locate the tiger moth because the clicking interferes with the bat's system of echolocation.

13

Word Workout

WORDS TO KNOW

chameleon generosity ricocheting scrounging

famine pathetic rummaged undetected

Try Two Let's try to think of sentences that use two vocabulary words. We'll check each other's sentences to make sure the words are used correctly.

SPELLING WORDS

search	sparkle	servant	fierce	court
starve	bargain	torch	pierce	weird
thorn	parched	earnest	urge	veer
reward	pursue	mourn	wharf	burnt

Missing Links We can make practice word cards. Write each list word on an index card. Leave a blank line for every vowel (**a, e, i, o, u**). Then we'll take turns picking a card and spelling the entire word.

Home-School Connection

Dear Family Member:

Every culture has its own stories and fables. This week, we're reading a remarkable fable from Mali titled *The Magic Gourd*. The setting might be far away, but the story's ideas about friendship and sharing are surprisingly close to home.

Of course, things don't always turn out the way you think they will. When one of the characters gives his friend a magic gourd, the results, or effects, of this gift are far from predictable. As we read the fable, we look at what causes each of the twists and turns in the tale.

THIS WEEK'S SKILLS

Comprehension: cause and effect

Vocabulary: context clues

Spelling/Phonics: vowels followed by **r**

Name _____

(fold here)

Why? Because!

Riddles often give silly reasons for things. Let's try to make up answers to the riddles. We'll be matching causes and effects.

Why did the farmer name his pig *Ink*?

Because it

Why did the bubble gum cross the road?

Because it was stuck

Why did the football coach give his team a lighter?

Because they were always

What happened because the plastic surgeon stood too near the oven?

He

What happened because the doctor yelled at everybody?

He ran out of

Why did the soccer coach throw Cinderella off the team?

Because she ran

melted.

kept running out of the pen.

patients.

losing their matches.

on the bottom of the chicken's foot.

away from the ball.

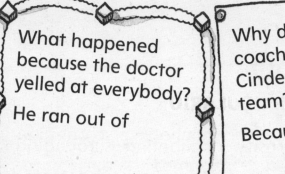

Ejercicio de palabras

PALABRAS DE VOCABULARIO

chameleon generosity ricocheting scrounging

famine   pathetic   rummaged undetected

De a dos Tratemos de formar oraciones con dos de las palabras de la lista. Verificaremos las oraciones de cada uno de nosotros para asegurarnos de que las palabras están usadas correctamente.

PALABRAS DE ORTOGRAFÍA

search	sparkle	servant	fierce	court
starve	bargain	torch	pierce	weird
thorn	parched	earnest	urge	veer
reward	pursue	mourn	wharf	burnt

Eslabones perdidos Vamos a hacer tarjetas de palabras para practicar. Escribe cada palabra de la lista en una tarjeta. Deja un espacio en blanco para cada vocal (**a, e, i, o, u**). Luego vamos a turnarnos para escoger una tarjeta y deletrear la palabra completa.

(fold here)

© Macmillan/McGraw-Hill

Conexión con el hogar

Queridos familiares:

Cada cultura tiene sus propios cuentos y fábulas. Esta semana estamos leyendo una excelente fábula de Mali llamada *The Magic Gourd*. Aunque la acción se sitúa en un lugar muy lejano, las ideas del cuento sobre la amistad y el compartir cosas resultan muy familiares.

Por supuesto no todo se resuelve siempre como uno espera. Cuando uno de los personajes le da a su amigo una calabaza mágica, los resultados, o efectos, del regalo no son nada predecibles. Al leer la fábula, observamos lo que causa cada uno de los enredos y peripecias del cuento.

Destrezas de la semana

Comprensión: causa y efecto

Vocabulario: claves de contexto

Ortografía/Fonética: vocales antes de **r**

Nombre _____

¿Por qué? Porque...

Las adivinanzas suelen dar razones sin sentido para lo que pasa. Vamos a tratar de encontrar las respuestas de las adivinanzas. Así haremos corresponder los efectos con las causas.

Why did the farmer name his pig Ink?

Because it

Why did the bubble gum cross the road?

Because it was stuck

Why did the football coach give his team a lighter?

Because they were always

What happened because the plastic surgeon stood too near the oven?

He

What happened because the doctor yelled at everybody?

He ran out of

Why did the soccer coach throw Cinderella off the team?

Because she ran

melted.

kept running out of the pen.

patients.

losing their matches.

on the bottom of the chicken's foot.

away from the ball.

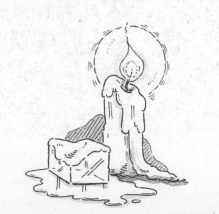

Comprehension Check

Summarize

How has each of the Navajo arts—basketmaking, weaving, silversmithing—changed over time? How do the materials they use reflect their environment? How do all of them reflect Navajo traditions? Use the Cause and Effect Chart to retell the story.

Cause	→	Effect
	→	
	→	
	→	
	→	

Think and Compare

1. Look back at page 15. Why was the art of Navajo basketmaking in danger of being lost? How did Mary Holiday Black help preserve the tradition? *(Identify Cause and Effect)*

2. Navajo weavings, baskets, and jewelry often have traditional stories to tell. If you could choose any story to tell through an artwork, what would it be? Which art form would you choose? Why? *(Apply/Analyze)*

3. People in every culture make art. Some use expensive materials, like oil paints or special papers. Others rummage through trash to find materials to recycle as sculpture. Why do you think it is so important to people to make art? *(Evaluate/Analyze)*

Arts of the
Navajo

by Helen Byers

Table of Contents

Introduction

The Navajo (NAH-vah-hoh) Indians call themselves the Dineh (dee-NAY). In Navajo, their name means "The People."

Over 255,000 Navajo live in the United States today. Their nation is the largest in the country.

For generations the Navajo have made beautiful weavings, baskets, and jewelry. Their arts reflect their traditions, their history, and their modern life.

Centuries ago, the Navajo settled in a part of the Southwest now called the Four Corners. It's called that because the borders of four states meet in one spot

⊙ Today Monument Valley is part of the Navajo Reservation.

Index

Glossary

ceremonial *(ser-uh-MOH-nee-uhl)* used in formal acts, done on special occasions *(page 14)*

cochineal *(koh-chuh-NEEL)* a small beetle found on a type of cactus; used to make pink or red dye *(page 9)*

fleece *(FLEES)* wool from an animal such as a sheep *(page 8)*

hogan *(HOH-gahn)* a small, round Navajo house made of logs or poles, earth, and brush, with a dirt floor and a hole in the ceiling for smoke to escape *(page 3)*

lichen *(LIGH-kuhn)* a type of plant that grows on another plant or on rock *(page 9)*

matrix *(MAY-triks)* a pattern *(page 20)*

mesa *(MAY-sah)* a high, flat-topped land formation (from the Spanish word meaning "table") *(page 3)*

peso *(PAY-soh)* a Mexican silver coin *(page 17)*

petroglyph *(PET-ruh-glif)* a design carved on rock, usually by ancient people *(page 19)*

piñon *(peen-NYOHN)* a type of pine tree (from the Spanish word meaning "pine") *(page 12)*

spindle *(SPIN-duhl)* a tool for spinning fiber *(page 8)*

sumac *(SOO-mak)* a type of bush or shrub *(page 12)*

treaty *(TREE-tee)* a formal agreement *(page 3)*

yucca *(YUK-uh)* a cactuslike plant *(page 12)*

© 2007 Macmillan/McGraw-Hill

The Four Corners area has beautiful canyons, **mesas**, rivers, and rock formations. But the high desert climate is harsh and dry. The Navajo lived in **hogans**. They moved often to find grass for their sheep and horses. When the climate permitted, they planted corn, squash, and melons. At times, on the brink of famine, they had to be good farmers to get by.

In 1868 the United States and the Navajo signed a **treaty**. The treaty promised them their own government, called the Navajo Nation. It also created the huge Navajo Reservation in the Four Corners area.

Navajo Indian Reservation

CHAPTER ONE
Weaving

Weaving has been a Navajo tradition for a long time. One Navajo legend tells how Spider Woman taught the Navajo how to weave. Her husband is Spider Man (but not the one you may have read about ricocheting from skyscrapers!). According to Spider Woman, he told her how to build the first loom. It was made of sky and earth, sunbeams, crystals, and lightning. For weaving tools, he recommended sunlight and shell.

4

Conclusion

All over the world today, people admire the skill and beauty of old and new Navajo weavings, baskets, and jewelry. In animal fiber, plant fibers, metal, and stone, Navajo arts celebrate the earth. They preserve ancient and modern Navajo ways and stories. Through their arts, the Navajo share their traditions, their history, and themselves.

21

The Sky Stone

When people think of Navajo jewelry, they think of turquoise as well as silver. To the Navajo, turquoise is a sacred stone. Many Navajo people believe that wearing it protects them. So some wear turquoise jewelry every day. Their rings, earrings, bracelets, necklaces, and belt buckles might include huge turquoise stones or an arrangement of many small ones.

But not all turquoise is the color of the sky. The color depends on what mine the stone came from. It might be blue-green, dark green, or even brown. The most valuable turquoise has brown or black veins in it that make an interesting **matrix** (MAY-triks), or pattern. One kind is called "spiderweb" turquoise.

Mining Turquoise

The turquoise in old Navajo jewelry came from mines in New Mexico, Arizona, and Nevada. These days, most American turquoise mines are closed. Navajo jewelers use turquoise from mines as far away as China.

© 2007 Macmillan/McGraw-Hill

Arts of the Navajo

Spider Rock

Spider Rock towers 800 feet (244 meters) above the clay floor of Canyon de Chelly (deh SHAY) National Park in Arizona. This canyon is one of the Navajo's sacred places. The red sandstone of Spider Rock has been shaped by wind and water swirling around it for 230 million years. The rock reminds the Dineh of their religious beliefs and history.

In Navajo legend, Spider Woman lives at the top of Spider Rock. Navajo children were told that if they misbehaved, Spider Woman would climb down her web, drag them to the top, and eat them.

But the legend also tells of Spider Woman's generosity. One time, a peaceful Dineh boy was chased by an enemy from another tribe. He had no place to hide. Suddenly he noticed a strand of silk dangling from Spider Rock. He climbed it to the top, undetected by his enemy. There he discovered that Spider Woman had rescued him. She pitied the pathetic boy. As a gift to the Dineh, she showed the boy how she spun and wove her magic thread. When the boy returned home, he shared Spider Woman's secret with his people. This is how the Navajo learned to weave.

This weaver uses a traditional loom.

Works in Wool

The first Navajo weavings were simple garments and blankets. But by the late 1800s, Navajo weavers were making strong, beautiful rugs with fancy patterns. Visitors to the Southwest admired the rugs and offered to buy them. It could take a weaver weeks or months to finish a single rug, but it could be traded at a trading post for food and other goods.

◑ This is a trading post where the Navajo traded goods.

Cody Hunter is a Navajo master jeweler who lives near Canyon de Chelly. He grew up exploring the canyon on foot and horseback. Today scenes and symbols from the canyon decorate his bracelets, which are called story bracelets. Clouds, rock formations, mountains, people, animals, hogans, and **petroglyphs** are all pictured on his bracelets.

◑ Story bracelets, like the one this woman is wearing, are just one style of Navajo jewelry. There are many others.

☾ Today the tradition of making jewelry is passed down from generation to generation.

Making Jewelry Today

These days jewelry is the most popular Native American craft. Navajo silversmiths in the Southwest sell thousands of jewelry items in galleries, at craft fairs, and over the Internet. Some Navajo jewelers today still use old stamps. They decorate their silver in ways that look traditional.

Other Navajo jewelers create highly polished modern designs. Today jewelers use a wider range of materials in their work. They might mix traditional designs and materials with new styles and materials.

Arts of the Navajo

In the 1880s, Navajo weavers used homemade looms like this one, made from tree limbs, rope, and string.

A Navajo rug is a labor of patience. It takes a long, long time to make.

Before the weaving itself can begin, a weaver needs fiber to use as thread or yarn. For Navajo weavers, the fiber is always wool.

Traditional Navajo weavers shear their churro (CHUR-roh) sheep. They wash and dry the **fleece**. They card, or comb, the wool to make the fibers straight and smooth. They use a tool called a **spindle** to spin the fibers into yarn. Next, if they plan to use colors other than the natural white, gray, brown, or black of the fleece, they dye the yarn.

☽ Weavers shear their sheep in the spring.

Collecting Silver

How did the Navajo get silver to make jewelry in the late 1800s? They traded weavings for silver wire, old teapots, solid "slugs" of silver, and coins. Silver made from Mexican **pesos** or American silver dollars was not the best, but it worked.

Most Navajo jewelers today have fine tools and materials. But the first Navajo silversmiths did not. They had no electric drills or polishing machines. They had to rummage for supplies. Their work surface was a rock or a scrap of railroad track. But they still made beautiful jewelry.

The silversmiths melted and softened their silver over an open fire. They hammered, twisted, and turned it. They filed and sanded to make the metal smooth and shiny.

As silversmiths began selling and trading more jewelry, they also began using finer tools. Their jewelry became more elaborate. They used metal stamps. By tapping the tip of a stamp into silver, a smith could make fancy designs. Other tools made it easier to form hollow beads. New machines made it easier to polish silver.

CHAPTER THREE
Silversmithing

Sometime in the mid-1800s the Navajo first began to make jewelry. They learned the craft from a Mexican *platero* (plah-TAY-roh), or silversmith. At that time Spanish settlers in the Southwest used silver in everything from horse saddles, bridles, and spurs to buttons, belts, and earrings.

◑ This silversmith displays a belt.

16

Special Sheep
Churro sheep came to the Four Corners area in the 1600s with Spanish settlers. These sheep are well suited to the desert because they are used to scrounging for food in the dry highlands of central Spain. Weavers who use the wool of the churro love its fleece. It is long, clean, and easy to spin.

To make a natural dye, weavers gather plants, nuts, berries, bark, roots, **lichens**, or tiny **cochineal** beetles. They pound the dyestuff into powder and dissolve it in water. Then they add the fleece and set the dye pot in the sun.

When the dye has done its work, the wool must be dried again. Finally it's ready to weave.

Because shearing, cleaning, dyeing, and spinning are so time-consuming, many Navajo weavers now use factory-made yarns and dyes. Others still prefer to prepare churro wool the old-fashioned way. They say the process helps them feel connected to their past.

9

🎧 Navajo rugs sometimes tell stories.

Reading a Rug

Over the years, the designs in Navajo rugs have become elaborate. Many rugs include symbols that can be "read." Some designs represent things in nature. A zigzagging line might stand for lightning. A series of steps might represent rainclouds. A cross may stand for Spider Woman or the morning star. Triangles might mean mountains. Bars might suggest a rainbow.

Preserving a Tradition

The art of Navajo basketmaking might have been lost. For years Navajo basketmakers could not earn enough money from their craft. By 1960 there were only about a dozen Navajo artists making baskets for a living.

But Mary Holiday Black was determined to save the basketmaking tradition. When she was 11, Mary learned how to make baskets from her grandmother. She kept making them. She taught nine of her 11 children and also her grandchildren. Now their work inspires others.

Today a single basket can take Mary four months to make. It may sell for as much as $8,000.

🔄 This ceremonial basket has a traditional design.

Reading a Basket

Navajo baskets tell stories. The stories are told through their colors and designs.

Some Navajo say that the center of a **ceremonial** basket represents the legendary spot where the Dineh emerged from the underworld. The part around the center is the earth. The black triangular designs in the middle represent the mountains. The red band stands for the life-giving rays of the sun. The black designs close to the rim represent the night and clouds that bring rain. The white pattern on the outer edge represents the dawn.

14

Even the colors in a Navajo weaving can have meaning. White suggests dawn. Blue suggests daytime. Yellow is for sunset. Black is for night.

Navajo weavers sometimes weave a secret message, such as a tiny good-luck seed into the fabric. Like a chameleon, these secret messages are always carefully hidden. Also the weavers always include a mistake so that the rug will not be perfect.

Giant Rugs

One of the biggest Navajo rugs ever made was woven in one piece by Minnie Manyhorses. It is 19 feet (6 m) wide and 31 feet (9 m) long. It took Minnie Manyhorses 23 months to weave this rug, and 23 helpers to prepare the yarn. Another enormous Navajo rug is called the Little Sisters Rug. It is actually many rugs woven by different weavers and joined together like a quilt. It measures 26 feet (8 m) wide by 28 feet (8.5 m) long.

11

CHAPTER TWO

Basketmaking

◆◇◆◇◆◇◆◇◆◇◆◇◆◇◆◇◆◇◆◇◆◇◆◇◆◇

For centuries, the Navajo have used and traded baskets. In ceremonies, the baskets are good for holding clay, cornmeal, or prayer sticks. They can even serve as drums.

Like rug weaving, Navajo basketmaking is a process that takes time. Each part of the process is as important as the others. It can't be rushed.

The fibers in Navajo baskets come from **sumac** and **yucca** plants. After gathering the plants, the basketmaker dyes some of the yucca fibers. Traditional baskets often use the colors black and red, made from natural dyes.

To make red basket dye, an artist might mix water with mountain mahogany root, juniper ashes, and black alder bark. To make black, the recipe calls for coal dust, **piñon** pine sap, and sumac leaves. When the dye is ready, the basketmaker soaks the yucca fibers in it.

Arts of the Navajo

To create a basket, Navajo artists use a method called coiling. The basketmaker twists sumac twigs together and forms a small loop for the center of the basket. Then he or she sews a strip of yucca fiber around the sumac core, covering it stitch by stitch. Slowly the basket grows. The finished basket will be round, shallow, and very strong.

🎧 Coiling takes skill and patience.

Word Workout

WORDS TO KNOW

analyzing dehydrated propelled speculated

conserve embedded sedated vital

In the Know Let's imagine we're researchers trying to protect endangered animals. We can try to act out a scene that uses all eight of these words.

SPELLING WORDS

heartbeat	seashell	brother-in-law
watermelon	after-school	northwest
twenty-five	old-fashioned	science fiction
teenager	seaweed	wading pool
full-time	self-respect	fingernail
eyelid	near-sighted	windshield
flashbulb	question mark	

Breakdown Each of these compound words includes two or more smaller words. I'll spell one of the smaller words and you can give the other word that makes the compound.

‹(fold here)›

Home-School Connection

Dear Family Member:

Things can get pretty tough for some animals. This week we're reading about sea turtles and the people who help them. Some sea turtles are endangered, which means the whole species is in danger of dying out. In *Interrupted Journey*, we're reading about the kinds of hard work it will take to keep these turtles around for the future.

I am learning to focus on the main idea in an article. Then I can connect all of the interesting details to this key idea.

This Week's Skills

Comprehension: main idea and details

Vocabulary: analogy

Spelling/Phonics: compound words, such as *doghouse*

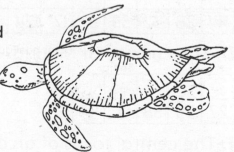

Name _____

What's the Idea?

Let's solve this puzzle to find a secret message.

- Write the answers to the clues.
- Then use the numbers under each letter to write the letters in the mystery message.
- You can check answers at the bottom of each page.

A. It pumps blood

35	43	12	32	22

B. Opposite of tall

15	7	31	21	34

C. The people in a movie theater

44	28	42	39	8	17	24	36

D. The country of Madrid

27	29	38	13	40

E. The events in a story

30	3	4	11

F. The central focus of an article

37	1	16	19

23	9	26	20

G. Another name for autumn

5	18	14	2

H. The name of a book or story

33	41	6	25	10

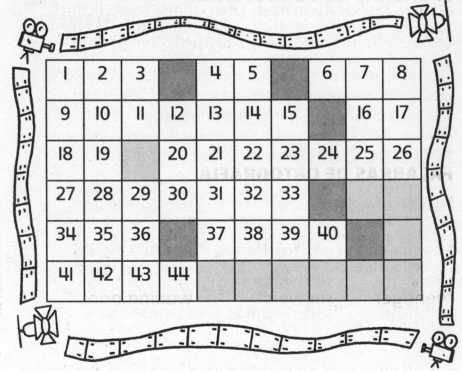

heart, short, audience, Spain, main idea, plot, tall, title: All of the details in an article support the main idea.

Ejercicio de palabras

PALABRAS DE VOCABULARIO

analyzing dehydrated propelled speculated

conserve embedded sedated vital

Expertos Supón que somos científicos y protegemos animales en peligro de extinción. Representemos una escena usando las ocho palabras de la lista.

PALABRAS DE ORTOGRAFÍA

heartbeat	seashell	brother-in-law
watermelon	after-school	northwest
twenty-five	old-fashioned	science fiction
teenager	seaweed	wading pool
full-time	self-respect	fingernail
eyelid	near-sighted	windshield
flashbulb	question mark	

Poco a poco Estas palabras están formadas por dos o más palabras más pequeñas. Deletrearé una de las pequeñas y tú vas a decir la otra palabra que forma la palabra compuesta.

(fold here)

Conexión con el hogar

Queridos familiares:

Para algunos animales la vida puede ser muy dura. Esta semana estamos leyendo acerca de las tortugas marinas y de la gente que las ayuda. Algunas tortugas marinas corren el riesgo de desaparecer, lo que significa que toda la especie está en peligro de extinción. En *Interrupted Journey* estamos leyendo sobre las duras tareas que habrá que realizar para que estas tortugas puedan seguir existiendo.

Estoy aprendiendo a distinguir la idea principal de un artículo. Así puedo conectar todos los detalles interesantes a esta idea clave.

Destrezas de la semana

Comprensión: idea principal y detalles

Vocabulario: analogía

Ortografía/Fonética: palabras compuestas, como *doghouse*

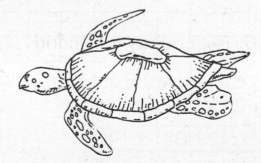

Nombre_____

¿Cuál es la idea?

Vamos a resolver este acertijo para descubrir un mensaje secreto.

- Escribe la respuesta para cada pista.
- Luego usa los números que aparecen debajo de cada letra para escribir las letras del mensaje secreto.
- Verifica las respuestas al pie de la página.

A. It pumps blood

35	43	12	32	22

B. Opposite of tall

15	7	31	21	34

C. The people in a movie theater

44	28	42	39	8	17	24	36

D. The country of Madrid

27	29	38	13	40

E. The events in a story

30	3	4	11

F. The central focus of an article

37	1	16	19

23	9	26	20

G. Another name for autumn

5	18	14	2

H. The name of a book or story

33	41	6	25	10

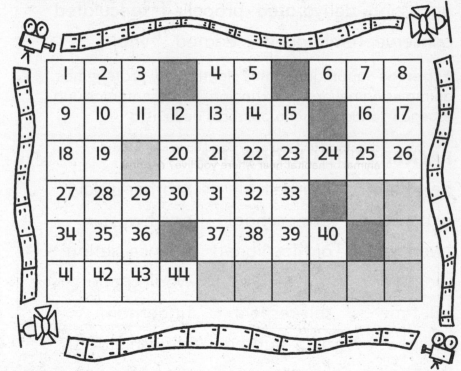

heart, short, audience, Spain, main idea, plot, tall, title: todos los detalles de un artículo apoyan la idea principal.

70

Comprehension Check

Summarize

Use a Main Idea Chart to list the main ideas and supporting details for each idea in *Saving Peregrine Falcons*. Then use your list of main ideas to write a summary blurb for a dust jacket for this book.

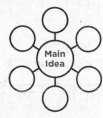

Main Idea

Think and Compare

1. Look back at pages 10 and 11. The author discusses DDT and its impact on peregrine falcons here. Write a sentence that summarizes the author's main idea for each paragraph. Add supporting details. *(Identify Main Idea and Details)*

2. Many people helped save the peregrine falcon. What is something that you do or could do to help protect an animal or habitat near where you live? *(Apply)*

3. Do you think it's important for people to try to save endangered species like the peregrine falcon? Explain why or why not and provide support for your position. *(Analyze)*

24

SAVING
Peregrine
FALCONS

by Barbara A. Donovan

Table of Contents

Introduction

A hunter spirals into the sky. Its prey—animals hunted for food—is below it. It spots the weakest flier in a flock of birds, and in an instant it aims downward. Propelled by gravity and rapid wing beats, it swoops through the sky. It dives at speeds that would kill other birds. Then when it nears its target, it kills or injures its prey with a blow from its feet. The predator, or killer, is the peregrine falcon. It's such a great hunter that it's been called the "king of birds."

↻ The name *peregrine* comes from the Latin word for "wandering."

2

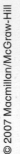

Index

23

Glossary

baffle *(BAF-uhl)* a device that slows or changes the flow of a fluid substance such as air or water *(page 4)*

captive breeding *(KAP-tiv BREED-ing)* producing and raising animals such as birds in a laboratory or a place other than its natural setting *(page 15)*

DDT *(dee-dee-TEE)* a powerful chemical that may harm animals and is used for killing insects *(page 10)*

extinct *(ek-STINGKT)* not existing any longer *(page 12)*

falconry *(FAL-kuhn-ree)* the sport of training falcons or other hawks to hunt and retrieve prey for humans *(page 12)*

fledge *(FLEJ)* the growing of flight feathers on a young bird *(page 17)*

flyway *(FLIGH-way)* a route that birds often follow as they migrate *(page 7)*

hacking *(HAK-ing)* raising birds in an artificial nest in such a way that they do not associate themselves with their human keepers *(page 13)*

migrate *(MIGH-grayt)* to move from one location to another and back according to the season *(page 7)*

raptor *(RAP-tur)* a bird such as a falcon, eagle, or owl that hunts other animals for food; a bird of prey *(page 4)*

stoop *(STOOP)* the high-speed dive or descent that a bird makes as it goes after its prey *(page 8)*

talon *(TAL-uhn)* an animal's claw, especially the claw of a bird of prey *(page 4)*

telemetry *(tuh-LEM-uh-tree)* the use of a device that measures heat or other quantities and sends that data to a receiver some distance away *(page 19)*

© 2007 Macmillan/McGraw-Hill

Peregrine falcons used to range across our country. Then over a period of about 20 years, they began to disappear. Scientists spent years trying to analyze why. It took the work of many dedicated people to bring back this falcon. Their efforts finally paid off. The peregrine falcon has made a comeback.

For years the peregrine falcon was endangered. Now office workers sometimes see them from skyscraper windows.

Chapter One

Mighty Hunter

The peregrine falcon is a **raptor**, a bird of prey. It has a body that is designed for hunting.

The falcon's eyes are set forward in its head. That gives it depth perception. Its vision is excellent. It can spot a bird in flight from a great distance away.

Inside its nostrils are **baffles**. Scientists have speculated that these small walls may slow the air rushing into the falcon's lungs as it dives. They let the falcon breathe. They also keep its lungs from bursting.

Like all raptors, the falcon's beak is curved. It's designed for tearing its prey's flesh. Unlike other raptors, the falcon also has a "tooth." This special notch on its beak breaks its prey's back.

The falcon's legs, feet, and curved **talons** are strong weapons. They can deliver a powerful blow to prey. Then, as the falcon flies away, it can grasp its prey.

Peregrine falcon's wings are long, narrow, and pointed. They help give this bird its incredible speed in a dive. In level flight its wings flap rapidly to keep it aloft.

Conclusion

Since 1973 the law has protected peregrine falcons. Breeding and release programs have built up their numbers. At last the peregrine falcon has staged a comeback from near extinction. DDT almost eliminated this raptor from our land. For 40 years people worked together to save this magnificent bird of prey. Biologists and other caregivers raised chicks in captivity and freed them. They built up the populations that we had knocked down. Now we understand that we must never again waste such a precious resource. We must conserve it for future generations. Peregrine falcons are here to stay, but only if we are careful.

Today city people as well as country people can see peregrine falcons flying around. As the birds struggled back from extinction, many found their old nesting spots were gone. Other predators, such as great-horned owls, had taken their nests. Some birds lost their nests as humans developed their habitats.

This time peregrine falcons adapted. They moved into cities around the country. Skyscrapers and bridges are now their cliffs and treetops. Pigeons and starlings provide a steady diet. It's not the life they used to have, but they've found a niche where they have no predators. And as long as humans don't interfere again, peregrine falcons might prosper.

On the Net

Many peregrine falcons now live on city rooftops. Others make nests on window ledges in skyscrapers. As a result, many people have set up Web cams to watch these birds and their nests. Search the Internet for "peregrine falcon web cam." Then sit back and watch these fascinating birds.

20

Nostrils

Forward-facing eyes

"Tooth"

Curved beak

Long, pointed wings

Strong legs, feet, and talons

5

Peregrine falcons live across the globe but not around very tall mountains or in Antarctica. They have one big requirement of their habitat. They must have lots of open space. That's because these falcons catch prey in the air. It takes a lot of room for a chase like that. That's why they choose open, flat land. Riverfronts or other shorelines also suit them. Their nests are on cliffs, ledges, or tall trees. From a high perch, they watch for prey.

An open meadow with lots of prey is a prime nesting site for a peregrine falcon. Birds are their favorite meal. They eat small birds and medium-size birds, such as grackles and flickers. They even hunt birds as large as ducks.

The Duck Hawk

The peregrine falcon is considered a kind of hawk because it hunts during the day. In fact, it is commonly called the "duck hawk."

© 2007 Macmillan/McGraw-Hill

Biologists also use high-tech ways to find out about peregrine falcons. Instead of having volunteers watching the skies, they watch computers instead. Scientists have started to put **telemetry** equipment on some falcons. These tiny computers send data about each bird to satellites. Biologists use that data to find out where the birds are nesting. They can tell where a falcon migrates. They can also tell where and for how long it stops to rest.

For years scientists and volunteers collected data on peregrine falcons. By 1999 there was cause for celebration. About 1,000 pairs nested in the United States. The peregrine falcon was not in danger anymore. It did not need to be on the endangered species list. It was, however, watched for five more years. By 2004 the watching time was over. The peregrine falcon was back!

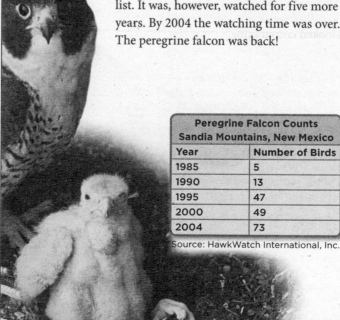

Peregrine Falcon Counts Sandia Mountains, New Mexico	
Year	Number of Birds
1985	5
1990	13
1995	47
2000	49
2004	73

Source: HawkWatch International, Inc.

Chapter Three

Success

The peregrine falcon needed our help, and we gave it. Year by year, thousands of falcon chicks were hacked. They'd been living in the wild. Had enough of them survived to make a difference? Biologists used many ways to check the populations. They needed to see if their plans had worked. If not, they needed new plans.

Groups like HawkWatch International count raptors as they migrate. Volunteers watch the skies. They identify each raptor they see. Then they count the birds. For the peregrine falcon, the counts from 1985 to 2004 looked encouraging.

DDT is still being sold in other countries around the world. Falcons and other birds that migrate to those countries are still in danger.

🎧 Four flyways cross the United States: the Pacific, Central, Mississippi, and Atlantic routes.

It is vital that peregrine falcons follow their prey when the seasons change. In winter, many birds **migrate**, or move, to warmer places with more food. The peregrine falcon follows. Some of these falcons move to southern states, such as Florida and Texas. Others fly much farther south. Some spend the winter in Mexico. Others fly all the way to South America. In spring they head north. It's time for them to breed.

To get where they're going, peregrine falcons travel along **flyways**. For birds a flyway is a migration super highway. Major flyways follow rivers, coastlines, mountain ridges, and valleys. And with other birds migrating at the same time, the flyway can be a movable feast for a hungry peregrine falcon.

When a falcon is on the hunt, a red-winged blackbird or other bird on the wing may never even see its predator speeding towards it. The peregrine falcon's **stoop**, or high-speed dive, is estimated to be between 100 and 120 miles per hour. Some estimates are as high as 200 miles per hour!

From the dead limb at the top of a tall tree or from the sky, a peregrine falcon seeks its prey. It looks for a weak, slow, or injured bird. Many birds fly around early in the day or evening. That's just when the falcon hunts.

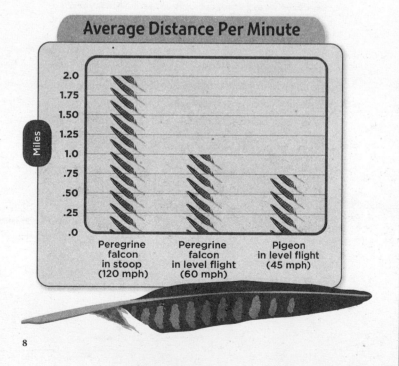

Average Distance Per Minute

Miles

2.0	
1.75	
1.50	
1.25	
1.0	
.75	
.50	
.25	
.0	

Peregrine falcon in stoop (120 mph)   Peregrine falcon in level flight (60 mph)   Pigeon in level flight (45 mph)

Once the chicks have **fledged**, or have grown the feathers they need to fly, then the rehabilitator gets them set for release. One goal is to make sure that the falcons don't identify with humans. They need to be birds. If they identify with humans, they won't be good hunters. They need to be able to hunt for their own food.

Rehabilitators want their falcons to steer clear of humans. To this end, Wingmasters has a noise program. They start it a few days before they set a bird free. They bang pots and pans. They make lots of loud noises to startle the fledgling. Surely this bird won't want to come near humans now.

Wildlife experts at Wingmasters care for raptors only. If a bird has serious injuries, they bring it to a veterinarian, where it is sedated. Then Wingmasters cares for it until it can be set free.

Some birds get better but still can't survive in the wild. For example, a broken wing may heal, but the bird may not be able to fly. These raptors may become part of Wingmasters' school programs. Having a live peregrine falcon in the classroom is fun.

Some peregrine falcon chicks lose their parents or their homes through storms or other means. Wingmasters tries to save them, too. They use a hacking box for this. With it they can care for the chick without having to handle it very much.

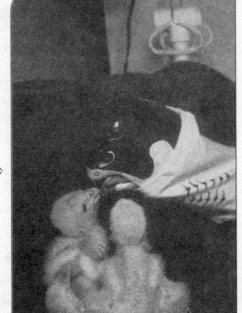

Rehabilitators use bird ⮌ puppets to feed chicks so that they will identify with birds and not with humans.

How a Falcon Hunts

1 Once a peregrine falcon chooses its victim, it begins its stoop. The falcon cups its wings and glides in tight S-curves. Like an acrobat, it loops through the air. Faster and faster it rockets toward its prey.

2 As it reaches its prey, the peregrine falcon uses its feet to strike it. Often the blow kills the victim. If the prey is still alive once they're on the ground, then the falcon uses its "tooth" to kill it.

3 If the prey falls to the ground, the falcon eats it where it fell. Because a peregrine falcon flies so fast, it can sometimes catch its prey before it hits the ground. Then the falcon carries its meal to a safe place to eat it. If the prey falls into the water, the falcon leaves it. Then it hunts again.

Chapter Two

Saving Peregrine Falcons

During the 1960s, scientists began to notice a decline in the population of birds. Peregrine falcons, condors, and other large birds were in serious trouble. Scientists soon discovered that **DDT** was the cause.

Back in 1939, scientists had found a new use for an old invention—DDT. When sprayed, DDT killed mosquitoes and other pests. Everyone hailed it as a miracle. It killed bugs that caused malaria and other diseases. It saved lives across the globe. But something was very wrong with DDT. It took about 20 years to find out how bad it really was.

Spotlight on Rachel Carson

In 1962 a scientist named Rachel Carson wrote *Silent Spring*. In this book she described how DDT and other chemicals affect us. She let people know that DDT was harmful. It was poisoning plants, animals, the soil, our water, and us. Rachel Carson led the charge to save our environment.

Animal Tracks Banding

Wildlife rehabilitators use banding to keep track of released raptors. A small metal band goes around one of the bird's legs. A number on the band tells where and when the bird was banded.

Not all peregrine falcons that need saving are part of a **captive breeding** program. Many people find injured peregrine falcons. They may be starving or dehydrated, in need of water. They may have dirt and lice embedded in their feathers. To save these birds, people call wildlife rehabilitators. These are people around the country who help make sick or injured animals well. One such group is in Springfield, Massachusetts. It's called Wingmasters.

🎧 A hacking box is set up just like a nest would naturally be.

Dr. Cade thought that hacking might work to save the endangered peregrine falcon. The difference would be that the falcons that he and others raised would be set free and not used for hunting.

In hacking a peregrine falcon is raised by people without the chick seeing them. A four-week-old chick is placed in a special hacking box, which is placed on a pole or cliff. For five weeks people feed the chicks and care for them the way adult falcons would do, but the chicks never see their human "parents." Soon they are big enough to hunt and survive on their own. That's when they fly away and make their own nests.

© 2007 Macmillan/McGraw-Hill

Effects of DDT on the Food Chain

DDT gets on plants and into the soil.

When the bird dies, bacteria returns DDT to the soil.

Insects eat the DDT as they eat the plants.

Peregrine falcons eat the birds that now have DDT in their bodies.

Birds eat the insects that ate the DDT.

Farmers had sprayed DDT on plants to kill insects eating their crops. The DDT stayed in the soil and on plants. Insects ate the plants and burrowed in the soil. DDT stayed in their bodies. From there the DDT worked its killing way along the food chain.

One deadly effect of DDT showed up in the peregrine falcons' eggs. DDT in the birds' bodies made their eggshells thin. When falcons sat on their eggs, the eggs broke. Soon too few young birds survived to replace their parents. By 1964 not one peregrine falcon nest could be found east of the Mississippi River. By 1970 the peregrines in the West were endangered. In 1972 the United States banned DDT.

In 1973 the United States government passed a law to protect animals in danger of becoming **extinct**. This law is the Endangered Species Act. When the peregrine falcon got on that list, it was officially an endangered bird. Now the federal government protected it. No one could kill or take a peregrine falcon, its young, or its eggs. No one could damage its nests. No one could bother its nesting places. It was against the law.

That plan worked fine for peregrine falcons that had survived DDT and other threats. But too few were left. Those few birds couldn't bring the peregrine falcon back from the brink of extinction. Then Dr. Tom Cade of Cornell University thought about **falconry**.

⦿ Scientists check the eggs and the chicks in falcon nests for any signs of trouble.

12

For hundreds of years, falconers had taken peregrine falcon chicks from nests for a sport called falconry. They raised these chicks in captivity as hunters. This is called **hacking**. First they tamed the falcons, and then they trained them to catch other wild birds for them. Using whistles and gestures, the falconer guided his hawk during the hunt. The falcon killed the prey and brought it back to its master.

⦿ Falcons do not like to be touched. Taming them for falconry takes patience and experience.

13

Word Workout

WORDS TO KNOW

embarrassment   grouchy   pennant

regulation   enthralled   inscribed

postmarked   resemblance

Put It in a Sentence I'll choose a word for you from the words above. You can put the word in a sentence. Then we'll try to make sentences that tell about someone who changed our world.

SPELLING WORDS

echoes   volcanoes   wolves   wives   sheriffs

photos   shelves   dominoes   cuffs   tornadoes

data   media   solos   staffs   sopranos

scarves   bacteria   buffaloes   thieves   loaves

Weird Ones Which three of these plurals do not end with **s**? Those words are almost always used only in the plural. The other words have common singular forms. I'll tell you the singular form, and you can spell the plural.

······(fold here)······

Home-School Connection

Dear Family Member:

Some people really know how to look at the best in other people. This week we're reading the story *How Tia Lola Came to Stay* about a family that is lucky to get a visit from Lola. She is their aunt, and she is a great judge of character. In fact, she can even see the good in people who try to keep it really well hidden.

While we read, we're making our own inferences about the characters and events. I'm learning how to use my own ideas about life to help me make sense out of what I read.

THIS WEEK'S SKILLS

Comprehension: make inferences

Vocabulary: word parts

Spelling/Phonics: plurals

Name _____

Home Hints

Imagine that we're planning to rent a house for a week this summer. Which of these ads sounds best to you? What information do you think they might be leaving out? Let's give our ratings and explain why.

	Ratings We Could Give
★★★★★	We'll Take It!
★★★★	Sounds Pretty Great
★★	Maybe, Maybe Not
★	We'd Rather Stay Home

Lots of Room Rent this sprawling mansion for the vacation of your life! Four big bedrooms, four baths, huge kitchen. Drive to Sunset Beach.

Rating:

Near the Best Beach in Town Cozy home with lots of rustic charm. Three bedrooms, one bath. Country kitchen with historic appliances. Perfect for a close family.

Rating:

Quirky Charm Interesting home in Sunset Cove with lots of unusual details. Two bedrooms plus a finished attic. Sleeps six at least.

Rating:

Home Away From Home Very comfortable ranch home. Close to the highway, convenient to shopping mall, movie theater, and miniature golf.

Rating:

Last-Minute Cancellation Our renters backed out at the last minute! Affordable two-bedroom townhouse. Newly painted, brand new appliances. Friendly community.

Rating:

Ejercicio de palabras

PALABRAS DE VOCABULARIO

embarrassment	grouchy	pennant
regulation	enthralled	inscribed
postmarked	resemblance	

Forma oraciones Voy a escoger una palabra de la lista de arriba. Forma una oración con esa palabra. Luego trataremos de formar oraciones que hablen de alguien que ha cambiado el mundo.

PALABRAS DE ORTOGRAFÍA

echoes	volcanoes	wolves	wives	sheriffs
photos	shelves	dominoes	cuffs	tornadoes
data	media	solos	staffs	sopranos
scarves	bacteria	buffaloes	thieves	loaves

Excepciones Hay tres de estos plurales que no terminan en **s**. ¿Cuáles son? Estas palabras se usan casi siempre sólo en plural. Las otras palabras tienen formas singulares. Te voy a decir el singular, y tú vas a deletrear el plural.

(fold here)

Conexión con el hogar

Queridos familiares:

Algunas personas realmente saben cómo ver lo mejor de los demás. Esta semana estamos leyendo el cuento *How Tia Lola Came to Stay* sobre una familia que tiene la suerte de que Lola los visite. Ella es una tía de la familia que sabe muy bien cómo juzgar el carácter de los demás. Hasta puede ver lo bueno en aquellos que tratan de esconderlo lo mejor posible.

Mientras leemos hacemos nuestras propias inferencias sobre los personajes y los sucesos. Estoy aprendiendo a usar las ideas que tengo sobre la vida para que me ayuden a comprender mejor lo que leo.

Destrezas de la semana

Comprensión: hacer inferencias

Vocabulario: partes de una palabra

Ortografía/Fonética: plurales

Nombre _____

¡A la búsqueda!

Piensa que estamos planeando alquilar una casa de verano por una semana. ¿Cuál de estos anuncios te parece mejor? ¿Crees que hay alguna información que no se menciona? ¿Cuál? Clasifiquemos cada anuncio y expliquemos por qué le damos esa clasificación.

	Ratings We Could Give
★★★★★	We'll Take It!
★★★★	Sounds Pretty Great
★★	Maybe, Maybe Not
★	We'd Rather Stay Home

Lots of Room Rent this sprawling mansion for the vacation of your life! Four big bedrooms, four baths, huge kitchen. Drive to Sunset Beach.

Rating:

Near the Best Beach in Town Cozy home with lots of rustic charm. Three bedrooms, one bath. Country kitchen with historic appliances. Perfect for a close family.

Rating:

Quirky Charm Interesting home in Sunset Cove with lots of unusual details. Two bedrooms plus a finished attic. Sleeps six at least.

Rating:

Home Away From Home Very comfortable ranch home. Close to the highway, convenient to shopping mall, movie theater, and miniature golf.

Rating:

Last-Minute Cancellation Our renters backed out at the last minute! Affordable two-bedroom townhouse. Newly painted, brand new appliances. Friendly community.

Rating:

Comprehension Check

Summarize

How does Jenna feel about her new school at the beginning of the story, and how do her feelings change? Use your Inference Chart to help you retell *The Right Move*. Analyze the clues the writer gives about Jenna, and make inferences about what you have learned.

Text Clues and Prior Knowledge	Inference

Think and Compare

1. Reread Jenna's conversations with her brother on pages 3, 7, and 10. What do you learn about the characters from these pages? How does Jenna feel about her brother? Explain your inferences with examples from the story. *(Make Inferences)*

2. What would you do if you had to move to a new school where you didn't know anyone? How would you try to fit in and feel comfortable? *(Evaluate)*

3. Why do you think Jenna's parents called her former coach, Gina, and told her about basketball tryouts at Jenna's school? Use clues in the text about Jenna's relationships with her parents and with Gina to explain your answer. *(Analyze)*

© 2007 Macmillan/McGraw-Hill

The Right Move

by Lisa Moran
illustrated by Sylvia Walker

Table of Contents

CHAPTER 1
New School Blues

Jenna McKinney lies on her bed with her hands folded under her head. She stares up at the ceiling, feeling more and more anxious. Tomorrow is the first day at her new school, Eastern Middle School. Dozens of questions run through Jenna's head. Will she find her way to her classes? Will the other students be friendly? What if she doesn't fit in? What if no one likes her?

Jenna turns her head to look at the pennant on the wall above her bed. It's from her old school basketball team, the Wilson Wildcats. Jenna had been a star forward on the team, and some of her best friends had played, too. Then again, Jenna had had a lot of friends at Wilson. She had lived in the same small town her whole life. Being at Wilson was like going to school with your extended family.

Now Jenna, her brother Sean, and her parents had moved into a new neighborhood in a big city. There were three times as many students at Eastern Middle School as there were at Wilson. Jenna let out a loud sigh. How was she ever going to make friends?

The Right Move

Her father laughs and tells Jenna to slow down. Sean tosses a piece of food at his sister, but she can tell by the gleam in his eyes that he is proud of her.

Jenna keeps babbling and her family listens and nods and eats. Jenna's mom brings out a special dessert, an orange pound cake with white icing with the number 14 on it. Sean fights Jenna for the numbers, but he lets her win.

"So, are you glad you tried out?" Jenna's mother asks in a playful, teasing tone.

"Definitely. I might sit on the bench the whole season, but who cares?" Jenna answers truthfully.

"I know one thing for sure. I'm glad I tried out."

She holds up a jersey from the team's regulation uniforms. Jenna's eyes light up. The team colors are orange and white, just like her favorite team, the Tennessee Volunteers. Jenna gets her jersey; it's number 14. She likes the sound of that.

Practice ends with the veteran players showing off a few cheers. Jenna likes the way that Coach Reynolds inspires everyone to work together as a team. Jenna has no trouble getting into the team spirit as the players try some cheers together. They do some last minute laps, and then practice is over. Jenna can hardly believe it, even though she knows that she will be so sore tomorrow. As they leave, everyone talks about the team and their chances of having a winning season. Most of the team members say good-bye to Jenna.

At dinner that night, Jenna is so enthralled with her new team that she talks a mile a minute. Her mother and father beam as they realize that at last, the real Jenna has surfaced—and is here to stay.

"The girls on the Hurricanes are so cool! I have a team buddy, named Mia, and she's a forward, too. I also met another girl who's new on the team, Rena. I invited her to come over to play basketball sometime."

The Right Move

After dinner the night before the first day, Jenna and her brother Sean play one-on-one basketball in the driveway. They've been shooting baskets together as long as Jenna can remember. Their evening games have always been Jenna's favorite part of the day.

"So, are you nervous about school tomorrow?" Jenna asks as she throws the ball toward the hoop. Sean is starting in the new high school and playing football for the team. She knows he must be at least a little bit worried.

"I don't know," Sean says without looking at his sister. "It'll be different. Why?"

"Well, I'm kind of nervous about Eastern. It just seems so big," Jenna confesses.

Sean grabs the rebound. "Don't worry, you'll be fine. Even if you are a terrible basketball player," he teases, and then smiles at Jenna.

The next morning, Jenna's stomach does flip-flops and she can't eat. Sean raises his eyebrow, as he knows breakfast is Jenna's favorite meal. When she arrives at Eastern, a wave of nausea passes through her entire body. The enormous building bears no resemblance to her old school, Wilson. Huge columns tower over three sets of double doors. Hundreds of students hurry up the wide staircase. A man with his shirtsleeves rolled up stands at the top of the stairs and shouts through a megaphone, urging students to hurry inside.

Jenna quickly joins the crowd and tries to blend in as students flow by her. They all seem to know one another! Groups of students talk and laugh together.

Suddenly Jenna realizes she's lost. Whom can she ask for directions without looking like an idiot? Jenna calls out to a girl walking by, "Excuse me, could you tell me where room 234 is?" The girl looks annoyed and points behind Jenna, who mumbles a thank you. "Great," Jenna thinks, "I'm going to be labeled the country bumpkin."

The rest of the first practice is difficult. Jenna sweats like crazy, and she can't remember ever working that hard in a Wildcats practice! Coach Reynolds expects the girls to give it their all, but she's fair, too. She expects them to make some mistakes. The seasoned players work hard, but they still find ways to joke around. They give their new teammates a lot of encouragement. Jenna is so glad that she made the team that she doesn't even realize how exhausted she is.

At the end of practice, Coach Reynolds gathers the team on the bleachers. She sends a player into the gym office, and the girl returns with a huge box. Coach Reynolds breaks out into a big smile as she tells the girls that she has something special for them.

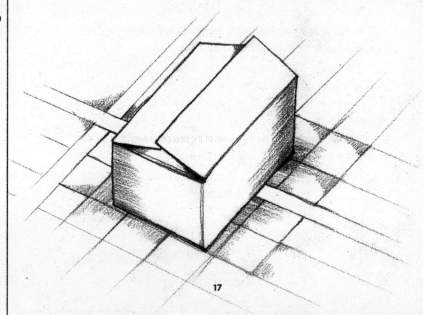

Jenna joins the other new players sitting on the bleachers. The veteran players are standing together in the middle of the gym floor.

"Okay, everyone. Settle down. I'm Coach Reynolds," the coach says in a booming voice. "Before we start practice, I've paired up each new player with one of our team members. You and your 'buddy' will have about five minutes to talk and get to know each other."

Coach Reynolds calls out the names of the new players and their buddies. Jenna is paired up with a girl named Mia. The two begin chatting. They hit it off and begin practice.

16

The Right Move

When the bell finally rings at the end of the first day, Jenna trudges home feeling pretty dejected. She is positive that she'll never make friends and will for all eternity be known as the idiot country girl.

Walking home alone, Jenna relives the nightmare that was math class. She had kept her head down trying to avoid being called on, but it proved futile. Suddenly Jenna heard the teacher asking her a question, and she was clueless as to the answer. Not wanting to seem ignorant, she gave the first answer that popped into her head. And it was wrong!

Jenna had sunk into her seat, as she knew how dumb her answer sounded. She thought she heard someone laugh in the back of the class, and as she glanced over her shoulder, she saw a girl whispering to her friend. Were the two girls laughing at her? Jenna had felt her cheeks redden in embarrassment. For the rest of the day, Jenna hadn't said another word.

"I've got to find a way to stay home sick from school tomorrow," Jenna thinks as she hurries home. "Or convince Mom to homeschool me."

5

Jenna arrives at home and wishes she could just dump her books and race over to her old friend Amy's house, but of course, she can't. Jenna takes a stab at doing her homework, but all she can concentrate on is how much she misses her friends.

At dinner, Jenna shuffles her food around on her plate without eating. Sean's seat is empty since he is at football practice. "He's probably already made friends," thinks Jenna.

Her mother tries to make conversation, but she gives up when Jenna manages only one-word answers and is sullen at best. Her parents exchange glances, and Jenna thinks her father mutters something about mood swings. Her parents drop the effort at conversation.

5

The following week at the first practice, Jenna has a bad case of butterflies. Jenna tries to push down the thoughts, but they keep surfacing.

Finding an empty locker, Jenna stores her stuff. Just as she's ready to leave the locker room, a girl says hello to her.

"Hi. I'm Rena," the girl says as she opens the locker next to Jenna's. Jenna looks up and smiles.

"I'm Jenna."

Rena babbles that she's only really played basketball with her brothers. Then she says that she'll probably get cut after practice today. Jenna reassures her that she won't. Jenna invites Rena to come over to her house to shoot hoops after school one day, and Rena accepts. Then Rena calls over another girl. Jenna turns around, and there staring at her is the girl who laughed at her in math class. Jenna wants to sink into the floor, but the girl just smiles and says, "Aren't you psyched about playing? I'm Bianca. Welcome aboard." Jenna smiles and nods.

15

CHAPTER 3
The Right Move for Jenna

Monday morning, Jenna makes her way slowly down the hall toward the gymnasium. The list of students who made the cut for the basketball teams is posted. Jenna desperately tries to maintain her cool, but her heart pounds a frantic rhythm.

Finding the list, Jenna moves in closely to read the small type. Jenna is sure her name is nowhere to be found on the list, but she quickly glances down the "M"s. Suddenly Jenna catches her breath and rereads the list two more times. No, there it is: "McKinney, Jenna." Jenna can hardly believe it—she made the team! She walks off as if floating on a cloud.

Jenna is so excited, she can't concentrate all day. At home that afternoon, she struggles to keep the surprise until dinnertime. When everyone is finally seated at the table, Jenna blurts out, "I made the team!"

Pandemonium breaks out. Her mom hugs her and her father and Sean cheer, with Sean cheering and clapping the loudest.

After dinner, Jenna quickly heads to her room and changes into sweatpants and a sweatshirt. Her eyes wander up to the trophy on the shelf above her desk. It's from last year's basketball division championships. The Wilson Wildcats were undefeated last season, with a 12–0 record. They won the championship game easily by a 22-point margin. The trophy is inscribed with the names of all of the players. Jenna runs her fingers over the list until tears blur her vision.

Suddenly she hears the front door slam. Jenna quickly wipes the tears from her eyes, and hurries to open her bedroom door. Sean soon comes bounding up the stairs with his backpack in one hand and a plate of food in the other.

"Got time for a quick game?" Jenna asks hopefully.

Sean shakes his head. Jenna can tell that he is exhausted. Sean mumbles something about "maybe tomorrow" if he can spare the time. Jenna wants to make a crack about his lack of enthusiasm, but decides she'd better not press him as lately Sean seems grouchy all the time.

Jenna gathers up her strength and goes down to shoot baskets alone. Again. Outside, the darkness makes Jenna feel even lonelier. Will she ever be a part of something special like she was at Wilson?

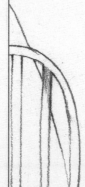

CHAPTER 2
"What If I'm a Big Flop?"

One Monday morning in late fall, Jenna takes her seat in homeroom as usual. She knows a few more students, but she still hasn't made any real friends. Jenna sighs. At least she's actually doing well in math.

During announcements, Jenna only half listens while she thinks over the material for her social studies quiz. Then she hears something that catches her attention.

"The boys' and girls' basketball teams will hold tryouts this Friday afternoon at 3:00 in the gym. All are welcome, but there are only a few places on the teams. So bring your best shot, and go Hurricanes!"

Jenna feels a rush of excitement. It would be so great to play her favorite sport again and be part of a team! Just as quickly, though, she feels her heart plummet. The new school is huge and must have a roster of players who are better than I am, thinks Jenna in despair. Jenna decides that she'll ask Sean what to do.

© 2007 Macmillan/McGraw-Hill

The Right Move

After the tryouts are over on Friday, Jenna hurries back to the locker room. "I am the worst basketball player of all time," Jenna thinks bitterly as she unties her shoes. She sits on the bench and keeps her head down so she won't have to look at the other girls' faces.

Jenna runs through the basketball tryouts in her head. Her ball handling was great, and she did fine on the dribbling drills. But she made only two of her five free-throw shots. Then the girl from the team who was guarding Jenna blocked her drive to the basket. Jenna never had an opportunity to show off her signature jump shot. Jenna groaned and thought, "I am such a loser."

Well, so I don't make the team, Jenna thinks as she stuffs her basketball shoes and clothes into her bag. It's not the total end of the world. Or is it? Plus it doesn't help that the girl from her math class, the one who laughed at Jenna on the first day, was at the tryouts, too. Jenna thought the other girl played well and would make the team. "I'm sure she'll tell all her friends what a loser I am," Jenna thinks dejectedly. She grabs her bag and runs out of the locker room, biting her lower lip to keep from crying.

© 2007 Macmillan/McGraw-Hill

The Right Move

"Guess what?" Jenna challenges her parents at dinner that night.

"I don't know. Why don't you tell us, since you seem to be bursting at the seams," her dad says with a smile. Jenna's mom is on her way back to the kitchen for another dish of food, but she pauses to hear what her daughter has to say.

"The girls' basketball team is holding tryouts on Friday," Jenna says. She waits for her parents to comment. Finally, they ask simultaneously if she is going to try out. Laughter breaks the tension.

"Part of me wants to," Jenna admits, "but I'm afraid I won't be good enough. Eastern is such a huge school. What if I'm a big flop?"

Both parents reassure Jenna that she is great. Jenna smiles, but secretly she knows tryouts might not have the perfect ending she wants.

After dinner, Jenna enthusiastically shoots a few warm-up baskets while she waits for Sean. As soon as she sees Sean, she almost pounces on him. Sean laughs and tells her to calm down.

After a quick first game, the two take a breather and sit in the driveway. "My school is holding tryouts for the girls' basketball team on Friday," Jenna bursts out.

Sean turns to look at Jenna. "Are you going to try out?" he asks. Jenna shrugs her shoulders and mutters that she doesn't know if she's good enough.

Sean tells her that she has to try out. "If nothing else," Sean says, "you have to keep up the family tradition of playing sports." Jenna smiles and agrees to try out. She crosses her fingers and hopes she makes it or at least makes some friends.

© 2007 Macmillan/McGraw-Hill

The Right Move

Wednesday afternoon, when Jenna arrives home from school, there's a letter in the mail addressed to her. It's postmarked with the name of her old town, but she doesn't recognize the return address. Jenna rips open the envelope and finds a letter from her former basketball coach, Gina. In the letter Gina tells Jenna that her parents contacted her because they were concerned that Jenna might not try out. Gina encourages her to go for it. After all, Gina had coached Jenna and her team to the championships.

Jenna puts down the letter and stares out the window. She thinks about Gina. Jenna knows in her heart that Gina would never recommend trying out for the team unless she thought Jenna had a good chance of landing a spot.

Jenna smiles as she remembers the championship game last year. It was such a rush when the final buzzer rang and the Wildcats won! She hit some big shots that game and scored 14 of the team's 44 points. Why shouldn't she at least try out for the Eastern Hurricanes? She has nothing to lose, and besides, it was high time Jenna stopped being such a wimp.

Word Workout

WORDS TO KNOW

broadcast   marveled   spicy   unsatisfactory

calculations   ravaged   undone   vigil

On the Page Let's think of a topic we both like. Then we can use the words above in talking about it.

SPELLING WORDS

permitting	patrolling	hovered	uttered
encouraged	marveled	accused	totaled
glimmering	confiding	reviving	stifling
unraveling	orbiting	labored	sloped
regretting	credited	referred	sipped

What Plus What All of these list words are a word plus an ending. I'll tell you two things to combine and you can spell it. For example, I'll tell you "**encourage** plus **ed**" and you'll spell **encouraged**.

(fold here)

Home-School Connection

Dear Family Member:

I know that school projects reflect the kids that make them. When I work carefully on a project, I know that it will turn out well. This week we're reading *The Night of the Pomegranate*, about a student who has some trouble with her science fair project. What makes this story interesting is that she does her project in a hurry even though she's very interested in the topic. I'm going to make inferences about how good her project turns out to be.

This Week's Skills

Comprehension: make inferences

Vocabulary: dictionary pronunciations

Spelling/Phonics: adding **ed** and **ing**

Name _____

Who Says?

What can you tell about people based only on what they say? Some of your inferences might be extremely accurate. Others might only be likely guesses.

Imagine that you overheard these comments at a school science fair. Let's talk about what we think each person is like. How old is each person? What can you say about their personalities? What might they look like?

I built the whole thing out of toothpicks and paperclips! It took me a long time to make.

My project shows all of the stages in the life cycle of a fruit fly. I worked hard and did my best. That's all that counts.

Ew! That one with worms on it is yucky.

My diagram explains how a DVD player works. It's very technical. Now I'm afraid people won't understand it. I should have thought of that.

Yikes! I almost smashed Mount Saint Helena with my elbow! I crushed it twice at home. Oh, no! I've spilled water on the volcano.

I can say with total confidence that this is will be the most interesting, best-prepared, and most imaginative project at the fair.

Ejercicio de palabras

PALABRAS DE VOCABULARIO

broadcast   marveled   spicy   unsatisfactory

calculations   ravaged   undone   vigil

Un mismo tema Pensemos en un tema que nos guste y hablemos de eso usando las palabras de arriba.

PALABRAS DE ORTOGRAFÍA

permitting	patrolling	hovered	uttered
encouraged	marveled	accused	totaled
glimmering	confiding	reviving	stifling
unraveling	orbiting	labored	sloped
regretting	credited	referred	sipped

Una cosa más otra Todas las palabras de esta lista están formadas por una palabra más una terminación. Te voy a decir dos cosas para combinar. Luego deletrea la palabra. Por ejemplo, si yo digo "**encourage** más –**ed,**" tú debes deletrear **encouraged**.

© Macmillan/McGraw-Hill

·······(fold here)·······

Conexión con el hogar

Queridos familiares:

Entiendo que los proyectos escolares son un reflejo de los estudiantes que los hacen. Cuando trabajo con cuidado en un proyecto, sé que va a quedar bien. Esta semana estamos leyendo *The Night of the Pomegranate,* acerca de una muchacha que tiene dificultades con su proyecto para la feria de ciencias. Lo que hace que este relato sea interesante es que la estudiante hace su proyecto de prisa, aunque el tema le interesa mucho. Voy a hacer inferencias sobre cómo va a quedar su proyecto.

Destrezas de la semana

Comprensión: hacer inferencias

Vocabulario: las pronunciaciones en el diccionario

Ortografía/ Fonética: agregar **ed** e **ing**

Nombre _____

¿Quién lo dice?

¿Qué puedes decir de la gente si te basas sólo en lo que dicen? Algunas de tus inferencias pueden ser muy precisas; otras, sólo conjeturas aproximadas.

Imagina que escuchas estos comentarios en una feria escolar de ciencias. Vamos a comentar cómo pensamos que es la persona. ¿Cuántos años tiene? ¿Qué podemos decir de su personalidad? ¿Qué apariencia tendrá?

Ew! That one with worms on it is yucky.

My diagram explains how a DVD player works. It's very technical. Now I'm afraid people won't understand it. I should have thought of that.

I built the whole thing out of toothpicks and paperclips! It took me a long time to make.

Yikes! I almost smashed Mount Saint Helena with my elbow! I crushed it twice at home. Oh, no! I've spilled water on the volcano.

My project shows all of the stages in the life cycle of a fruit fly. I worked hard and did my best. That's all that counts.

I can say with total confidence that this is will be the most interesting, best-prepared, and most imaginative project at the fair.

Comprehension Check

Summarize

What do you think are some of the most important discoveries made by ancient astronomers? Use an Inference Chart to support your findings.

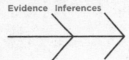

Evidence Inferences

Think and Compare

1. Ancient peoples had a keen interest in watching the sky. Why do you think people in ancient civilizations were so interested in astronomy? *(Make Inferences)*

2. Sky watchers in ancient times developed calendars, recorded eclipses and other events, and built observatories. These tasks required various skills in math, science, writing, engineering, and construction. If you were an ancient astronomer, which task would you have most wanted to take part in? Why? *(Evaluate)*

3. What do you think was the most important discovery made by ancient astronomers? Explain why you think so. *(Analyze)*

24

Stargazers
Astronomers in Ancient Times

by Jo Pitkin

Table of Contents

Introduction

Have you ever gazed up into a clear night sky? Did you wonder about what you saw? Since ancient times, people have marveled at the sights they have seen in the sky.

Astronomy is the study of stars, **planets**, and other objects in space. The term comes from two Greek words that mean "star" and "to name."

Astronomers are people who observe stars, planets, **comets**, and other distant objects. Modern astronomers use instruments to observe the sky. They have computers to make calculations about data. They record what they see on computers, too. Calculators help them solve mathematical problems. Powerful **telescopes** give them a clear look deep into the universe. They launch space probes and satellites into space. These broadcast photographs of planets and **galaxies** far from Earth.

© 2007 Macmillan/McGraw-Hill

Stargazers of Ancient Times

Index

Glossary

astrolabe *(AS-truh-layb)* an ancient instrument used to measure the height of objects in the sky *(page 4)*

astronomer *(uh-STRAWN-uh-mur)* a person who observes the stars, planets, comets, and other distant objects *(page 2)*

astronomy *(uh-STRAWN-uh-mee)* the scientific study of stars, planets, and other objects in space *(page 2)*

comet *(KOM-it)* a bright object in space that looks like a star with a long tail of light *(page 2)*

constellation *(kon-stuh-LAY-shuhn)* a group of stars that forms a pattern in the sky that looks like a picture *(page 6)*

eclipse *(i-KLIPS)* a darkening or hiding of the sun, a planet, or a moon by another heavenly body *(page 3)*

galaxy *(GAL-uhk-see)* a very large group of stars *(page 2)*

observatory *(uhb-ZUR-vuh-tawr-ee)* a special building that has telescopes for observing and studying the sun, moon, planets, and stars *(page 5)*

petroglyph *(PET-ruh-glif)* an ancient carving or drawing made on rock *(page 7)*

planet *(PLAN-it)* one of nine large heavenly bodies that orbit the sun *(page 2)*

solstice *(SOHL-stis)* one of the two times a year when the sun is farthest from the equator of Earth *(page 11)*

telescope *(TEL-uh-skohp)* an instrument that makes distant objects seem larger and nearer *(page 2)*

Stargazers of Ancient Times

Ancient astronomers didn't have scientific equipment. They had no binoculars or telescopes or computers. But they did carefully observe the closer planets and the stars. They used their eyes. What they saw helped them develop ideas about the universe. They created theories about the size and shape of Earth and how it was positioned in space.

Ancient sky watchers kept records of their observations. They noted how the stars and planets moved. They recorded **eclipses** of the moon and sun. They studied falling stars and followed the changing shape of the moon. Sometimes they recorded what they saw in pictures or in writing on bark, shell, bone, or papyrus. Sometimes they kept records by carving notches on sticks. Some made paintings on cave walls using inky black and spicy red colors that have survived until modern times.

Studying the Sky

Why did early peoples study the sky? They were curious about their world. Knowing about the stars and skies helped them in their natural world. They followed stars when they sailed the sea. They used their observations of the motions of the sun and the cycles of Earth's moon to tell time. The sun's position in the sky pointed to the changing seasons, and it told them when to plant and harvest their crops.

What kinds of tools did these ancient astronomers use? The oldest tool is likely a straight stick called a gnomon (NOH-man). Ancient astronomers measured the shadow cast by the stick as Earth moved around the sun. In this way they could tell the time of day and the season of the year.

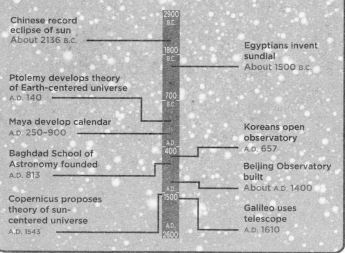

A Greek astronomer probably ⮌ invented the **astrolabe** in the second or third century B.C. The astrolabe measured the height of objects in the sky above Earth's horizon.

Conclusion

From one side of the globe to the other, people long ago watched the skies. They observed the sun and tracked the movements of the planets and stars. They identified comets and noted eclipses of the sun and moon. They built observatories and recorded what they saw. The work of ancient astronomers helped set the stage for the great strides of the present day.

Stargazing Through Time

Chinese record eclipse of sun
About 2136 B.C.

Egyptians invent sundial
About 1500 B.C.

Ptolemy develops theory of Earth-centered universe
A.D. 140

Maya develop calendar
A.D. 250–900

Koreans open observatory
A.D. 657

Baghdad School of Astronomy founded
A.D. 813

Beijing Observatory built
About A.D. 1400

Copernicus proposes theory of sun-centered universe
A.D. 1543

Galileo uses telescope
A.D. 1610

2900 B.C.
1800 B.C.
700 B.C.
A.D. 400
A.D. 1500
A.D. 2600

Italy

The telescope was invented in Holland in 1608. Galileo Galilei (gal-i-LAY-oh gal-i-LAY-ee) from Italy made his own improved telescope in 1610 and used it to discover many stars. He saw the craters on the ravaged surface of the moon. He discovered four moons of Jupiter. He learned about the phases of Venus. The invention of the telescope was a milestone in astronomy. Many ancient theories were undone. This invention marked the beginning of modern astronomy.

This is the telescope ↪ that Galileo used.

©2007 Macmillan/McGraw-Hill

Later the sundial was invented in Egypt, in about 1500 B.C. Like a gnomon, the sundial shows daylight hours by means of the shadow cast as Earth moves around the sun.

Some ancient peoples built observatories. An **observatory** is a special building where astronomers observe and record things that happen in the sky. There are ancient ruins of observatories in many different parts of the world.

England's Stonehenge

In England, Ireland, and Scotland, ancient people built circles of standing stones and stone pillars. Some modern scientists believe that these stone circles functioned as astronomical observatories. England's Stonehenge is the most famous of these circles.

The large monument features stones set in a pattern. Some of the positions of the stones seem to show where the sun and moon would rise and set. Stonehenge may have helped ancient people predict the seasons, eclipses, and other important events in nature.

CHAPTER ONE

Sky Watchers in the Americas

Ancient peoples in what are now North America, Central America, and South America studied the sky. They developed myths and stories about what they saw. They built huge, ornate temples where they could watch the skies and record their observations. They then created detailed calendars based on their observations.

Mound Builders

From 1000 B.C. to A.D. 1400, Mound Builders lived in a large area between the Great Lakes and the Gulf of Mexico. These Native Americans built enormous, flat-topped mounds of dirt in valleys and plains. Some mounds are in the shapes of birds, snakes, and other animals. Others are circles, squares, and straight lines. Some scientists believe that these mounds represent individual stars or groups of stars in **constellations**.

◖ Did ancient peoples use this mound to help predict eclipses?

Differing Views

Compare Copernicus's view of the universe with that of Ptolemys.

◖ Ptolemy's view

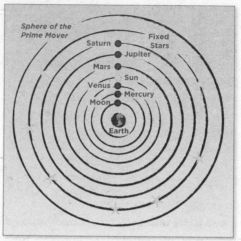

◖ Copernicus's view

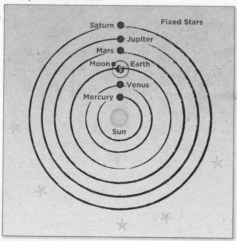

CHAPTER FOUR

From Ancient Astronomers to Galileo

Ancient European astronomers also made many contributions. Most sky watchers in Greece believed that Earth was a huge ball in the center of the universe. The Greek astronomer Claudius Ptolemy (TAW-luh-mee) collected their ideas in a book.

Poland

In Poland an astronomer named Nicolaus Copernicus (koh-PUR-ni-kus) found theories about the universe to be unsatisfactory. Copernicus believed that the sun was the center of the universe. He also believed that the planets and other objects in our solar system circled around the sun.

↻ This bronze monument shows Copernicus holding his model of the solar system.

↻ This rock art drawing, called a **petroglyph**, was made by the Anasazi thousands of years ago.

Anasazi

The Anasazi (ah-nuh-SAH-zee) lived in cliff dwellings, clusters of apartments carved from rocky hillsides in the Southwest. The Anasazi built observatories to track the sun's movement. They sketched drawings of the moon and a star on rocks in Chaco Canyon in present-day New Mexico. These ancestors of today's Pueblo Indians also began to build a stone sun temple in what is now Colorado. This temple may have been used to help mark the change of the seasons. Its windows seem to face the direction of the setting and rising sun.

Maya

The Maya (MIGH-uh) lived in what is now southern Mexico and Central America. The Mayan culture reached its height from about A.D. 250 to 900. The Maya observed the movement of the sun, moon, and planets and predicted eclipses based on the movements of the sun and moon. The Maya built temples for observation.

The Maya developed a calendar. Their calendar is based on the daily and yearly movements of the sun. It is also based on the phases of the moon and the rising and setting of Venus. Mayan astronomers figured out that the solar year is 365.2420 days, which is very nearly correct. They used their calendar to track time.

This observatory ⮌ helped the Maya study the movement of the planet Venus.

This manuscript ⮌ shows ancient Arabic astronomers at work.

Arab Empire

During the Middle Ages astronomy in most parts of the world entered a dark period. But it flourished in the Arab Empire. Beginning in the 600s, Arabs discovered, translated, and studied Greek astronomy books. In the 700s Arab astronomers founded observatories in Damascus and Baghdad. In the 800s an Arab astronomer wrote tables that predicted star and planet positions in the future. In the 900s an Arab astronomer discovered a new way to figure out the positions of the planets and made a detailed list of the stars.

CHAPTER THREE

Astronomers in the Middle East

Like their counterparts in Asia, the Americas, and Africa, ancient astronomers in the Middle East observed the movements of the moon and planets. Somehow they were able to do this with few tools.

Babylon (BAB-i-lon) was an ancient civilization near what is now Iraq. Ancient astronomers in Babylon studied the movements of the planets over 3,000 years ago. They observed five "wandering stars." These "stars" were the planets Mercury, Venus, Mars, Jupiter, and Saturn. Babylonians also predicted eclipses of the moon.

Babylonians recorded observations of Venus in about 1600 B.C. They made records of eclipses in about 800 B.C. and also created a star calendar about 100 years later.

⌒ Babylonians recorded their sightings on clay tablets.

Aztecs

The Aztecs lived in Mexico from about A.D. 1200 to 1521. They believed that their sun god led them to found a city on a small island in the valley of Mexico. Like the Maya, the Aztecs also built temples where they spent vigils observing the sky. They also developed a sun calendar.

The Aztecs carved a giant sun calendar out of stone. The 12-foot-wide calendar weighs 24 tons. It was originally painted white, red, blue, and yellow. The center of the calendar is a circle with an image of the sun god. The calendar also has pictures that symbolize the Aztec days, months, and sun cycles. The calendar was originally placed facing south in the capital of the Aztecs. After the Spanish conquered the Aztec's capital, however, the calendar was buried. It was found again in 1790.

Incas

The Incas lived in what is now Peru in South America from about 1438 to 1535. They believed that their people were born of the sun god. The Incas watched the movement of the sun to help them figure out when to plant crops on terraces on steep hillsides. They built a series of tall sticks on the hills. When the sun rose or set between the sticks, the Incas knew it was time to plant at that particular spot.

10

Egypt

Ancient Egyptians needed water to grow their crops. They needed to know exactly when the Nile River would flood so that they could plant their crops after the flood. Egyptian astronomers discovered that the Nile flooded its banks when a star called Sirius appeared in the east at dawn. By observing and then predicting the star's appearance, the Egyptians knew when to plant, grow, and harvest their crops.

Egyptian astronomers also developed a calendar. The calendar, like our own, had $365\frac{1}{4}$ days. Each day was divided into 24 hours. There were 12 hours of daylight and 12 hours of darkness.

↻ The Egyptians measured time with sundials.

15

The Mysterious Dogon

The Dogon live in Mali, West Africa. Their culture has myths and legends, which date to before 3200 B.C., and reveal the Dogon's great knowledge of astronomy. They knew about the star Sirius, the brightest star in the sky. They also knew about its small companion star, Sirius B, which cannot be seen with the naked eye. They knew about Saturn's rings. The mystery is how the ancient Dogon were able to obtain this knowledge. These astronomical features can only be found with a telescope, which the ancient Dogon did not have.

This African cave art appears to show planets.

Africa

People in ancient African cultures also studied the skies. Tribes in East Africa developed calendars based on astronomy. For example, the Mursi people in Ethiopia developed a calendar based on the cycles of the moon. Scientists have also discovered a Stonehenge-like structure in Kenya. It was built about 300 B.C. This circle of stone columns seems to line up with the positions of certain stars and constellations.

Like the Maya and Aztecs, the Incas also built temples that were used as observatories. One of their most important observatories was the Temple of the Sun. It was covered in gold, which the Inca called "the sweat of the sun." The location of the temple helped the Incas predict events, such as the sun's solstices. A **solstice** happens two times a year when the sun is farthest from the equator of Earth.

◔ Ancient astronomers watched the skies from the Temple of the Sun, located in Cuzco, the capital city of the Inca Empire.

CHAPTER TWO

Astronomers in Asia and Africa

People in ancient Asia and Africa also watched the sky. They, too, recorded what they saw and built observatories.

In ancient China priests recorded important questions on shells and animal bones. Some of the writing refers to stars and eclipses. The earliest known record of an eclipse of the sun was found on an animal bone in China. The description was written in about 2136 B.C. It says "three flames ate the sun and a great star was seen."

Ancient Chinese astronomers often worked for the rulers of China. They recorded the appearance of comets. They identified 300 constellations. The Chinese felt that the stars could tell what would happen on Earth.

☻ The Beijing Observatory was built in the 1400s in China.

12

In about A.D. 675 a Japanese astronomer named Mim opened the first observatory in Japan. Mim also founded the Imperial Department of Astronomy. In October A.D. 684, Japanese astronomers observed Halley's Comet, a ball of snow, ice, and dust with a glowing tail. Halley's Comet regularly passes by Earth every 76 years. The last sighting of the comet was in 1985.

The oldest known existing observatory is in Korea. Korean astronomers climbed to the top of the 30-foot tower to make their observations through an opening in the roof.

This beehive stone ⤸ structure in Korea was built in about A.D. 657.

13

Word Workout

WORDS TO KNOW

administer   devastating   mitigate

calamities   evacuate

In the News Let's try to imagine a news story that might use all five of these words. We'll take turns making up sentences about the topic we choose.

SPELLING WORDS

vault	noodle	fraud	thaw	rookie
slouch	blouse	sought	groove	scoot
poise	boost	scowl	corduroy	avoid
scrawl	sooty	employ	browse	snoozed

Color Cards The vowels in these words are tricky. Let's make a special set of practice cards. We'll need two pens: one black and one red. We'll write the consonants in black, but the vowels in bright red.

Home-School Connection

Dear Family Member:

Tough times can bring out the best in some people. That's a broad statement, but I know it's true. This week we're reading "Helping Hands," which has several articles about how real people have really helped. One of the articles tells how people in Florida worked together to save zoo animals after a terrible hurricane. The details are fascinating, but this week we're focusing on what big ideas we can form based on what we read.

This Week's Skills

Comprehension: make generalizations

Vocabulary: context clues

Spelling/Phonics: vowels

Name _____

In General

Only some general statements are true. Others are false or just plain silly. Look at the following generalizations. Do you think they are true, false, or ridiculous?

Examples of Generalizations

All dogs have to go to school.

A team of scientists can help others.

One tree can save the world.

Now we can make some generalizations of our own. We'll choose one word from column A and add it to ideas from columns B and C. Then let's talk about whether each generalization is true, false, or too ridiculous for words.

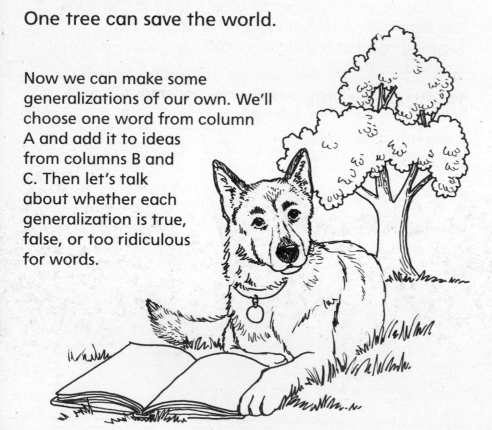

A	B	C
All	teachers	breathe
No	students	work to improve the world
Every	people	can help others
Some	dogs	hope that the future will be better
Almost no	scientists	read the news every day
Almost all	trees	have to go to school
Quite a few	politicians	are honest
One	babies	learn something new every day
A team of	musicians	can save the world

Write here if you want to make notes.

_____

_____

_____

_____

Ejercicio de palabras

PALABRAS DE VOCABULARIO

administer   devastating   mitigate

calamities   evacuate

En las noticias Imaginémonos una noticia del periódico que contenga estas cinco palabras. Nos turnaremos para formar oraciones sobre un tema que escojamos.

PALABRAS DE ORTOGRAFÍA

vault	noodle	fraud	thaw	rookie
slouch	blouse	sought	groove	scoot
poise	boost	scowl	corduroy	avoid
scrawl	sooty	employ	browse	snoozed

A dos colores Las vocales de estas palabras son un poco complicadas. Vamos a hacer un juego de tarjetas para practicar. Necesitamos dos lápices: uno negro y uno rojo. Vamos a escribir las consonantes en negro y las vocales en rojo vivo.

(fold here)

© Macmillan/McGraw-Hill

Conexión con el hogar

Queridos familiares:

Los momentos difíciles pueden hacer resaltar las mejores cualidades de la gente. Aunque esto es muy general, creo que es verdad. Esta semana estamos leyendo *Helping Hands*, que contiene varios artículos sobre personas reales que han sido realmente de gran ayuda. Uno de los artículos cuenta cómo la gente de Florida colaboró para salvar a los animales del zoológico después de un huracán terrible. Los detalles son fascinantes, pero esta semana nos concentramos más en las ideas generales que nos podemos formar basándonos en lo que leemos.

Destrezas de la semana

Comprensión: hacer generalizaciones

Vocabulario: claves de contexto

Ortografía/Fonética: vocales

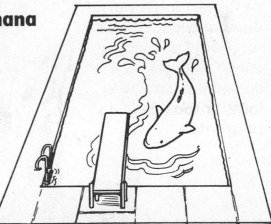

Nombre_____

En general

Sólo algunos enunciados generales son verdaderos. Otros son falsos o no tienen ningún sentido. Mira las siguientes generalizaciones. ¿Piensas que son verdaderas, falsas o absurdas?

Examples of Generalizations

All dogs have to go to school.

A team of scientists can help others.

One tree can save the world.

Ahora podemos hacer algunas generalizaciones por nuestra cuenta. Vamos a escoger una palabra de la columna A y a agregarle ideas de las otras dos columnas. Luego veremos si cada generalización es verdadera, falsa o totalmente absurda.

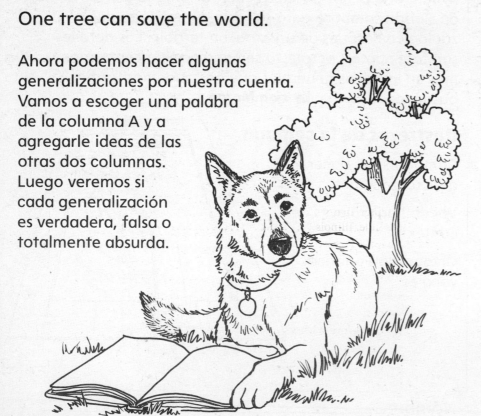

A	B	C
All	teachers	breathe
No	students	work to improve the world
Every	people	can help others
Some	dogs	hope that the future will be better
Almost no	scientists	read the news every day
Almost all	trees	have to go to school
Quite a few	politicians	are honest
One	babies	learn something new every day
A team of	musicians	can save the world

Tus notas:

_____

_____

_____

_____

_____

116

Comprehension Check

Summarize

Retell the story of *The Great Flood of 1993*. For each chapter in the book, write down two details. Then make a generalization about that chapter.

Think and Compare

1. Reread pages 7–9 and 17. What were some of the ways disaster relief organizations like the Red Cross and the Salvation Army helped during the flood? Use details from the story to form generalizations about how some charities aid disaster victims. *(Summarize/Identify Details)*

2. Was there ever a time when you volunteered to help during a disaster? If not, how do you think you might pitch in if a disaster ever strikes your community? *(Apply)*

3. During a response to a disaster, relief organizations need all kinds of help from volunteers. Besides donating money and supplies, how could people help a relief agency during a crisis? *(Evaluate)*

The Great Flood of 1993

THE GREAT FLOOD OF 1993

by Lisa Moran

Table of Contents

Introduction

The Great Flood of 1993 was the worst flood in modern U.S. history. The flood affected nine Midwestern states during the spring and summer of that year. The entire state of Iowa was declared a disaster area. Nearly 50 people died. About 54,000 people had to **evacuate**, or leave their homes. The flood damaged or totally destroyed at least 50,000 homes.

But the victims of the floods were not alone. Thousands of people came out to help. Relief workers rescued homeowners and provided food and shelter. Volunteers worked to hold back floodwaters.

Area newspapers and magazines reported daily on the flood. Here are just a few of the stories they told of the many helping hands during the Great Flood of 1993.

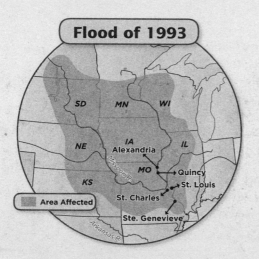

Flood of 1993

SD MN WI

NE IA
Alexandria

KS MO Quincy
St. Louis
St. Charles
Ste. Genevieve

Area Affected

Index

Glossary

breach *(BREECH)* to break through *(page 12)*

calamity *(kuh-LAM-uh-tee)* deep trouble or misery *(page 10)*

crest *(KREST)* to reach the highest point *(page 16)*

donate *(DOH-nayt)* to give or contribute *(page 6)*

evacuate *(i-VAK-ew-ayt)* to remove from an area of danger *(page 2)*

levee *(LEV-ee)* man-made wall built to hold back floodwaters *(page 4)*

mildewed *(MIL-dewd)* covered with a fungus that grows in damp conditions *(page 9)*

nonprofit *(non-PROF-it)* not producing a profit *(page 7)*

peninsula *(puh-NIN-suh-luh)* a piece of land that sticks out into water from a larger body of land *(page 16)*

personnel *(pur-suh-NEL)* people employed in work or service *(page 8)*

relief *(ri-LEEF)* easing distress *(page 7)*

sewage *(SEW-ij)* the waste matter carried off by drains *(page 11)*

sludge *(SLUJ)* mud, muck, or ooze *(page 9)*

treatment plant *(TREET-mohnt PLANT)* the facility in a city that cleans wastewater so that it can be used for drinking and other purposes *(page 4)*

The Great Flood of 1993

CHAPTER ONE

Dateline: Iowa

The Midwest floods hit Iowa in July 1993. On July 10 heavy rains poured down on ground that was already soaked. The next day, the rising Raccoon River flooded. River waters broke through the **levee** protecting Iowa's capital city of Des Moines. A levee is a man-made wall. Levees keep river waters from flooding populated areas. But sometimes they fail.

The raging waters flooded Des Moines's water **treatment plant**. The plant shut down. For 12 days 250,000 people in Des Moines were without clean water for drinking. Residents couldn't bathe, wash their clothes, or even flush their toilets. There wasn't enough water to use in fighting fires. The mayor of Des Moines shut down all but the most essential businesses. Des Moines needed clean water—and fast. Soon help was there.

Help came from the Federal Emergency Management Agency, or FEMA. FEMA goes in to help when the President of the United States declares a place a disaster area. The agency tries to mitigate, or help make better, some of the problems. It finds people shelter. It repairs buildings and provides insurance money. In Des Moines, FEMA took charge of getting fresh water to the city.

Workers used boats and walkie-talkies ➲ to organize rescue efforts.

Conclusion

Thousands of volunteers and relief workers helped when disaster struck. Help came from government agencies, charities like the American Red Cross, and ordinary citizens who pitched in to help in any way they could. The states affected by the Great Flood of 1993 have rebuilt their towns and recovered from the flood.

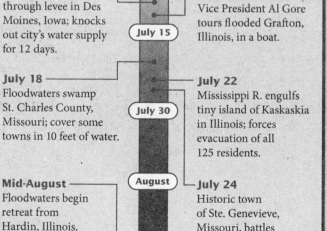

The Great Flood of 1993

July

July 11
Raccoon R. breaks through levee in Des Moines, Iowa; knocks out city's water supply for 12 days.

July 15

July 13
Vice President Al Gore tours flooded Grafton, Illinois, in a boat.

July 18
Floodwaters swamp St. Charles County, Missouri; cover some towns in 10 feet of water.

July 30

July 22
Mississippi R. engulfs tiny island of Kaskaskia in Illinois; forces evacuation of all 125 residents.

August

Mid-August
Floodwaters begin retreat from Hardin, Illinois.

July 24
Historic town of Ste. Genevieve, Missouri, battles flooding Mississippi R.

Kids Help

Young people pitched in all over the Midwest during the Great Flood of 1993.

In Ste. Genevieve, Missouri, 18-year-old Jennifer Murphy helped fill sandbags until she had blisters.

A fifth-grade class in St. Charles County, Missouri, collected games and toys for children in a flood shelter.

Twelve-year-old Billy Johnson delivered sandwiches and drinks from a Salvation Army van in St. Louis, Missouri.

Many others did what they could. And that was more than enough.

The floodwaters receded in the fall of 1993. The Midwest began to clean up. Relief organizations continued to help. The Salvation Army started an effort called Operation Noah's Ark. The operation was a long-term recovery effort. It helped victims rebuild after the flood. Operation Noah's Ark collected hundreds of thousands of dollars. It provided cleaning supplies, building materials, clothing, furniture, and food.

The Great Flood of 1993 destroyed many lives. But many more people were saved, thanks to the heroic efforts of countless volunteers and aid workers.

FEMA gave the task to the Army Corps of Engineers. The Corps is part of the U.S. Army. It provides help during disasters. In Des Moines, the Corps began pumping floodwaters out of the treatment plant. It set up emergency water stations and trucked in gallons of fresh water. Des Moines residents used anything they had—empty water bottles, milk jugs, coolers—to collect water from the Corps's stations.

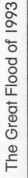

It took 12 days to restore the flooded water treatment plant in Des Moines, Iowa. But it was another week before the water was safe enough to drink.

Another organization that stepped in to help with the water shortage was the National Guard. Each state has its own National Guard units. The Iowa National Guard found a special way to help the residents of Des Moines. It offered free showers at its headquarters in Camp Dodge, eight miles outside of Des Moines.

A member of the Guard spoke to a reporter for *National Geographic* magazine. He said that more than 5,000 people had used the showers in less than a week. A local hotel had **donated** soap for people who had not brought their own.

The Great Flood of 1993

Every day Anderson held a strategy meeting at a command center in the city hall to administer everyone's efforts. He met with workers from the National Guard, the Coast Guard, the Red Cross, and even prison inmates. He divided the 4,400 residents of Ste. Genevieve into "sectors." Volunteers checked and sandbagged the levee. Dump trucks loaded rocks from a nearby quarry behind the floodwall.

In the end Ste. Genevieve was spared severe damage. The historic district remained intact. It was a bright spot in a long, dark summer.

People worked in relay teams to block the flood with sandbags.

Not all the news from Missouri was bad, though. A heroic effort by townspeople and disaster response teams helped save the historic town of Ste. Genevieve. The town's historic district dated back to the eighteenth century. The rising waters of the Mississippi River threatened to breach the town's levee. But Ste. Genevieve had time to build up and extend its levee.

Mayor Bill Anderson took charge. "Ste. Genevieve is a civilian war zone," he said. "The Mississippi River is now our enemy, and we're fighting it."

The Red Cross Responds

Clean water was not the only problem for the people living in Des Moines and West Des Moines. Thousands of people had to leave their homes. They had no place to live and no food to eat. Some left with nothing more than the clothes on their backs.

As soon as the flooding began in the Midwest, the American Red Cross responded. The Red Cross is a **nonprofit** disaster **relief** organization. It provides all kinds of services to people in need across the country. During the floods of 1993, the Red Cross spent $44 million to help families throughout the Midwest.

⊙ During the flood, residents of Des Moines got around by boat.

The Red Cross set up flood headquarters in Des Moines County. More than 200 volunteers worked there. The volunteers helped people find shelter. They also collected and distributed donations of money for flood victims.

One of the most important services the Red Cross provided was serving meals. Not only did residents of Des Moines and West Des Moines need food, but so did the hundreds of volunteers and relief workers.

The Red Cross ran a 24-hour kitchen that fed emergency **personnel**. Kay Plummer, a Red Cross volunteer, ran the kitchen. "I've never seen such an outpouring of support," she said in a Red Cross news bulletin. "I had no kitchen experience and there was still no running water, but we made sure families and responders had warm meals every day."

☀ President Bill Clinton visited flood victims.

By July 18, 40 percent of the county was under water 10 feet deep. More than 7,000 residents had to be evacuated. Some left on their own. Others needed help. The U.S. Coast Guard provided boats for people stranded by floodwaters.

Help was already waiting for St. Charles County flood victims. The Salvation Army, a charity organization, had been on the scene in the Midwest since early summer. The group set up a shelter in the town of St. Charles. It also ran a mobile field kitchen that served more than 18,000 meals to flood victims and volunteers.

☾ The bright orange jackets and boats of the Coast Guard became a familiar sight in many counties.

CHAPTER THREE

Dateline:
Missouri

In Missouri, St. Charles County faced a two-fisted punch from the flood. The county lies on a **peninsula**. The Mississippi River runs along one side, and the Missouri River runs along the other. When the floodwaters **crested** high enough to overflow, the two rivers joined about 20 miles north of where they usually meet.

16

The floodwaters finally receded from Des Moines a couple of weeks later. But flood victims faced a new set of challenges. Thick **sludge**, or muck, covered the floors of buildings. Walls and furniture were soaked and **mildewed**. The river had washed up all sorts of wildlife, like frogs, fish, snakes, and worms. These creatures found new homes in people's houses.

One resident, Barbara Long, told the Red Cross, "There was mud and dead fish everywhere. The stench was just awful . . . It . . . looked like we had been bombed." The cleanup would take months.

Fortunately, the Red Cross was still there to help. They sent out ERVs, or Emergency Response Vehicles, to give out food and supplies to families cleaning up.

Iowa was beginning to rebuild. But it was not the only state feeling the wrath of the Great Flood.

9

CHAPTER TWO

Dateline: Illinois

Even the smallest towns hit by the flood received help from some faraway places. The town of Grafton, Illinois, sits where the Mississippi and Illinois Rivers meet. On July 10 all of Grafton's 900 residents had to evacuate. The flood swallowed 150 homes. Three days later Vice President Al Gore visited Grafton. He announced the opening of a disaster assistance center.

The vice president was not the only one to help Grafton. Television stations and newspapers, like the *St. Louis Post-Dispatch*, brought the **calamity** to the entire nation. Paul Arnold was Grafton's flood commissioner. He told the *St. Louis Post-Dispatch* that he had received about fifty calls a day from people offering assistance.

© 2007 Macmillan/McGraw-Hill

The Great Flood of 1993

Everyone tried their hardest to protect the island, but it was no use. On July 21 workers noticed a dangerous break in the levee. The Army Corps of Engineers woke the islanders just after midnight. They told everyone to grab what they could and flee.

The Corps brought two giant barges to evacuate the island. Corpsmen loaded up Kaskaskia's residents. People took personal belongings, furniture, even farm animals. One little boy was in tears over the dog he had left behind. Someone went back and saved his pet.

Later that morning the flood broke a 10-yard hole through the levee. The Mississippi River poured in. Within hours, the entire 15,000-acre island was under water. Residents of Kaskaskia were devastated.

Everyone assumed that animals left on the island had drowned. But they were wrong. About 50 pigs died in the flood, but many survived and were recaptured.

↻ "I must have hugged about 300 hogs on Kaskaskia that day," the county sheriff, Ben Picou, told *National Geographic* magazine.

Rescue on Kaskaskia Island

Nowhere in Illinois was the flood more threatening than on tiny Kaskaskia Island. The island sits in the middle of the Mississippi River. It is home to about 125 people, most of whom are farmers. A levee that is 52 feet tall usually protects the island. In the summer of 1993, Kaskaskia's residents needed extra help.

The Army Corps of Engineers worked alongside Kaskaskia's residents to strengthen the island's levee. They put sandbags in place to keep the water out.

How a Levee Works

Most rivers are bordered by floodplains. A floodplain is the area of land that lies next to a river. Floodplains absorb water that overflows from a river, and they drain as the river water recedes.

As more and more people settled on floodplains in the Upper Mississippi River Basin, they built levees to protect farmland and cities. But floodwaters sometimes rise so high they breach a levee.

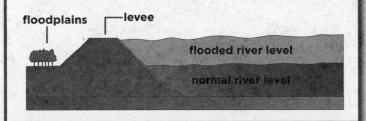

floodplains — levee

flooded river level

normal river level

The Great Flood of 1993

Arnold said that people had brought food, clothing, and supplies from states as far away as Texas. "Four children, the oldest of them just 11, . . . brought us $180 in an old ice cream container."

The flood brought communities together. In the town of Hardin, Illinois, there were no levees to protect the community from rising floodwaters. On every block of every street, neighbors helped fill sandbags. People worked in teams, one holding a bag open while the other shoveled in the sand. Then they piled the bags up to make a temporary wall.

One of Hardin's schools became a community center. A nurse gave free tetanus shots to protect people against the dangerous disease. Tetanus could be picked up from **sewage** (SOO-ej) flooding into homes.

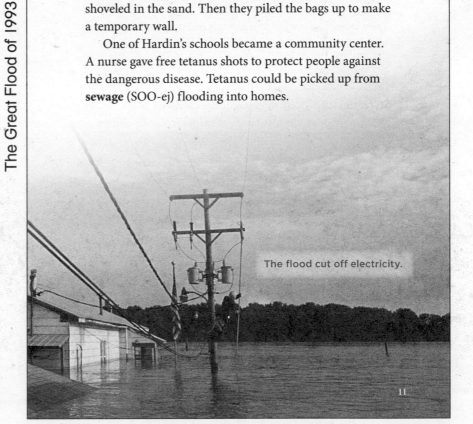

The flood cut off electricity.

Sometimes the effort against the flood was just too much for a community to handle by itself. In Hardin, the floodwaters **breached** the sandbags. The downtown area was under water. The town was cut off from the nearest larger town. Residents had to drive 100 miles to a town with a grocery store. The community was helpless.

Disaster agencies moved in. The Red Cross set up a relief center and shelter nearby. The National Guard flew in food, drinking water, and other essentials to residents stuck in the town. A charity group sent volunteers from North Carolina. They brought a tractor-trailer with cooking supplies. Local women had been serving food at the school cafeteria to more than 1,500 people a day. Now volunteers took over serving meals.

◯ Sandbags couldn't stop the downtown from flooding.

The Johnstown Flood of 1889

One of the worst floods in history happened in Johnstown, Pennsylvania, in 1889. A dam near Johnstown burst, sending a wall of water more than 60 feet high crashing down on the town. The floodwaters carried away buildings, trees, and anything else in its path. More than 2,200 people died in the flood.

After the devastation, the survivors of the flood needed help. Anyone who was able immediately got to work clearing debris and building shelters.

The first national organization on the scene was the American Red Cross. In 1889 the Red Cross was made up of nurses. Its president was Clara Barton. The Red Cross set up a camp and hospital near the disaster area. Its nurses visited the survivors and provided medical care.

Food, clothing, and other supplies poured in from cities and towns nearby and far away. In the end people from around the world contributed $3 million.

It was five years before Johnstown fully recovered.

Word Workout

WORDS TO KNOW

coincidences   mufflers   prospered   sumptuous

hobbled   phase   sheepishly   sweeten

Narrow It Down I will choose one of these words. You can ask me yes-or-no questions about my secret word. How many questions will it take you to guess each word?

SPELLING WORDS

factor   formal   pumpkin   barren   funnel

banner   pantry   muffler   necklace   dwelling

victim   ballot   ragged   wallet   fabric

snapshot   mental   prosper   kingdom   ponder

What's in the Box? We can box the consonants in the middle of these words. We'll box two or three consonants in each word. Then let's say the syllables of the words.

(fold here)

Home-School Connection

Dear Family Member:

Problems can be challenging in real life, but they can also make stories interesting and exciting. This week we're reading *Rumplestiltskin's Daughter*, a surprising new version of the tale of Rumpelstiltskin. In this version a lot of the characters face tough problems, but they always find clever and successful solutions. The characters in this story show me that smart thinking can help you solve tough problems. Of course, I also know that not every solution is successful in real life. Sometimes you have to try, try again.

This Week's Skills

Comprehension: problem and solution

Vocabulary: dictionary

Spelling/Phonics: syllables

Name _____

What Worked?

Let's try to find the solution that helped take care of each of these real-life problems. Which solutions match each problem? One problem has not been solved yet. What ideas can we come up with to solve this problem?

PROBLEMS

A. The Colorado River Basin often flooded. Farming communities near the river experienced terrible damages during these floods.

B. People who worked with the United States Department of Defense needed a way to share information on different computers.

C. Dirt covered the surface of Michelangelo's famous statue of David.

D. There is not enough room to store all of the garbage that people create every day.

E. When actors need to make a quick costume change, buttons and zippers can take too long.

Ejercicio de palabras

PALABRAS DE VOCABULARIO

coincidences mufflers prospered sumptuous

hobbled phase sheepishly sweeten

Basta con un sí o un no Voy a escoger una de estas palabras. Para saber cuál es mi palabra secreta, debes hacerme preguntas que tengan sólo sí o no como respuesta. ¿Cuántas preguntas deberás hacerme para adivinar cuál es la palabra?

PALABRAS DE ORTOGRAFÍA

factor formal pumpkin barren funnel

banner pantry muffler necklace dwelling

victim ballot ragged wallet fabric

snapshot mental prosper kingdom ponder

¿Qué hay en cada recuadro? Vamos a marcar las consonantes en el medio de estas palabras. Haremos un recuadro alrededor de dos o tres consonantes en cada una. Luego diremos las sílabas de cada palabra.

© Macmillan/McGraw-Hill ··········· {fold here}

Conexión con el hogar

Queridos familiares:

Los problemas pueden ponernos a prueba en la vida real, pero también pueden agregar interés y emoción a un cuento. Esta semana estamos leyendo *Rumpelstiltskin's Daughter*, una fascinante versión nueva del cuento de Rumpelstiltskin. En esta versión, muchos de los personajes se enfrentan con grandes problemas, aunque siempre encuentran soluciones inteligentes y exitosas. Los personajes del cuento demuestran que el ingenio puede tener un papel importante para resolver problemas difíciles. Por supuesto, también sé que no todas las soluciones tienen éxito en la vida real. A veces hay que intentar una y otra vez.

Destrezas de la semana

Comprensión: problema y solución

Vocabulario: diccionario

Ortografía/ Fonética: sílabas

Nombre _____

¿Qué funcionó?

Vamos a tratar de encontrar la solución con la que se pudo resolver cada uno de estos problemas de la vida real. ¿Qué solución corresponde a cada problema? Un problema no ha sido resuelto todavía. ¿Qué ideas se te ocurren para resolverlo?

PROBLEMS

A. The Colorado River Basin often flooded. Farming communities near the river experienced terrible damages during these floods.

B. People who worked with the United States Department of Defense needed a way to share information on different computers.

C. Dirt covered the surface of Michelangelo's famous statue of David.

D. There is not enough room to store all of the garbage that people create every day.

E. When actors need to make a quick costume change, buttons and zippers can take too long.

Comprehension Check

Summarize

What was Princess Amber's problem in this story? How did she solve it? Use the Problem and Solution Chart to help you organize your ideas.

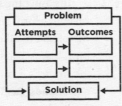

Problem

Attempts → Outcomes

Solution

Think and Compare

1. Look back at page 6. How did coincidence play a part in Amber's problem? Now look back at page 19. How did coincidence play a part in the solution to Amber's problem? *(Identify Problem and Solution)*

2. In the story, Beryl pretended to be someone he was not. Do you think that this is acceptable behavior or that you should always be true to yourself? Explain your answer. *(Evaluate)*

3. Does the story *The Princess and the Gnome* remind you of any other fairy tale? How is it the same? How is it different? *(Analyze)*

The Princess and the Gnome

by Nomi J. Waldman

illustrated by Judy Stead

Table of Contents

The Gnome

Long ago in a land of forests and mountains, two kingdoms sat side by side. One, on the borders of a forest, was inhabited by men and women who lived and worked on farms and in villages. In this place, the sun shone on most days and rain fell only when it was really needed. As any traveler through the region could report, the people there were always busy, usually happy, and never sad for long.

The second kingdom, however, was hidden from sight. For it lay mostly beneath a mountain whose base went so deep that it seemed to reach almost to the fiery center of the earth. This was the kingdom of the gnomes, and its ruler was one Beryl Hardstone.

Beryl was a princely sort, given his fabulous wealth. Beryl had all the traits and powers of gnomes. He was small, bearded, and not particularly handsome, at least in human terms. He could move through solid earth as easily as through air. And he could carry with him whatever he held in his hands. This was useful because, in true gnome fashion, Beryl was a miner and he liked to take his precious stones with him.

The Princess and the Gnome

Instantly the butterfly changed into a giant, ravenlike bird. Hopping on its back, the princess directed it to take her home. And, this being a magic bird, that is exactly what it did.

Amber's return brought great joy to her father and friends. And the real Ruby, Pearl, and Jade laughed and wept in turn as Amber told them of their vegetable twins.

As for the gnome, when he returned to find the princess gone, he decided that he'd had enough of human beings. "I will go back to my own home underground," he said. And since gnomes can live hundreds of years, he may be there even now.

He was wrong. Though she still sighed and wept over her friends' fate, Amber's mind was actively working on her problem. In a way, the absence of her friends— and certainly of the gnome—was helpful. Now she would not be distracted from the truth of her situation by cheerful playmates or a lovesick prince.

"I want to go home," she said to herself. "I want to see my father and sleep in my own room. If I could only think of a way to get back!"

She sat quietly, trying to think of a way to escape. A large black butterfly was drawn to her still figure. As it settled on Amber's hand, the flutter of its wings gave Amber an idea. Finding the glass wand, she gently touched the insect and pictured a way out of her situation.

Now, Beryl wasn't one of those princes who just sat around counting his treasures. He did some of that, of course, since there was so much treasure. Hundreds and hundreds of other gnomes toiled for the prince, gathering rocks big and small. Then Beryl would work his magic, turning them into precious stones and metals. For another talent this gnome had was the ability to change the form of any living or nonliving thing as it suited him.

Although Beryl prospered beyond the wealth of most gnomes, he was not completely happy. It is said that gnomes have yet another special trait and not an especially welcome one. That trait was that being anywhere near a gnome could make a person feel sad, no matter what else was going on.

It seems that Beryl himself was a victim of this very effect. Or maybe it was just that the need to supervise his many workers meant that he spent long days in the gloomiest of regions, miles below ground. Either way, it is true that sometimes Beryl longed to be outside, where the world was green with growing things and the sky was blue and filled with bird songs. At those times he would take on the form of a human and travel through the mountain to spend some time with the creatures who lived their lives in the sun and shade of the world outside his own kingdom. And that is how he happened to fall in love with one of those very creatures.

On this last adventure, Beryl had not gone very far when he heard sounds of merriment. That in itself would have been enough to draw his attention, for laughter in a gnome's kingdom was rare. It's not that it was banned. It's just that there was very little reason for it.

© 2007 Macmillan/McGraw-Hill

The Princess and the Gnome

Amber finally understood that her friends had mysteriously aged overnight. And now they were actually wasting away. They had turned into old, shriveled women who leaned on sticks and walked with bent backs and trembling legs.

Running from the sight of them, Amber ran to find the prince. "What have you done to my friends?" she cried after telling him what she had seen.

"There's nothing I can do," he replied sheepishly. "As the sap in the plants from which they were formed dried up, so did the beings they had become." He promised to go immediately in search of other roots and restore her friends to her.

Once again the princess was overwhelmed with sadness. She found herself drifting toward the garden, hoping that the cheerful flowers might give her comfort. But even the gnome's magic could not hold back the changing seasons. It was autumn, and the flowers were fading. Even the grass had lost its sheen. And the songs of the remaining birds were less cheerful. Every chirp seemed to say "Good-bye."

Meanwhile, the gnome was searching the fields, moving farther and farther from the castle. The fields were now covered with fallen leaves, and deer had cropped the tops of the plants. Still, Beryl felt certain that he could make everything right again.

Chapter 4

Changes

Then came the morning when the princess went looking for her friends, only to find that they had not even left their rooms. She ran from one chamber to another, calling to them: "Ruby, Pearl, Jade! What is the matter?"

One by one they answered her in the much the same way.

"Oh, only let me rest," said Ruby. "I have no strength for your girlish games." And with that, she hobbled to the fireplace. There she sat down in a rocking chair from which she could reach out to the fire and warm her shaking hands.

"Foolish girl," croaked Pearl, barely moving in the softest chair in her room, "don't you see, these old limbs want only to rest?"

Of the three, Jade's reply was the hardest to bear.

Lifting her head from her pillow, she said, "Young woman, I don't know who you are. I do know that you have disturbed the sleep that is my only comfort."

Beryl was still in the forest, but close to its farthest edge. There the trees had dwindled into a pleasant woodland. The open spaces of farm, village, and castle were just beyond. Hiding behind a screen of leaves, Beryl peered at the scene ahead of him. Four young women danced by a little brook that ran at the foot of a sparkling waterfall.

Each of the young women bore herself proudly, as suited someone of noble birth. One woman, though, was especially lovely, and Beryl could hardly keep his eyes off her. As he moved closer, a twig snapped underfoot. All the women turned in his direction. In an instant, Beryl made himself invisible, but he did not leave. Instead he kept his place and watched and listened.

Chapter 2

The Princess

"Did you hear that?" Princess Amber asked her ladies-in-waiting. For, in one of those important coincidences, the woman Beryl had fixed his attention on was the princess of this human kingdom.

There was a buzz of conversation as the women around the princess offered different explanations for the sound.

"It was probably a deer," said the Lady Ruby brightly. "Nothing to fear there."

"I suppose it could have been a bear," whispered the Lady Pearl, looking around nervously.

"Clearly it's nothing important," said the Lady Jade, waving her hand as though to drive away any disagreement. "Please, go on with what you were saying."

"I don't remember," said the princess. She was still staring at the very spot where Beryl stood, unseen, for the strangest feeling had come over her.

"About the ball, about the grand ball," the three ladies chimed in together.

6

The four young women hugged each other as though it had been only hours since they parted. Princess Amber was happy to see her friends again. Now she could once again spend all her waking hours in their merry company. But the gnome, though pleased to see the princess happy again, also realized that he would have less time to spend with her. And that meant less time to win her heart.

15

Every day the princess grew sadder. She spoke less and less to Beryl, no matter how hard he tried to amuse her. Often she simply sat by a window and sighed. Finally, the gnome decided that she probably missed human company. So he went into the fields that lay beyond the garden and gathered several root vegetables, one each of carrots, radishes, and beets.

Laying the roots at Amber's feet, he said, "I realize that you must miss your friends. Take this wand and touch each root with it. As you do, wish it to take whatever familiar form you want, and it will happen." With that, he handed her a tiny glass wand.

Thinking of the young women she had left behind, the princess touched each root with the wand. She thought of the Lady Ruby with her long red hair and rose-pink cheeks. And suddenly, Ruby was there. Then she wished as hard as she could for the Lady Pearl with her soft blond hair and shy smile. And suddenly, Pearl was there. And finally she closed her eyes and pictured the Lady Jade with her green eyes and playful grin. And suddenly, Jade was there.

With that, Amber finally turned her gaze away to chat with her friends. Beryl found that he had been holding his breath, so sure was he that the princess would somehow spot him. But once he knew that he was safe, he began to listen.

The topic of the grand ball led to talk about ball gowns, dancing shoes, flowers, and food, each of which seemed to delight the young women.

Beryl tried to remember them all. If he could supply the princess with such pleasures, he thought, it would surely win him her love. For he had decided that he must have the Princess Amber for his wife.

Suddenly, though, the princess said, "It's getting dark. We must get back to the castle." Once they had left, Beryl put his plan into action.

The next afternoon, the princess and her three ladies returned to the same spot. Except it had changed. Where once a waterfall had made its way over rough, red rocks to the brook, now smooth white marble walls enclosed a still, clear pool. There was a sparkling fountain in the middle of the pool. It sang as it rose and fell, and the sun lit up each drop. Instead of pale, weedy grasses, there were sweet-smelling flowers. And around the edges were rows and rows of rosebushes in many colors.

8

13

As they explored the grounds outdoors, Amber saw, on three sides of the castle, velvet lawns and a lovely garden filled with flowers. On the fruit trees hung both golden and rosy apples, and birds seemed to sing in every bush. Only the fourth side of the castle was bare of any living thing, for there the mountain loomed, barring the way like some giant wall.

And so the time passed, with sunny days and moonlit nights following one after another. There were pleasant walks and conversations with the prince. Delicious meals appeared as if by invisible hands. And to sweeten the pot, in every room there was beautiful music. It seemed to come from the very walls because there were no musicians to be seen.

In her own rooms, Amber was well cared for by a number of helpful, though rather short, servant women. Yet there was little else that she could learn about any of them. While they took care of her every wish, they never spoke. And, strangest of all, though the air was mild both indoors and out, they all hid their features in huge, winding mufflers.

Hardly able to believe their eyes, the young women ran about, crying out over each wonder—first the water, then the marble, and finally the sumptuous flower beds.

All of this, of course, was the result of the gnome's magic. He was delighted at the pleasure it was giving the princess. But there was more to come.

Looking down into the clear water of the pool, the princess announced that she simply had to wade in it. That was what the invisible Beryl was waiting to hear. In a moment the princess had removed her shoes and was making ready to step into the pool.

Only the Lady Pearl protested. Magic was not something to be taken lightly.

"But, my lady, please . . ." she began.

Yet the princess only waved her away, saying, "Come, all of you, follow me."

But no one had the chance, for the instant Amber stepped into the pool, she sank down, down, down and disappeared.

Screaming, tears running down their cheeks, the three called and called to the princess. They ran in every direction looking for her, until finally they faced the truth. Princess Amber was gone.

Chapter 3
In Another World

For Princess Amber, the next phase of her adventure was like a dream. She was hardly aware of being carried along underground rivers and through the roots of the mountain. When she awoke at last, she found herself in the grandest castle she had ever seen. Compared to it, her father's palace was little more than a villager's hut.

She was seated on a great couch that was covered in a thick, rich material. She herself was dressed in a satin gown. Before her was a table set with dishes made of gold. Each one held the freshest and most colorful fruit possible.

At her feet knelt a pleasant young man. He was noble in bearing, spoke softly, and gave her the greatest care and attention. It was Beryl Hardstone himself. The gnome had changed himself into the form of a man he was sure the princess would most admire.

He introduced himself by his proper name but said little else about himself. Nor did he answer the princess when she pressed him to tell her how she came to be there. Instead he invited her to take his arm and let him show her the rest of his great estate.

The princess hesitated, though she had no fear of the young man. Still, she was aware of another feeling. It was the very feeling, in fact, that had come over her by the brook when she thought someone was watching her. Having had only the happiest of lives, Amber had no name for it, because until then she had never known sadness.

Finally, she took the young prince's arm, and he led her through the many rooms and halls of the palace. Each one was filled with rare and wonderful treasures.

Word Workout

WORDS TO KNOW

epidemic outskirts plight rendezvous

intercept pedestrians quarantine unbearable

Ask Me Another Let's take turns thinking of questions that use this week's vocabulary words. For example, I might ask you "What would make a vacation unbearable?" Then we'll answer each other's questions.

SPELLING WORDS

brutal	fever	detect	rival	unit
secure	voter	resist	recite	rotate
panic	vanish	labor	topic	vital
cabin	nylon	focus	amid	lament

Star Power Ask me to spell the list words. Draw a star next to any words I misspell. When we're done, we can make reminder cards that show the correct spellings of the words I misspelled.

© Macmillan/McGraw-Hill • (fold here)

Home-School Connection

Dear Family Member:

Teamwork can accomplish amazing feats. On some teams animals and people pull together to achieve greatness. This week our class is reading the remarkable true-life story of *The Great Serum Race*. In 1925 an outbreak of diphtheria in Nome, Alaska, threatened to wipe out the entire town. A serum could save many lives, but the only way to get it there was by sled dog team. We are reading about the exciting series of events that happened as a series of dog teams worked together to save the people of Nome.

This Week's Skills

Comprehension: sequence

Vocabulary: thesaurus/dictionary

Spelling/Phonics: syllables

Name _____

Out of Order

When the sequence of events isn't clear, lots of clues can help you figure out what happened when. Clues such as dates and events give information. So do signal words such as *then, next, before, after*, and *finally*.

Let's see if we can put these events in order. They describe moments in the life of Alice Coachman.

_____ Coachman continued to run barefoot in high-school and college competitions. She broke many records and won twenty-five national titles.

_____ After her victory she became a coach. She trained many women athletes, helping them to always do their best.

_____ In the 1948 Olympics, Coachman won the long jump. She was the first African-American woman to win an Olympic gold medal.

_____ Alice Coachman was born in Georgia in 1923. She was the fifth of ten children.

_____ The Olympics were cancelled in 1940 and 1944 due to World War II. Coachman could not compete when she was at her peak.

_____ As a child Alice loved running and jumping. Although African-Americans were not allowed to use the public facilities, Alice trained anyway. She ran barefoot and jumped over everything from ropes and sticks to rags she tied together.

Ejercicio de palabras

PALABRAS DE VOCABULARIO

epidemic outskirts plight rendezvous

intercept pedestrians quarantine unbearable

Por turno Vamos a turnarnos para hacernos preguntas que tengan las palabras de vocabulario de esta semana. Por ejemplo, te puedo preguntar *"What would make a vacation unbearable?"* Cada uno debe contestar las preguntas que se le hacen.

PALABRAS DE ORTOGRAFÍA

brutal	fever	detect	rival	unit
secure	voter	resist	recite	rotate
panic	vanish	labor	topic	vital
cabin	nylon	focus	amid	lament

Las estrellas lo dicen Voy a deletrear las palabras de la lista. Dibuja una estrella junto a las palabras que deletree mal. Cuando terminemos, podemos hacer tarjetas recordatorias que muestren la ortografía correcta de las palabras que yo haya deletreado mal.

(fold here)

Conexión con el hogar

Queridos familiares:

El trabajo en equipo puede producir grandes logros. En algunos equipos, animales y humanos colaboran juntos para alcanzar grandes metas. Esta semana nuestra clase está leyendo un admirable relato de la vida real *The Great Serum Race*. En 1925 un brote de difteria en Nome, Alaska, amenazaba con exterminar toda la ciudad. Un suero podría salvar muchas vidas, pero la única forma de conseguirlo era con un equipo de perros de trineo. Estamos leyendo acerca de la emocionante serie de sucesos que tuvieron lugar cuando varios equipos de perros colaboraron para salvar a la gente de Nome.

Destrezas de la semana

Comprensión: orden de los sucesos

Vocabulario: enciclopedia/diccionario

Ortografía/Fonética: sílabas

Nombre _____

Aquí falta orden

Cuando el orden de los sucesos no es claro, hay pistas que pueden ayudarte a deducir qué pasó y cuándo. Pistas como fechas y sucesos proporcionan información. Lo mismo pasa con palabras como *entonces, luego, antes, después* y *finalmente*.

Vamos a ver si podemos poner estos sucesos en orden. Narran momentos de la vida de Alice Coachman.

_____ Coachman continued to run barefoot in high-school and college competitions. She broke many records and won twenty-five national titles.

_____ After her victory she became a coach. She trained many women athletes, helping them to always do their best.

_____ In the 1948 Olympics, Coachman won the long jump. She was the first African-American woman to win an Olympic gold medal.

_____ Alice Coachman was born in Georgia in 1923. She was the fifth of ten children.

_____ The Olympics were cancelled in 1940 and 1944 due to World War II. Coachman could not compete when she was at her peak.

_____ As a child Alice loved running and jumping. Although African-Americans were not allowed to use the public facilities, Alice trained anyway. She ran barefoot and jumped over everything from ropes and sticks to rags she tied together.

Comprehension Check

Summarize

Use a Sequence Chart to summarize the history of the Iditarod.

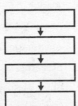

Think and Compare

1. Look at pages 9–11 in this book. Who led the effort to clear the trail for the centennial Iditarod? How long did it take until enough of the trail was cleared to hold the first long Iditarod? *(Identify Sequence of Events)*

2. If you competed in the Iditarod, what do you think would be the most difficult thing about it for you? Would you enjoy racing in the Iditarod? Why or why not? *(Evaluate)*

3. The Iditarod challenges mushers to compete under very harsh conditions in nature. Can you think of any other sports or activities in which people must work to survive extreme cold, heat, rough terrain, or other dangers? Why do you think athletes enjoy these sports and activities? *(Analyze)*

24

Sled Dog Heroes

by Sarah Jane Brian

Table of Contents

Introduction

On the outskirts of Anchorage, Alaska, 12 dogs jump and bark. They have been training for months. Now these furry athletes and their human driver, or **musher**, are about to set off on an amazing journey. They're going to race the Iditarod. They'll run more than 1,100 miles up snow-covered mountains, through blizzards, and across frozen **tundra** and jagged ice sheets. Temperatures may fall to minus 50 degrees **Fahrenheit** (-45° Celsius). Most animals couldn't hope to survive such dangerous conditions. But these dogs can't wait to begin! They are Alaskan huskies, bred for this weather and this job. They love to run through the icy north.

↺ Alaskan huskies have thick warm coats to keep them warm as they race through the Arctic cold.

Index

Glossary

caribou *(KAYR-uh-boo)* a large reindeer that lives in northern climates *(page 14)*

centennial *(sen-TEN-ee-uhl)* the one hundredth anniversary of an event, or the celebration of that anniversary *(page 8)*

epidemic *(ep-i-DEM-ik)* an outbreak of a disease that makes many people in an area ill at the same time *(page 7)*

Fahrenheit *(FAR-uhn-hight)* a scale that measures temperature in degrees. Water freezes at 32°F and boils at 212°F. *(page 2)*

glacier *(GLAY-shur)* a large body of ice that moves and spreads out over land *(page 4)*

musher *(MUSH-ur)* a person who drives a dog sled *(page 2)*

quarantine *(KWAWR-uhn-teen)* the keeping of a person, animal, or thing away from others to stop the spreading of a disease *(page 7)*

sound *(SOUND)* a long and wide bay along the coast of an ocean *(page 16)*

terrain *(tuh-RAYN)* ground or land *(page 16)*

tundra *(TUN-druh)* a huge plain with no trees that lies in Arctic regions *(page 2)*

Sled Dog Heroes

In the late 1800s and early 1900s, many people who lived in Alaska depended on sled dogs. They lived far from transportation. Winters there were harsh. The best way to get around was to use sled dogs. Over the years, the dogs saved many lives. They helped people keep in touch with each other and the outside world. Without the dogs, life might have been unbearable for some of the settlers.

Today, the Iditarod celebrates the history and heroism of sled dogs in Alaska. The dogs who run in today's race are heroes, too. They inspire people from all over the world with their loyalty, bravery, and hard work.

Sled dogs work hard, but they love their work.

Frontier Dogs

Alaska was not always a part of the United States. The United States purchased the land from Russia in 1867. Many Americans thought that buying Alaska was a waste of money. The territory was huge, and the land was cold and harsh. Few people lived there. Large stretches of tundra, mountains, and huge ice sheets called **glaciers** covered the land.

Then, in the late 1880s, settlers made an exciting discovery—gold! Thousands of miners flocked to Alaska. Small villages grew into bustling cities as their population exploded. Alaska was in the middle of a gold rush.

Conclusion

Long ago, just about every Alaskan had a team of sled dogs. More than just pets, the dogs provided transportation, entertainment, and even saved lives.

People still love to remember the sled dogs of the past and the spirit they represent. Mushers dedicate time and effort to the Iditarod, crowds of volunteers come to help, and fans around the world follow the race each year. They are reliving Alaska's past through the amazing sled dogs of today's "Last Great Race."

↻ The mushers must wear warm clothing to protect them from harsh weather during the race.

It takes more than frisky dogs and dedicated mushers to make the Iditarod happen. Each year thousands of people volunteer to help with all kinds of jobs. Snow machine crews brave freezing temperatures and harsh weather to clear the trail for the dog teams. Veterinarians take time off to care for dogs. Pilots fly airplanes loaded with food and supplies to the checkpoints and sometimes search for and rescue teams that have lost the trail. Other volunteers relay messages, make dog booties, cook food for mushers, and help handle dogs at the checkpoints.

⋂ Four-time-winner Susan Butcher is one of the Iditarod's most famous mushers.

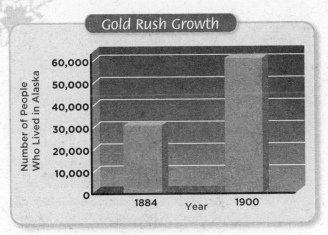

Gold Rush Growth

⋂ Thanks to the discovery of gold, Alaska's population doubled at the end of the nineteenth century.

Miles of snowy wilderness separated the mining towns. In the winter only sled dogs could get through. Teams of dogs pulled sleds loaded with much-needed supplies and mail. They also took sick miners to doctors in towns. They even transported heavy sleds full of gold. The sled dogs would travel on trails, or paths, that went from mining town to mining town. One of these trails went from Seward in the south to Nome in the north. It was called the Iditarod Trail.

⋐ Native Americans like this Athabascan man used sled dogs long before Alaska became part of the United States.

Meet Baldy

One famous sled dog was Baldy. He led his team through a terrible blizzard to victory in the 1909 race. They won again in 1911 and 1912. In the 1910 race, the entire team fell down a 200-foot cliff. Five dogs were injured, but Baldy still guided the team to an amazing third-place finish.

One winter, some sled dog owners in Nome decided to rendezvous for a race. At first, the children of Nome drove the dog teams in short races. Soon mushing, or dog sled racing, became the most popular sport for boys and girls in the area. Then the adults wanted to join in. In 1908, they organized a 408-mile (657 km) race over ice, mountains, forest, and tundra that was called the All-Alaska Sweepstakes.

The annual All-Alaska Sweepstakes became a popular event. Each year schools and businesses closed down so that everyone could cheer on their favorite teams.

◑ Mushers and their dog teams competed in the All-Alaska Sweepstakes until World War I, when the race was discontinued.

6

The Junior Iditarod

Racing through the snow behind a pack of energetic dogs isn't just for adults. In 1977, Joe Redington organized the first Junior Iditarod. It's a race for teens aged 14 to 17. The race is held each year on the last Saturday in February. It is a week before the start of the full Iditarod.

At 150 miles (241 km), the two-day Junior Iditarod is shorter than the full version, but it is still hard. The teens spend long hours training their dogs and preparing for the race. They face the same dangers on the trail and carry the same equipment. At the end of the race, all mushers who finish attend an awards ceremony. They get a special patch and a trophy honoring their hard work. A veterinarian gives an award to the musher with the best-cared-for team, and other awards go out for sportsmanship and best lead dog.

This is the Junior trophy. ➲

19

CHAPTER FOUR

Today's Iditarod

These days about 65 teams race in each Iditarod. The winners usually finish in 9 to 12 days. That is because of improvements in training. Also sleds are now much lighter. Men and women travel with their dogs from around the world to compete. Each year the Iditarod changes its route for part of the race. On even years, the trail follows a northern route, and on odd years it takes a southern route. The trail changes a bit each year due to weather, but it is always more than 1,100 miles (1,770 km) long from start to finish.

↻ The Iditarod race begins in downtown Anchorage.

18.

Sled Dog Heroes

During the winter of 1925, more than 100 of Alaska's racing dogs made a run that would go down in history. Twenty teams ran a relay over 674 miles (1,085 km) of Alaska's most brutal land in just 5 and one half days and nights.

An **epidemic** of the disease diptheria had broken out in Nome. It was too late for a **quarantine**. Children were dying, and the town needed medicine fast. The medicine was hundreds of miles away, and the city was snowed in. The only way to get the medicine was to use sled dogs. For speed, each dog team ran a leg of the journey. The following team had to intercept, or catch and stop, the team carrying the medicine. The mushers handed off the medicine to the next team. That team then took off. At 5:30 A.M. on February 2, 1925, the final team raced into Nome—and into the history books. The relay became known as the Great Serum Race.

Great Serum Race, 1925

Nome

Nenana

ALASKA

CANADA

Serum Race Route

↻ This is the route of the 1925 Great Serum Race.

7

CHAPTER TWO

A Race to Remember

By the 1960s, few Alaskans used dog sleds for transportation. Now people used snowmobiles and airplanes. They carried people and supplies where they needed to go. Dog sled racing was no longer the major sport it had once been in Alaska.

Most people had forgotten about the Iditarod trail and its importance in Alaskan history. Dorothy Page, a local historian, wanted to keep alive Alaska's sled dog traditions and history. It was also the one hundredth anniversary of the purchase of Alaska. She came up with the idea of a race along part of the old Iditarod trail. The race would help celebrate the **centennial**, or one hundredth anniversary.

⋒ Dorothy Page had the idea for the first Iditarod race, which earned her the nickname "mother of the Iditarod."

© 2007 Macmillan/McGraw-Hill

Sled Dog Heroes

⋒ Musher Susan Butcher kept training her dogs even when there was no snow.

Dog Dictionary

Mushers use these command words to communicate with their teams:

Gee: turn right

Haw: turn left

Whoa: stop (Mushers also use brakes on the sled to stop.)

Hike Up: start moving, or go faster

Butcher's lead dog, Granite, rescued her from this plight by pulling her to safety. With ice forming on her soaked clothes, Butcher kept going. Her team took second place that year. Butcher has won the Iditarod four times.

Mushers spend months or even the whole year training their dog teams for the Iditarod. They practice moving together as a team and running at different speeds over all kinds of **terrain**. Most important is the lead dog. That dog runs at the front of the team. The lead dog is responsible for steering around danger on the trail, finding the way if the team gets off the trail, and following all of the musher's commands.

Out on the trail, every bit of training counts. In several Iditarods, the winner of the race has been just five minutes ahead of the second-place team. In 1978, the top two teams were just a second apart, even after racing for more than 14 days!

Over the years, Iditarod dogs and mushers have had unbelievable adventures. They have also shown incredible courage. One example is Susan Butcher. In the 1983 race, Butcher was traveling with her team over 10-foot-tall mounds of ice on the frozen waters of Norton **Sound,** off the Bering Sea. Suddenly the ice cracked open, dropping Butcher and her sled into the freezing water.

© 2007 Macmillan/McGraw-Hill

Sled Dog Heroes

🎧 Joe Redington rode parts of the Iditarod trail every year whether there was a race or not. Redington's whole family loved the trail, and his daughter even got married there!

By this time, the Iditarod trail was overgrown and mostly unusable. But since the early 1950s, musher Joe Redington had been clearing sections of the trail. He wanted it to become an official part of the U.S. National Historic Trail System. In 1966, Page told Redington about her plan for a centennial race and asked if he would help.

Redington thought the race was a great idea. He raised $25,000 in prize money. It was the biggest prize ever awarded in a dog race at that time. Then he gathered volunteers. Using tractors and chain saws, they cleared away overgrown trees and shrubs from the trail. Thanks to everyone's hard work, the centennial Iditarod was a huge success. Altogether, 58 teams competed in the race, which covered about 56 miles (90 km).

Why the Iditarod Trail?

The Iditarod Trail got its name from the town of Iditarod. The town was halfway between Nome and Seward. In the early 1900s, Iditarod was a booming gold rush town. More than 40,000 people lived there. Today it's a ghost town.

Redington wanted to make the Iditarod an annual event. But in 1968, he was able to raise only $1,000 in prize money, and just 12 mushers competed with their dog teams. The race was canceled for a few years, but each year Redington and some of his friends would ride out onto the cleared part of the trail with their dogs to keep the Iditarod spirit alive.

10

Must-Have Equipment

Iditarod rules say that every team must carry these items at all times (mushers pick up extra supplies at each checkpoint):

- Cold weather sleeping bag and parka
- Snowshoes
- 2 pounds (1 kg) of food per dog
- A day's food for the musher
- 8 booties per dog (These socklike coverings strap over paws to protect them from getting hurt in the ice and snow.)
- An ax with a handle 22 inches (56 cm) or longer that weighs at least $1\frac{3}{4}$ pounds ($\frac{4}{5}$ kg)
- A stove for cooking and heating water

Volunteers make ➲ the socklike booties that all the dogs wear to protect their paws.

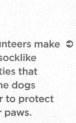

15

A musher and his or her dogs never know what dangers may lie just around the next bend in the trail. Moose, buffalo, **caribou**, and wolves sometimes attack teams. Dogs and sleds can fall through holes in the ice. In mountainous parts of the trail, avalanches may occur. Fallen trees can block the trail in the forest. Long hours on the trail may cause a musher to fall asleep and tumble from the sled. The team keeps going. The musher must run ahead to catch up with the team!

At about two dozen spots along the trail are a series of checkpoints. They are often located in small, remote villages. The distance between checkpoints varies. Some are located 14 miles (22.5 km) apart, while others are as far as 100 miles (161 km) apart. Mushers feed and rest the dogs at these stops. They also pick up extra supplies and food and make repairs to equipment. Vets check each dog. If a dog cannot run any farther, it remains at the checkpoint. Later it is flown back to the owner when the race is over.

All the mushers have a plan. They decide when and how long to rest the dogs. They also have a special menu for feeding the dogs. They feed them everything from fish, beef, chicken, or even seal meat to a special high-energy dog food. Some mushers prefer to run during the daylight hours while others choose to race at night. To increase their speed, mushers try to keep their sleds as light as possible.

Then, in 1972, the U.S. Army cleared a large part of the remaining overgrown Iditarod trail. This gave Redington an idea. His plan was to create a marathon race of more than 1,000 miles (1,609 km) through the wilderness from Anchorage to Nome. Much of the trip would follow the old Iditarod trail that was now clear.

Many people said it couldn't be done. Few thought that dogs could run that far. But Redington was determined to make his dream come true. After years of mushing, he was convinced that well-trained dogs and mushers could travel the long distance.

With the support of Dorothy Page and others, Redington raised $50,000 in total prize money for the first long Iditarod in 1973. Thirty-four mushers entered their teams in what he called "The Last Great Race." In all, 22 teams completed the entire race. The winning team crossed the finish line in Nome 20 days after setting out from Anchorage.

⟳ The route of the Iditarod has changed since the first race, but the finish line is always in Nome.

CHAPTER THREE

Tales from the Trail

Each year since 1973, the Iditarod has thrilled fans all over the world. On the first Saturday in March, pedestrians crowd along the sides of a wide street in Anchorage. More than 1,000 sled dogs bark and howl in anticipation. Then they're off!

The teams must cross bridges of ice to get across rivers. They go up and down trails so steep and slippery, the dogs sometimes slide more than they run. Many obstacles block the teams' path.

⟳ Harsh conditions like running water and deep snow make the Iditarod even more difficult.

⟲ As the Iditarod begins, the dogs and mushers can't wait to get started.

Machines clear deep snow away from the trail. Then the race can begin. But fierce winds and blizzards sometimes blow the snow right back by the time the mushers and dogs arrive. The dogs must fight their way through the deep drifts. This slows the race.

Alaskan huskies are built for winter weather, but even these tough dogs can run into trouble in extreme cold. During the Iditarod, temperatures on the trail can reach minus 50°F (-45°C) or below. Perhaps even more dangerous is flowing water that sometimes gets trapped on top of ice sheets. Besides creating slippery conditions, the water can freeze paws as well as a musher's boots.

Word Workout

WORDS TO KNOW

employee	foreman	gleefully	gritted
flourish	fulfill	gloated	vigorously

Act It Out Can you get me to guess a word without saying anything yourself? Let's take turns choosing a word and then either play charades to get me to say the word, or act it out. You can go back and forth depending on which way is easier to express the word.

SPELLING WORDS

ignore	enroll	debate	forlorn	saunter
wealthy	accept	prepare	shoulder	falter
fulfill	parchment	repair	abroad	install
healthy	dismay	applaud	flounder	bounty

Rhymes with Spelling Let's find words that rhyme with the words on the list. Which rhymes have the same end spellings? Which are different?

(fold here)

Home-School Connection

Dear Family Member:

Why are some stories good enough to tell again and again? Every culture has fables that have been around for generations. This week we are reading *Juan Verdades, The Man Who Couldn't Tell a Lie,* a new version of a story that has been told and retold in Mexico. The setting is interesting, but it's the characters and plot that make the story truly memorable. In fact, the same story could probably be set in another place. Of course, the feeling of the tale would be different, but the theme of the fable would remain the same. I'm learning to analyze stories using different perspectives.

This Week's Skills

Comprehension: character, setting, plot

Vocabulary: word parts

Spelling/Phonics: syllables

Name _____

Weird Fiction

Good writers use the elements of setting, character, and plot very carefully. Their choices make stories fun and interesting. We'll make some random choices to write a story that's just plain weird.

- Write a word for each item in the list. Then we'll add our words to complete the story.
- When we read it aloud, let's listen to how our choices changed this tale.

A. woman's name: _____

B. adjective: _____

C. profession: _____

D. city: _____

E. man's name: _____

F. action verb: _____

G. city: _____

H. adverb: _____

_____ was a very _____
　　　　　(A)　　　　　　　　　　　　　　　　　(B)

_____ . She lived in _____ .
　　　　　(C)　　　　　　　　　　　　　　　　　(D)

One day, _____
　　　　　　　　　　(E)

moved in next door. He was also an unusual

neighbor because he liked to _____
　　　　　　　　　　　　　　　　　　　(F)

every day. Of course, _____
　　　　　　　　　　　　　　(A)

and _____ fell in love. For their
　　　　(E)

honeymoon, they went to _____ and had
　　　　　　　　　　　　　　(G)

so much fun that they decided to move there.

Needless to say, they lived _____
　　　　　　　　　　　　　　　　　(H)

ever after.

160

Ejercicio de palabras

PALABRAS DE VOCABULARIO

employee	foreman	gleefully	gritted
flourish	fulfill	gloated	vigorously

¡A representarlo! ¿Puedes hacer que yo adivine una palabra sin decir tú nada? Vamos a turnarnos para escoger una palabra y luego jugar a las charadas o a representar la palabra para que el otro la adivine. Podemos usar un método o el otro, según cómo resulte más fácil expresar la palabra.

PALABRAS DE ORTOGRAFÍA

ignore	enroll	debate	forlorn	saunter
wealthy	accept	prepare	shoulder	falter
fulfill	parchment	repair	abroad	install
healthy	dismay	applaud	flounder	bounty

Rimas con deletreo Vamos a buscar palabras que rimen con las palabras de la lista. ¿Qué rimas tienen un final que se escriba igual? ¿Cuáles son diferentes?

(fold here)

© Macmillan/McGraw-Hill

Conexión con el hogar

Queridos familiares:

¿Por qué algunos cuentos son tan buenos que se pueden narrar una y otra vez? Cada cultura tiene fábulas que se han contado de generación en generación. Esta semana estamos leyendo *Juan Verdades, The Man Who Couldn't Tell a Lie,* una nueva versión de un relato que ha sido contado y vuelto a contar innumerables veces en México. El ambiente es interesante, pero son los personajes y el argumento los que hacen que el cuento sea verdaderamente memorable. De hecho, el mismo relato podría estar ubicado en otro lugar. Por supuesto, el efecto emocional del cuento sería diferente, pero el tema de la fábula no cambiaría. Estoy aprendiendo a analizar cuentos desde diferentes perspectivas.

Destrezas de la semana

Comprensión: personajes, ambiente, argumento

Vocabulario: partes de una palabra

Ortografía/Fonética: sílabas

Nombre _____

Extraña ficción

Los buenos escritores usan el ambiente, los personajes y el argumento con mucho cuidado. Sus opciones hacen que los relatos sean divertidos e interesantes. Vamos a escoger algunas opciones al azar para escribir un cuento realmente extraño.

- Escribe una palabra para cada elemento de la lista. Luego agregaremos nuestras propias palabras para completar el cuento.
- Al leerlo en voz alta, escucharemos cómo nuestras opciones cambiaron el relato.

A. woman's name: _____

B. adjective: _____

C. profession: _____

D. city: _____

E. man's name: _____

F. action verb: _____

G. city: _____

H. adverb: _____

_____ was a very _____
(A)   (B)

_____. She lived in _____.
(C)   (D)

One day, _____
(E)

moved in next door. He was also an unusual

neighbor because he liked to _____
(F)

every day. Of course, _____
(A)

and _____ fell in love. For their
(E)

honeymoon, they went to _____ and had
(G)

so much fun that they decided to move there.

Needless to say, they lived _____
(H)

ever after.

Comprehension Check

Summarize

What is Benny's mood as he travels southwest at the beginning of the story? As the story develops, how does his mood change, and why? How do his mother's feelings change? Use the Summary Chart to summarize the big events.

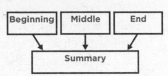

Think and Compare

1. Why do you think that Benny's mother wants to write a memoir? How will finding the family papers help her to write it? *(Analyze Character, Setting, Plot)*

2. What sort of relics—writings, photographs, heirlooms, etc.—survive from your family's past? What do these items reveal about who your ancestors were, where they came from, and the times in which they lived? *(Synthesize)*

3. Name one type of artifact that helps us learn about the past. (Some examples are tools, art, ruins, mummies, books, clocks, buildings, and photographs.) Why did you choose this? Describe what we can learn from this type of artifact. *(Evaluate)*

The Secrets of
Old Mesilla

by Becky Cheston
illustrated by KE Lewis

Table of Contents

Chapter One

November 20, 1854

Today, our small town makes history. Ten million dollars has already changed hands. Mexico may be richer, but here in Old Mesilla we have a new home: the United States. Any moment now, U.S. General Sam Garland and Mexican General Angel Trias will sign the Gasden Purchase. By day's end Mesilla Valley, part of 30,000 square miles along the Mexican border, will change hands from Mexico to the United States. Already flags from both countries ripple from the plaza bandstand. . . .

If Benny Stone could see what lay ahead, he'd probably be itching to get to Old Mesilla. Instead, he squirmed. The car seat was hot and made him sweat more. His shirt itched and he wished he were back home.

His mom, however, was a different story. The farther they got from Minneapolis, the lighter Benny's mother seemed. It was as if she was shedding burdens onto the highway as they traveled southwest, the convertible top pulled back.

Suddenly, she jabbed her finger at the windshield. "Look! There it is!" In the backseat, Garcia, Benny's black Labrador retriever, turned obediently, whipping himself in the face with one wind-blown ear.

The explorers emerged onto a floor made of hard-packed earth. Their flashlights illuminated a small room furnished with an old sofa, a wooden desk and chair, and a low cupboard with a sliding door.

Benny slid open the cupboard. "Look, Mom!" Inside, loose papers, leather-bound notebooks, and yellowed newsprint stood in tight stacks.

Even in the dim light, Benny could see excitement flare in his mom's eyes. She'd have plenty of family stories now. And so would he.

Epilogue

May 6, 1902

For my birthday today, Isabel, my son-in-law Francisco, and my three grandchildren have given me a cedar cabinet to store my writing. Built in Francisco's own workshop, it has two shelves behind a sliding door. My dear Sofia had a hand in this, even though, when the papers pile up, she nags me to throw some on the fire. But Isabel understands for she keeps treasures from her childhood. She knows my words are my treasures. I am not a rich man. What legacy do I have to pass down, other than these words. . . .

Fifteen minutes later, they had pried up slats of old, crumbling floorboards, revealing a three-foot-square metal hatch. But when they tried to lift the door, it wouldn't budge. Benny tied a strong rope to the loop, and when the three of them pulled together, it finally rose with a rusty squeak. They sat in awe around the dark hole until Benny finally ran to fetch Carla. Cole tracked down his dad, who brought Cole's Uncle Bob, flashlights, and more rope.

Now, with ropes around their waists, Cole's dad, Carla, and Benny descended a ladder, while Cole and Kip lay flat on their stomachs, pointing flashlights to guide them. Uncle Bob secured the safety ropes.

18

A large sign loomed on the side of the road. "Welcome To New Mexico, the Land of Enchantment," Benny read as it zoomed out of view. He had stopped complaining. Seeing his mom all grinning and light was almost worth the trip. Well, almost. He could still name about ten things he'd rather do this summer than spend it with his mother in some tiny southwestern town.

"So you're excited about seeing your old homestead, huh, Mom?"

"As a matter of fact, I am!" Carla Diaz-Stone leaned over to ruffle her son's hair, which was already seriously mussed.

Benny envied his mom's enthusiasm. After publishing three novels, she was working on a memoir. And she was stuck. No doubt about it—his mom had a genuine case of writer's block. The ideas just weren't flowing and she couldn't seem to write. This trip would hopefully bring back a ton of family memories. Still, did *he* have to tag along?

Benny sat back and studied the strange scenery. Dry, caked earth, cactus plants, scruffy sedge grass, and the occasional cottonwood tree decorated the land. Nothing at all like the dense brush and woodlands that lined the highways of the Midwest.

Benny stared out the window and read the exit signs as they went by. He squinted to read the names: Tucumcari, Santa Rosa, Albuquerque—that one sounded familiar. "So how far now?" Benny asked his mom.

"New Mexico's a big state, honey," Carla replied. "And Old Mesilla is about as far south as you can go before you hit the border."

Benny didn't like the sound of that. "Which means . . . ?"

"About two hours. Want to stop for lunch?"

© 2007 Macmillan/McGraw-Hill

"In here!" Benny called.

In a flash Kip raced into the room. "I have to talk to you!" she said. "I have this idea—*yikes*!" One of Kip's baseball cleats snagged on a loose carpet thread. She slid, which shoved the rug into a heap. Then her feet kicked out from under her.

"You okay?" Benny asked.

Kip gritted her teeth. "Yeah," she said. "Sorry about the floor." One of the floorboards had splintered, leaving a six-inch gash.

"Maybe we can glue it." He tried to position the broken slat back in place. "What's that?"

"Looks like a ring," said Cole. "Pick it up."

Benny tried, but the ring was welded onto something. Under the floorboards, they could see a metal plate.

"Hey—that's not a ring," said Cole. "It's the loop you grab onto to open a hatch. Maybe this was an old doorway down into the basement."

"I knew it!" Kip was actually gloating. "I tried to tell you before I fell. You know how in Isabel's note, she said she was burying her things for safekeeping *just like her papa does*?"

"You think Orlando Diaz hid his papers underground?" asked Benny.

Kip's eyes shone with excitement. "There's only one way to find out."

"But Orlando Diaz, Isabel's father, was a writer," Kip chimed. "Didn't he leave notes and letters and stuff?"

Carla shook her head. "There's nothing left of the old newspaper office. And no one ever found anything here."

"Maybe it's not somewhere obvious," said Benny.

"Yeah!" said Cole. "What if there's a secret hiding place somewhere in the house?"

Carla rolled her eyes and started clearing the table. "Now *that* sounds like a good fiction plot."

At that moment Benny and Cole (and Kip) latched on to the idea that Orlando Diaz's writings existed—somewhere. How cool would it be to discover real stuff from Benny's ancestors! And besides, his mom needed material for her book, not to mention inspiration.

But more than a week later, their search had turned up precisely nothing.

"There's got to be something we missed," said Cole.

"What would a detective—or an archaeologist—do now?" Benny mused.

From the backyard came the sound of Garcia and Woody barking. Both boys scrambled to the window and saw Kip skipping into the yard, dressed in her Little League uniform. Then the screen door slammed. "Benny? Hey, Benny?"

© 2007 Macmillan/McGraw-Hill

The Secrets of Old Mesilla

Chapter Two

February 12, 1862

Almost a year has passed since the Confederates captured Mesilla. I watch with caution as Colonel Baylor, our self-appointed governor, struts to and from his headquarters near the plaza. It is no secret that he likes it here, but I do not trust the man. Others may believe in his confederate paper money but not me. Yet I fear what will happen to our merchants if Mesilla finds itself once again in Union hands. . . .

"I can't believe this restaurant is still here!" Carla finished the last bite of her taco and took a long sip of lemonade. "But there does seem to be a lot of new shops in Santa Rosa."

Benny had finished his chili and was now studying the map of the Santa Rosa area on his paper placemat. "Blue Hole natural springs: The scuba diving capital of the Southwest. Now that sounds interesting. Or these cliff dwellings—wait! Right here's Billy the Kid's grave. Check it out!"

"We can see all that stuff if you want, Benny," said his mom. "But let's get settled in Old Mesilla first. Then we'll have all summer."

"Don't remind me," Benny muttered.

"You know," said Carla, "Billy the Kid was tried and sentenced right in my old hometown—at the county courthouse. They turned it into a Billy the Kid Gift Shop. Really."

"A gift shop? For a notorious outlaw?"

"There's a lot of history in Old Mesilla." Carla got up to pay the bill. "You'll see."

Outside on the restaurant's porch, Garcia dozed in the shade. Kneeling beside him, Benny unwrapped a piece of cornbread he'd saved in a paper napkin. He put it in front of Garcia and vigorously shook the last crumbs from the napkin. Instantly, Garcia awoke and gobbled up the treat. Benny chuckled. Garcia would, and did, devour any food.

Chapter Four

April 13, 1881

Today Billy the Kid has finally been sentenced to death for his crimes. He has agreed to meet with me later, at the jail. But he will grant Newman's Semi-Weekly *from Las Cruces no more interviews. "Newman gave me a rough deal," he said at the courthouse. "But I believe the* News *is always willing to give its readers both sides of a story." I sense we have not heard the last from the Kid. . . .*

They had been there for 11 days, and so far, the summer had more than fulfilled Benny's expectations. Though he had dreaded coming, he was now having fun. But for his mom, the excitement of the first few days had quickly worn off. Her not being able to write still worried her.

"When I write fiction, the plots come so easily. Maybe I just can't write a memoir," she remarked one evening over dinner. Benny had invited Cole over, and Carla had insisted that Kip stay, too. "When I came down here, I thought I'd discover so much to write about. But all the memories seem to have died with my ancestors."

"Come on, Mom. What's it say?" asked Benny. Carla translated it aloud:

Dear Mother Earth,
   Today I am giving you my most precious things for safekeeping. Just like my Papa does. Papa has told me that the bad man Billy the Kid has escaped from prison. I am afraid he will steal my things. My doll likes it when you sing to her. Her name is Maria.

They sat in wonder at this voice from long ago. Then Kip's shriek broke the silence. "Woody! Give me back my hat!"

Benny saw Kip was a girl. Kip was a girl.

14

"Okay, guys!" Carla called out. "Back in the car!"

Benny couldn't believe she hadn't visited New Mexico since she'd married his dad. The two had met at the University of Minnesota, where they both taught English. When his parents divorced three years ago, Benny thought she might move back to the Southwest. "If I did that, you wouldn't be able to grow up with both your parents," she'd told him. So Carla had stayed, teaching part time and writing her novels, while Benny lived one week with his dad, one week with his mom. Not the perfect life, but not bad either. His parents at least were always civil to each other, and Benny appreciated it.

They drove the rest of the way with the convertible top up, protecting them from the sun. At some point Benny crawled into the backseat. He was so tired that he fell asleep with his head on Garcia's fuzzy belly. In his dreams Benny dove into Blue Hole springs. Billy the Kid chased after him on horseback, wearing a scuba mask. At the bottom of the lake was his home in Minneapolis—if only he could reach it. A school of tacos swam by. His face was wet, so wet—but it was only Garcia's tongue, licking him awake. And there was his mom, standing over him, whispering gleefully, "We're here!"

7

Chapter Three

April 1, 1881

Today a sad event occurs for Old Mesilla. Since the Gasden Purchase, we have enjoyed great prosperity as a major trade and transportation center in the Southwest. We lay a proud claim to a central station on the Butterfield Stagecoach line. But today progress will pass us by as the first Santa Fe Railroad train arrives in Las Cruces. . . .

Benny felt strange walking into the house that had been in his mother's family for almost 200 years. His Aunt Mia, who lived in Albuquerque, helped maintain the place, often vacationing here on weekends. Benny strode over to check out the fridge. Aunt Mia had left a welcome note—and lots of groceries.

As he helped his mom unpack, Benny marveled at how cool the house stayed in the summer heat. Like many of the original homes here, it was built of adobe—bricks made from mud and straw. Inside, bright woven rugs lay scattered across polished wood floors. Benny dragged his stuff into the back bedroom. Here two large windows looked out onto a small backyard. Benny pushed aside the curtains. There was Garcia, sniffing around in the dirt.

Or—wait a minute. It *was* a Lab, but a deep, chocolate color, not black. There was his Garcia sniffing along behind this other dog, followed by a boy in denim shorts, who looked about Benny's age. The boy waved.

© 2007 Macmillan/McGraw-Hill

The Secrets of Old Mesilla

"I see something in here! Mom—look at this." Benny knelt down and smoothed handfuls of dirt away with his hands until a brownish object appeared.

"It looks like . . . I don't know—like a piece of pottery," she said. Benny lifted out a wide-mouthed vase and carefully handed it to his mom. Its rim was chipped in a few places, and a large crack ran from top to bottom. Carla turned it over and over. Things fell out: a carved brush made of bone and an old, hand-sewn doll.

Benny picked up the brush. "There's something written on the back," he said. *"Por Isabel Pilar Diaz."*

"Let me see that." Carla grabbed the brush. "Isabel Pila . . . that was my great-grandmother."

"Hey—take a look at this." Inside the vase, Cole had discovered a piece of yellowed parchment. He handed it to Benny's mom. "Careful—it's almost ripped there, along the folds."

The three of them sat cross-legged in the dirt as Carla slowly unfolded the paper. "Isabel wrote this—it's in Spanish," she said. She read silently for a minute.

Benny leapt up. Cole and Kip followed him to the edge of the yard, where Garcia and Woody were vigorously digging a huge hole. Snouts to the ground, they scratched rapidly at the earth, scattering it in all directions.

"No digging, dogs—NO DIGGING!"

Each time one boy grabbed his dog by the collar, the other would jump up and knock him free. Meanwhile Kip emerged from the hole with the red ball. "They were trying to bury this." Kip threw the ball. The dogs ran to fetch it.

Carla and the boys could now inspect the damage. "That is one totally gigantic hole," said Benny. Cole ran next door, returning with a pair of shovels. Cole started to scoop the dirt back inside the hole, but Benny shouted for Cole to stop.

Benny ran through the kitchen and out the back door. The boy stuck out his hand. "I'm Cole Sullivan. We live right next door."

"I'm Benny Stone. I see you've met Garcia. Shake, boy." Garcia offered his paw to Cole.

"This here's Woody—well, Haywood, actually."

Benny laughed. "Haywood, huh? He could have some wild nicknames."

"You mean, like, 'Haywood I. Care'? Heard 'em."

"I was thinking, 'Haywood U. Buzzoff,'" said Benny. They both chuckled. "Is that your brother over there?" A skinny kid about nine or ten years old stood at the edge of the yard.

The Secrets of Old Mesilla

Cole turned. "Definitely not. That's Kip, who's about to GET LOST."

"Come on," the kid whined. "I've got a right to see the new neighbor, too, you know." Kip tossed a red ball and the dogs dashed after it.

Benny and Cole walked over to a small, brick patio, where they sat on cedar chairs. "If you let Kip hang around, pretty soon you're going to have a shadow," Cole advised.

Benny laughed. "I'm not sure what else I'll be doing this summer." He told Cole about why he and his mom had made the trip.

"I'm doing a little work for my dad, painting houses and stuff," said Cole. "I'm sure he could use another part-time employee." Cole's father, who owned a small remodeling company, had a foreman on vacation and jobs were piling up.

Kip still hovered at the edge of the yard, as Cole told Benny how his family had moved from Houston, Texas, to Old Mesilla. When he was about five, Cole's parents had vacationed here and loved the little village. With Las Cruces just five miles north and El Paso, Texas, only 40 miles east, Cole's dad hoped his remodeling business would flourish here—and it had.

Benny's mom interrupted the boys. "Two new friends, already?" she exclaimed. Then she suddenly turned, shouting, "Benito—the dogs!"

10

11

Word Workout

WORDS TO KNOW

embarked	lamented	precarious
sensational	extravagant	limousine
promenade	unimaginable	

One Remarkable Day Let's describe an amazing day that could never happen. We'll use these words to describe events that are way beyond reality.

SPELLING WORDS

actor	platter	mirror	calendar	observer
stroller	customer	vinegar	waiter	wander
scatter	ancestor	bachelor	singular	traitor
gutter	flavor	behavior	maneuver	janitor

Three Ways I notice that these words have three different endings: **or, er,** and **ar.** Look at the words now. I'm going to spell each word without the ending and ask you to supply the missing ending.

········ (fold here) ········

Home-School Connection

Dear Family Member:

Did you ever notice how a little imagination can turn a lousy day into a great one? This week we're reading *Nothing Ever Happens on 90th Street,* a story about a character named Eva. She's really stuck on a writing assignment until she lets her imagination run wild. The story is humorous because Eva thinks up all kinds of funny things that might happen on the street where she lives.

While we're reading, we're also practicing drawing conclusions about what we read. This is an important part of reading. When I form a conclusion, I show that I can put the ideas in a story together and tell what they add up to.

This Week's Skills

Comprehension: draw conclusions

Vocabulary: dictionary

Spelling/Phonics: words with **or, er,** and **ar**

Name _____

The Stores on Moore Street

We can put information together to draw conclusions. Let's see what we can conclude after reading this quick story.

After school, Alison stopped in to visit her father at the store on Moore Street and buy a music CD. She told him about her day at school and then went to visit Ms. Wayne in her shop down the street.

"You look terrific today," said Ms. Wayne, "I'm going to give you a rosebud for your hair."

Then Alison said good-bye and stopped in the store next door. She needed to get a special treat for her brother Samson. She decided to stop in and say hello to Mrs. Nahun. "I've seen you running up and down the street," laughed Mrs. Nahun. "You'll be in here again to buy some new sneakers soon!"

	My Conclusions
Alison's father works at	
Ms. Wayne works at	
Samson needs	
Mrs. Nahun works at	

Ejercicio de palabras

PALABRAS DE VOCABULARIO

embarked	lamented	precarious
sensational	extravagant	limousine
promenade	unimaginable	

Un día memorable Vamos a describir un día asombroso que nunca podría suceder de verdad. Vamos a usar las palabras de la lista para describir sucesos que van más allá de realidad de todos los días.

PALABRAS DE ORTOGRAFÍA

actor	platter	mirror	calendar	observer
stroller	customer	vinegar	waiter	wander
scatter	ancestor	bachelor	singular	traitor
gutter	flavor	behavior	maneuver	janitor

Falta el final Observo que estas palabras tienen tres finales diferentes: **or, er** y **ar**. Mira todas las palabras. Voy a deletrear cada palabra sin la terminación y tú deberás decirme qué terminación corresponde.

(fold here)

© Macmillan/McGraw-Hill

Conexión con el hogar

Queridos familiares:

¿Han visto alguna vez como un poco de imaginación puede hacer que un mal día se transforme en uno bueno? Esta semana estamos leyendo *Nothing Ever Happens on 90th Street,* un cuento sobre un personaje llamado Eva. Ella tiene un montón de problemas con una tarea de escritura hasta que deja correr su imaginación. El cuento es humorístico, porque a Eva se le ocurren toda clase de sucesos graciosos que pueden suceder en la calle donde vive.

A medida que leemos, estamos también tratando de sacar conclusiones acerca de lo que leemos. Ésta es una parte importante de la lectura. Cuando llego a una conclusión, demuestro que puedo unir las ideas de un cuento y darme cuenta de qué es lo que quieren decir.

Destrezas de la semana

Comprensión: sacar conclusiones

Vocabulario: diccionario

Ortografía/Fonética: palabras con **or, er** y **ar**

Nombre_____

175

Las tiendas de la calle Moore

Podemos reunir la información que tenemos para sacar conclusiones. Vamos a ver qué conclusiones podemos sacar después de leer este breve cuento.

After school, Alison stopped in to visit her father at the store on Moore Street and buy a music CD. She told him about her day at school and then went to visit Ms. Wayne in her shop down the street.

"You look terrific today," said Ms. Wayne, "I'm going to give you a rosebud for your hair."

Then Alison said good-bye and stopped in the store next door. She needed to get a special treat for her brother Samson. She decided to stop in and say hello to Mrs. Nahun. "I've seen you running up and down the street," laughed Mrs. Nahun. "You'll be in here again to buy some new sneakers soon!"

	My Conclusions
Alison's father works at	
Ms. Wayne works at	
Samson needs	
Mrs. Nahun works at	

Comprehension Check

Summarize

Use the Draw Conclusions Chart to draw conclusions about the story. Did Julie and Peter change their opinions of their hometowns? How do you know?

What I Know	Text Evidence	Conclusions

Think and Compare

1. Look back at page 4. How can you tell that Julie is very interested in writing? *(Draw Conclusions)*

2. How do you feel about your own community? What is something you like about it? What is something you wish were different about it, and why? *(Evaluate)*

3. Julie and Peter shared writing and revision ideas. Which of their ideas have you used, too? What are some of the ways they gathered information about their hometowns that you could try? *(Apply)*

© 2007 Macmillan/McGraw-Hill

The Great American Hometown Homework

by Joyce McGreevy
illustrated by Marcy Ramsey

Table of Contents

CHAPTER 1 Mystery Homework

September 15, 3:41 P.M.

Hello, Peter Smith of Portland, Oregon. This is Julie Taylor of Monterey, California. You may wonder why I'm writing to you, since we don't know each other. It's because my entire class is abuzz. Everybody is talking about Mr. Mora's big announcement today. Mr. Mora is my teacher. Well, not just mine, of course, but he's the teacher for our whole class. My school is called Old Monterey Middle School, which is a boring name. I would have called it the Monterey School for Future Writers and Other Geniuses.

Mr. Mora laughed when I told him that. He said, "Well, Julie, that name is a bit long, don't you agree?"

Mr. Mora is always asking us if we agree. Most of the time I do. Mr. Mora knows a lot, especially about writing—which brings me to the exciting announcement.

2

19

Epilogue

October 29, 7:25 A.M.

Dear Julie,

It was great to meet you and your parents. Isn't it funny how we walked right up to each other at Dulles Airport like we'd known each other for life? And how about that ride in the limousine? All this writing has put us on the same page. (Get it?)

The awards ceremony was fun! But the best part was visiting all the monuments and landmarks. Hey, we should write about it for our classes! What do you think? It's the next big mystery to solve: What is Washington, D.C., really like?

Your friend,

Pete

October 29, 7:43 A.M.

Dear Pete,

Great minds think alike! I was going to suggest the same thing. We'll need to do more reading and gather research materials. It will be a whole new adventure. Ready for countdown? Three, two, one, blast off!

Julie

"Settle down, please," said Mr. Mora. It was almost three o'clock, and we were getting restless. "I'm going to give you a homework assignment—with a twist."

We were about to groan at the word *homework* when Mr. Mora explained that there would be something surprising about the homework.

That's where you come in!

"Each of you is going to work with a writing partner," Mr. Mora informed us.

Patti Ackley, who is my best friend, raised her hand.

"But Mr. Mora, that's nothing new. We work with writing partners all the time."

"That's true," admitted Mr. Mora. "But usually your writing partner is sitting at the next desk, not living in another state."

Now that got our attention. We all leaned forward so we could catch every detail of our new writing assignment.

Mr. Mora explained that we would each write something creative and work with a partner by email to share our writing. We would read each other's work, ask questions, and help each other with revisions.

I love to write, but I need all the help I can get when it comes to revisions. As long as the other person is polite and doesn't just say something like "That's boring" or ask me why I wrote what I did, I am only too happy to hear his or her ideas. Mr. Mora is not extravagant with compliments, but when he writes "Good work!" on your essay, you know he really liked it.

By now you've probably guessed that you and I are writing partners. I hope that's all right. If not, you can probably switch names and addresses with somebody else in your class.

October 10, 3:37 P.M.

Hi Pete,

Did you check the mail? I received a fat envelope. They must have sent back my essay.

Julie

October 10, 3:46 P.M.

Julie,

I got one, too! Why don't we open our envelopes together? Can you meet me online after dinner?

Pete

October 10, 6:51 P.M.

Julie: Are you ready to rip open the envelope?

Pete: I'm ready when you are!

Julie: Here goes nothing!

Pete: Hey! That's great!

Julie: We . . . won <u>second</u> place!

Pete: We <u>won</u>!

Julie: It's amazing!

Pete: Super—they're sending us to
        Washington, D.C.!

Julie: I'm over the moon!

Pete: We cracked the case! Let's tell our folks!

Julie: I'm on my way!!

© 2007 Macmillan/McGraw-Hill

Julie: My essay is too long. What can I do?

Peter: Well, you have some interesting details about Santa Cruz. But Santa Cruz is another city and not part of the main idea. Take that part out. Okay?

Julie: Roger! Copy that! Thanks! Just think, tomorrow we turn in our final drafts.

Peter: Then our teachers will send off copies to the contest. Good luck, partner!

October 1, 7:32 A.M.

Pete,

Have you heard anything?

Julie

October 1, 7:42 A.M.

Julie,

I haven't heard a word.

Pete

October 4, 4:29 P.M.

Pete,

I hate waiting.

Julie

October 4, 5:02 P.M.

Julie,

That goes double for me.

Pete

However—just a warning—you might end up with Calvin Landers. He's a nice guy in my class, but he only likes to write about surfing. Calvin says we should elect a surfer as President of the United States, send a surfer into space, and make surfboards the official state symbol of California. If you like to surf, then Calvin Landers is the partner for you.

I have two more things to share, and then I'm done. Mr. Mora says we are going to enter our writing in a contest! Plus, I'm going to write an adventure story about a girl and her friends who build a rocket ship and go to the moon.

My plan is to have the space ship crash on the edge of a giant crater. That way the crew inside will be in a precarious position, with the rocket hanging on the edge. That's what famous writers call a cliffhanger.

So, Peter, what do you think? Are you interested?

Sincerely,

Julie Taylor

Old Monterey Middle School in Monterey, California

P.S. The bell rang before Mr. Mora could tell us the rest of the assignment. I can't wait to hear what it is! Do you know anything? Did your teacher spill the beans?

September 15, 6:14 P.M.

Hi Julie,

So that's the definition of a cliffhanger. Your idea sounds more like a crater hanger! (Get it?) Yes, I have an obnoxious sense of humor.

You wrote to the right person, because I like writing, too. Our teacher, Ms. Greenleaf, told us she would "tell all" tomorrow.

I like your space story idea. I'm going to write about a boy detective who travels around the world solving mysteries.

I like to ask questions and figure things out. I'm absolutely certain the world is fascinating once you get outside boring old Portland.

Mom just called me to dinner.

See you (sort of),

Peter "Pete" Smith

CHAPTER 4 Revise and Conquer

September 22, 4:39 P.M.

Hey, Pete,
All systems are go! My first draft is attached.
Julie

September 22, 6:54 P.M.

Peter: Your essay made me want to visit Monterey again! Does the aquarium have other animals, too?

Julie: Oh, yes! Everybody watches the sea otters play. I'll add other examples. Thanks for the hint!

Peter: You're welcome. What did you think about my essay?

Julie: I never knew that Portland had a floating museum. Maybe you could add the name of it.

Peter: Good idea! Sometimes I have trouble with spelling. Do you have any more tips?

Julie: I use a dictionary, and try to match the first few letters. Once I find the word, I add it to my list. That helps me memorize it.

Peter: Cool! I'll try that.

15

September 21, 11:23 A.M.

Julie,

You've done some great research! I've been a sleuth, too, hot on the trail—the Oregon Trail, that is. I went to the library to check out books about Portland's history. You won't believe what I found out.

After 1847, the city grew so rapidly that people were cutting down trees for buildings faster than they could clear away the stumps. So people nicknamed the city Stumptown! I'm glad it didn't stick. Today we have a much better nickname, the City of Roses. We're famous for our rose gardens and our parks. One city park, Mount Tabor, sits on top of an extinct volcano!

I've also been taking pictures. The one I've sent you is Pioneer Courthouse Square. I like the red brick, all the hanging flowers, and the sculpture. People call it "Portland's living room" because everybody comes here for special events, to visit friends, or just to enjoy being downtown.

Are you ready to trade first drafts tomorrow?

Pete

14

CHAPTER 2

Bad News

September 16, 4:07 P.M.

Hi again, Peter "Pete,"

I've got bad news! Mr. Mora says we have to write about what we know. And as if that weren't bad enough, we have to describe a place. But this assignment gets worse. The description has to be about the place where we live. I've lived in Monterey my whole life. Believe me, there's nothing interesting about it.

So much for my sensational story that was going to thrill the judges. I lamented to Mr. Mora, saying how disappointed I was. Do you know what he said? Smiling like the superior teacher he thinks he is, Mr. Mora said, "By writing about the place where you live, you will make amazing discoveries, don't you agree?"

I don't. Mr. Mora says we will enter our "hometown homework" into a national contest. Students whose essays win will travel to Washington, D.C. Their two cities will be named as sister cities. That's supposed to encourage people from Monterey to visit Portland, and vice versa.

7

I guess the contest isn't <u>too</u> boring, but writing about this pathetic old place sure will be. If only I could embark on a cruise ship in Monterey Bay and sail to a more exciting and exotic place, maybe somewhere across the Pacific Ocean. You're absolutely luckier than I am. At least you live in a big city, filled with excitement. Mom says, "When you walk in a city, you don't just walk. You promenade in a grand style." What is that supposed to mean?

Julie

© 2007 Macmillan/McGraw-Hill

September 20, 10:03 A.M.

Hi Pete,

The author you're thinking of is John Steinbeck, who lived here and wrote about Monterey. Cannery Row was one of his favorite places. A long time ago, fishermen brought their daily catch in to be canned in all the canneries, or factories, there.

Now the canneries are museums, shops, and restaurants. It is a really fun place, which I remembered when I looked through some travel brochures. I picked some up at the tourism office on Alvarado Street. I forgot that even when you live in a place you can play tourist, too.

I never thought I'd say this, but it's unimaginable that anyone could ever be bored here in Monterey. It's like I'm exploring a whole new planet!

Julie

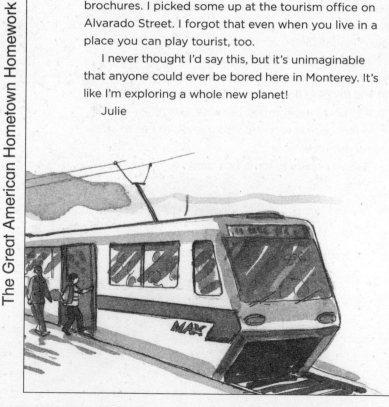

September 18, 7:43 A.M.

Hi Julie,

The MAX (Metropolitan Area Express) is Portland's light rail system, which takes you all over the city. I like the freedom it gives me. I just hop on in front of my apartment and the MAX zips along.

On weekends, I take the MAX to the Oregon Zoo. Sometimes my family takes the MAX to visit the Oregon Museum of Science and Industry. As a fan of outer space, you would love OMSI.

Every summer, we take the MAX to Portland International Airport. That's how I know about Monterey. My family flew there once for a wedding. It was great! (Monterey, not the wedding, which was a bunch of people getting dressed up and dancing to silly music.) I'd welcome the chance to solve the mysteries of Monterey. For instance, how did Cannery Row get its name? Didn't a famous author write about it?

Bye!

Pete

© 2007 Macmillan/McGraw-Hill

September 16, 8:15 P.M.

Julie,

Who are you kidding? Portland isn't exactly a hotbed of excitement and adventure. This city is what a detective hero would call "Dullsville." Nothing ever happens here except rain, and people living the same old lives. Pioneer Middle School is an old, red brick building surrounded by a bunch of trees. Every day I take the MAX to get there. But I must admit that Ms. Greenleaf makes class fun. It's kind of cool when a teacher makes school tolerable.

You, however, live in marvelous, fantastic Monterey, California. You can explore tide pools, take photographs of the seals and seagulls in Monterey Bay, visit the Monterey Bay Aquarium, and watch thousands of Monarch butterflies migrate to and from Mexico. (Migrate is my newest science word.) If I were a detective looking for a great city, I would follow the trail south from Oregon to California. Then I would gather clues, like great beaches, warm sun, and friendly people. That would lead me right to Monterey!

Hey, I have to run. Mom says that since I got dust all over the kitchen table, I have to clean it until it sparkles. (Did I mention that I'm trying to develop my own fingerprint-dusting powder?) She says the dust might make everyone lose their appetite for dinner. Man, how is an aspiring detective ever supposed to learn his craft?

I rest my case.

Pete

© 2007 Macmillan/McGraw-Hill

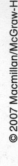

CHAPTER 3

No Place Like Boring Old Home

September 17, 3:45 P.M.

Pete,

How can you say that nothing ever happens in Portland? My dad helped me find a map of your neighborhood. You reside (which is a synonym for live, which is my word of the day) right near the center of the city! Dad says that your family lives close enough to go see the Blazers play basketball at Rose Garden Arena any time you like! I love basketball, but I have to watch it on television.

I see that Portland has a beautiful river called the Willamette. Its seven bridges look spectacular.

I'm off to launch some new ideas, since the space story crash-landed. Thanks for the reminders about Monterey. I guess exploring it could be an adventure—just not as exciting as blasting off with my imagination.

So that's one small step for a kid, and one giant leap for the writing kind. (Get it?)

Julie

P.S. Who is the mysterious MAX?

Word Workout

WORDS TO KNOW

adverse	generate	renewable
apparatus	nonrenewable	

Challenge I'll choose a word and challenge you to use it in a sentence. Then you can challenge me. We can keep challenging each other in several rounds.

SPELLING WORDS

burden	civil	normal	villain	curtain
carton	dwindle	novel	urban	peril
hasten	gallon	basin	organ	gravel
cable	fumble	whistle	satin	dangle

Back Writing I am going to trace a spelling word on your back with my finger. Can you tell which word I am spelling? Is it easier with your eyes open or shut?

(fol d here)

Home-School Connection

Dear Family Member:

This week we're reading "Building Green," an article about some clever ways to save our natral resources. Some adventurous people are building houses that are made from surprising materials such as recycled car bodies or hard-packed straw. We won't use trees for lumber that way. I'm seeing how one thing causes something else to happen, both good and bad.

This Week's Skills

Comprehension: cause and effect

Vocabulary: context clues

Spelling/Phonics: words ending in **en** and **il**

Name _____

One Thing Leads to Another

All of the things we do can affect the future. Choices big and small lead to changes. Unscramble the words on the next page and write them in the puzzle. Read down the letters in the circles to find the secret word.

1. S R C O E U
2. O T O R
3. C N A I H
4. S S I B A
5. E C T F F E
6. E S U T Q I N O
7. E S C U A
8. W A E N R S
9. O N C I T A
10. O M U E T O C
11. U R L E T S

1. _____ _____ _____ _____ _____ _____
2. _____
3. C _____
4. B _____
5. _____
6. _____ _____ _____ _____ _____
7. _____
8. _____
9. _____
10. _____
11. _____

The secret word is _____.

Ejercicio de palabras

PALABRAS DE VOCABULARIO

adverse   generate   renewable

apparatus   nonrenewable

La energía en casa Vamos a turnarnos para formar oraciones acerca de cómo usamos la energía en casa. Primero yo elijo una palabra para que tú hagas la oración. Luego tú haces lo mismo conmigo, y así sucesivamente.

PALABRAS DE ORTOGRAFÍA

burden	civil	normal	villain	curtain
carton	dwindle	novel	urban	peril
hasten	gallon	basin	organ	gravel
cable	fumble	whistle	satin	dangle

En la palma Muéstrame la palma de tu mano. Voy a escribir en ella con un dedo una de las palabras de la lista. ¿Puedes decirme de qué palabra se trata? ¿Cómo es más fácil adivinar, con los ojos abiertos o cerrados?

(fold here)

Conexión con el hogar

Queridos familiares:

Esta semana estamos leyendo *Building Green*, un artículo sobre algunas soluciones ingeniosas para conservar nuestros recursos naturales. Algunas personas arriesgadas están buscando nuevas maneras de edificar casas "verdes." Estas casas están construidas con materiales novedosos, como carrocerías recicladas de automóviles o paja comprimida. Así no tenemos qeu cortar árboles para usar madera. También estamos estudiando cómo una acción causa otra, ya sea buena o mala.

Destrezas de la semana

Comprensión: causa y efecto

Vocabulario: claves de contexto

Ortografía/Fonética: pronunciación de palabras terminadas en **en** y **il**

Nombre_____

Una cosa lleva a la otra

Todo lo que hacemos puede afectar el futuro. Grandes y pequeñas decisiones producen cambios. Desenreda las palabras que están en la página siguiente y escríbelas en los espacios. Lee las letras de los círculos para encontrar la palabra secreta.

1. S R C O E U   **2.** O T O R   **3.** C N A I H

4. S S I B A   **5.** E C T F F E   **6.** E S U T Q I N O

7. E S C U A   **8.** W A E N R S   **9.** O N C I T A

10. O M U E T O C   **11.** U R L E T S

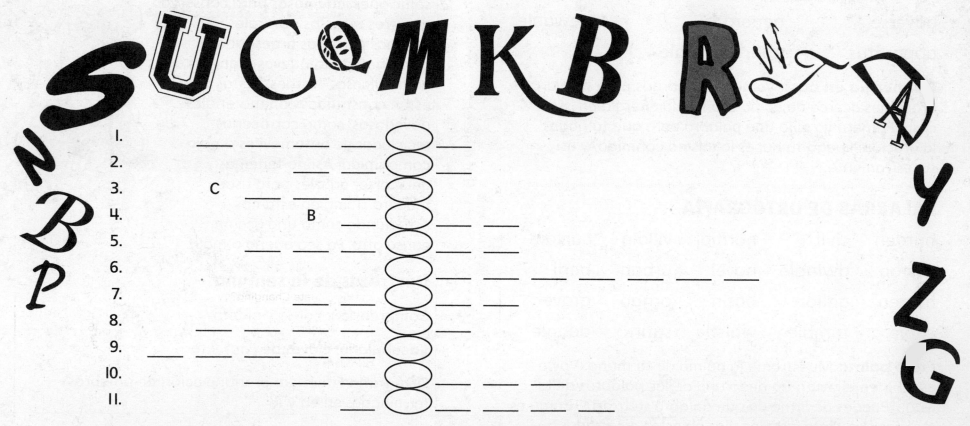

1.
2.
3. C
4. B
5.
6.
7.
8.
9.
10.
11.

The secret word is _____.

Comprehension Check

Summarize

How has the use of fossil fuels affected Earth? Review Chapter 1 on fossil fuels. Make a chart that lists both the causes and effects that using fossil fuels has on Earth.

Think and Compare

1. Review the section on the greenhouse effect. What is it? How does it work? *(Summarize)*

2. The author tells different ways that people can work to conserve energy. How would you work to conserve energy? *(Apply)*

3. Do you think it is important for people to find new forms of energy? *(Evaluate)*

Energy
Problems and Solutions

by Glen Phelan

Table of Contents

Introduction

During a space shuttle flight, an astronaut passed some time trying to find his home. As the spacecraft orbited Earth, the astronaut peered through the shuttle's windows to the world far below. Finally, he found it—the twinkling lights of the city where he lived. What a thrill! It was comforting to see home when he was so far away.

But then a strange thing happened. On the next orbit, he looked out the window again. This time the entire region around the city felt like home. On the orbit after that, he only had to look for his country to feel at home; then only at the continent. Eventually the astronaut saw the entire Earth as home sweet home.

Earth is our home in the universe. Are we taking care of it?

2

Index

23

Glossary

acid rain *(AS-id rayn)* rain or snow full of poisonous chemicals *(page 8)*

energy *(EN-urj-ee)* the capacity for doing work *(page 3)*

fossil fuel *(FOS-uhl FYEW-uhl)* a fuel formed from the remains of prehistoric plants and animals *(page 5)*

generate *(JEN-uh-rayt)* to bring about or produce *(page 5)*

glacier *(GLAY-shuhr)* a large mass of ice in very cold regions *(page 10)*

global warming *(GLOH-buhl WAWRM-ing)* an increase in the average temperature of the atmosphere of the earth *(page 12)*

greenhouse effect *(GREEN-hows i-FEKT)* the trapping of heat from the sun within the earth's atmosphere *(page 9)*

hybrid car *(HIGH-brid kahr)* a car that can switch from gasoline-powered to battery-powered, using less nonrenewable energy *(page 19)*

nonrenewable *(NON-ri-new-uh-bul)* relating to a resource that is gone forever once it is used up *(page 5)*

pollution *(puh-LEW-shuhn)* harmful materials such as certain gases, chemicals, and wastes that pollute the air, water, or soil *(page 8)*

renewable *(ri-NEW-uh-bul)* relating to a resource that is replaceable *(page 5)*

smog *(SMOG)* a combination of smoke and fog in the air *(page 8)*

strip-mine *(STRIP-mighn)* to remove topsoil in order to dig out a mineral that lies close to the surface, especially coal *(page 6)*

22

Energy Problems and Solutions

The astronaut understood a simple yet important idea—all of Earth is our home. But lately we haven't been too kind to our home. In fact you might say our home is in need of repair. Many of the problems facing the planet come down to one thing—our quest for **energy**. This book explores how the use of energy affects the environment. Yes, there are problems. But there are solutions, too.

3

CHAPTER 1

The Costs of Energy

Click on the TV. Turn up the heat. Go for a ride in the car. What do all these actions have in common? They all use energy. Energy is an important part of our lives. Try to imagine going through a day without it. First take away everything that uses electricity. No refrigerator, no TV, no light bulbs. Then shut down everything that runs on gasoline or fuel. No cars, trucks, planes, or trains. Next turn off the natural gas or oil that keeps your home warm on bitter cold nights. You get the idea—energy powers our lives.

A Kitchen Without Electricity

It may be hard to imagine life with no electricity, but your ancestors got along just fine without it. For example, 100 years ago there were no refrigerators that ran on electricity. How did people keep food cold? They used iceboxes. Most iceboxes were wooden boxes lined with metal. A large block of ice placed in one part of the box kept food cool in other parts of the box.

4

Conclusion

The costs of energy include more than how much money one has to pay to use an energy source. Costs also include the environmental effects of using the energy source and how much of the source we are using up if it's nonrenewable. Right now fossil fuels are the cheapest to use, but the costs to the environment and the limited supply may force us to use renewable energy sources more fully. Meanwhile, everyone can help by conserving energy.

What You Can Do

Conserving energy isn't just for carmakers and housing developers. Everyone can get involved. Here are some things you can do every day to save energy and take better care of our planet at the same time.

- Use less electricity whenever possible. Turn off lights that you aren't using. Don't run any electrical device unnecessarily.
- Ask a family member about replacing incandescent lights with compact fluorescent lights.
- Walk or ride a bike instead of asking for a ride.
- If you're cold, put on a sweatshirt instead of turning up the heat.
- Keep the curtains closed or shades drawn on hot, sunny days so that it stays cooler indoors without running the air conditioner.
- Use less hot water by taking showers instead of baths, running dishwashers only with a full load, and doing laundry in cold water.
- Recycle and reuse things whenever you can. Recycling aluminum cans uses only 5 percent of the energy required to make new cans from raw materials. The more you reuse, the less energy will be spent to make new items.

ALUMINUM   NEWSPAPER   PLASTIC

The Problems with Fossil Fuels

Most of the energy we use comes from **fossil fuels**—coal, oil, and natural gas. These energy sources are called fossil fuels because they formed from plants and animals that died millions of years ago.

⋒ Oil gathers in rocks underground—both on land and beneath the sea. Pumps pull the oil out of the ground.

Fossil fuels have many uses. Power plants burn coal and oil to **generate** electricity. Gasoline and fuel for most cars, planes, trains, and ships come from oil. Oil and natural gas provide heat for homes. In many ways fossil fuels are excellent sources of energy.

What's the problem? Fossil fuels are **nonrenewable**. Once we use them up, they are gone forever. Other energy sources, such as sunshine and wind, are **renewable**. They cannot be used up.

No one knows for sure how long our fossil fuels will last. However, one thing is for sure: sooner or later we will run out of fossil fuels.

Mining and Drilling

Some problems with fossil fuels come from the way we get them. Most coal, for example, is **strip-mined**. Huge earth-moving machines strip away the top layers of soil and rock to get to the coal beneath. Strip mines become giant scars on the land. Exposed metals and chemicals from the mines often wash into streams and pollute the water. Laws require mining companies to restore strip-mined land close to the way it was before being mined. Some mines have been successfully restored, but it is expensive and time-consuming.

Oil and natural gas cause some problems, too. More than half of the oil the United States uses comes from other countries, such as Saudi Arabia and Venezuela.

⊕ Pipelines carry oil over land. Some of them stretch for thousands of miles across the landscape. What problems might pipelines cause for animals that travel in herds?

Industries everywhere are looking for ways to use less energy and use it more efficiently. Housing developers are getting involved, too. A trend called "building green" is taking hold. It means building houses that are environmentally friendly. "Green" houses are energy efficient. They are well insulated to keep heat in on cold days and keep heat out on warm days. They use energy-efficient lighting and appliances. Some green houses even use recycled building materials that require less energy to make than new materials.

⊕ This "green" house is energy efficient.

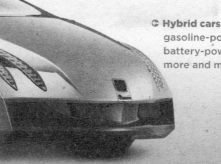

⊕ **Hybrid cars** that can switch from gasoline-powered to cleaner battery-powered are becoming more and more popular.

Using Less and Getting More

Today everything from light bulbs and windows to kitchen appliances, cooling systems, and entire buildings are being designed for greater energy efficiency. Replacing an incandescent bulb with a fluorescent one would save the buyer up to $50 over the 10-year life of the bulb. Cars are becoming more efficient, too. Carmakers can produce cars that can go farther on the same amount of gasoline.

One of the biggest wastes of energy happens in power plants. Generating electricity gives off a lot of waste heat. But this heat can be recovered and put to use. Some power plants redirect the waste energy to heat buildings and water. Other power plants use the waste heat to operate machines at the plant such as scrubbers, which remove harmful gases from the smokestacks.

The *Exxon Valdez*

The worst oil spill in history happened on March 24, 1989. The oil tanker *Exxon Valdez* crashed on rocks near Alaska, dumping 41 million liters (11 million gallons) of oil into the sea. The spill killed 250,000 seabirds, 2,800 otters, hundreds of seals, and 22 killer whales in addition to an unknown number of fish.

You may have heard the saying, "Accidents are bound to happen." This is true when you are riding a bike. It is also true when ships the size of several football fields are carrying oil on the high seas. Sometimes tankers slowly leak oil into the water. Sometimes a storm or navigation error causes a shipwreck that releases tons of oil into the sea. Either way the oil spill can be devastating to the environment. When the oil washes up on beaches, it harms the animals and plants there. Animals become coated with oil and cannot swim or fly. The oil poisons and kills some animals. It can take years to clean up an oil spill.

♦ Smog is most common in cities where many vehicles are burning gasoline.

The Costs of Using Fossil Fuels

Mining, drilling, and transporting fossil fuels certainly can have some adverse effects on the environment. But the biggest problems with these fuels come from actually using them.

If you have ever gotten stuck behind a car or truck belching exhaust into the air, you know how unhealthy air **pollution** can be. Burning gasoline in an engine releases gases into the air, including nitrogen oxides. These gases form a yellowish-brown haze called photochemical **smog**.

Motor vehicles are the single largest source of air pollution in the United States. But they are not the only one. Electric power plants and factories burn coal and oil, releasing nitrogen oxides and sulfur oxides into the air. These gases can cause **acid rain** that damages plants, kills fish, and even damages stone and metal statues.

8

Solar energy has some big advantages over fossil fuels. Sunlight is a renewable energy source—it won't run out. It is a clean source of energy—it doesn't pollute. But solar energy has some disadvantages, too. It is difficult to store solar energy at night and on cloudy days.

There are other renewable energy sources that are clean. But each has some disadvantages. Wind turbines can generate electricity. But not all places on Earth have strong, steady winds. Flowing water at a dam or waterfall also turns a turbine to make electricity. But dams cause problems, too. When a river is dammed and the area behind the dam floods, it forces people to move, changes wildlife habitats, and interrupts the natural flow of water.

Scientists and engineers are working on ways to make renewable energy sources more affordable as well as more practical.

♦ Wind farms in California produce one percent of the state's electricity.

17

CHAPTER 3

Energy Smarts

One solution to the energy problem is to find ways to use other forms of energy. Using solar energy is as simple as raising the window blinds and letting the sun shine in. The sunshine warms the inside so that on a chilly day, you can use less oil or natural gas to run the furnace. Some buildings are

⋒ Solar panels heat water used for cooking, washing, and heating.

designed to take advantage of solar energy. For example, sections of the roof might hang over the sides of a house. The overhang shades the windows in the summer when the sun is highest in the sky and you want to keep the house cooler. The overhang lets more light enter in winter, when the sun is lower in the sky and you welcome the warmth.

Fossil Fuels and the Greenhouse Effect

Have you ever been in a greenhouse? A greenhouse is made almost entirely of glass. Sunlight shines through the glass and warms up the inside. The heat cannot escape back through the glass so the greenhouse stays warm. In our atmosphere carbon dioxide, water vapor, and other gases act like the glass on a greenhouse. These gases let sunlight pass through but prevent most of the heat from escaping back into space. This trapping of heat is called the **greenhouse effect**. It causes Earth to stay warm enough to support life.

There is evidence that the greenhouse effect is getting stronger. Many scientists say it is because of fossil fuels. Burning the fuels adds enough carbon dioxide to the air to trap more heat, making the planet warmer.

⋒ Sunlight changes to heat when it strikes Earth's surface. Certain gases in the atmosphere prevent most of the heat from escaping into space.

CHAPTER 2

Is Our Climate Changing?

Glaciers carved the landscape of Glacier National Park in northern Montana. During the last Ice Age, these tongues of ice slowly crept down the mountainsides, gouging out deep valleys. Today 26 glaciers remain in the park. But maybe not for long. The glaciers are melting away. Grinnell Glacier, for example, covered 440 acres in 1910. Today it's less than 180 acres. As the glacier melts, the meltwater feeds a growing lake nearby.

1932

1988

Energy Problems and Solutions

Scientists also disagree about the future effects of global warming. Many factors affect climates:

- Carbon dioxide dissolves in ocean water. It is unclear whether more or less carbon dioxide will dissolve in the oceans as the water temperatures rise.
- Trees and other plants absorb carbon dioxide. If Earth gets warmer, more plants might grow. The extra plants will absorb more carbon dioxide from the air. But if more trees are cut down, more carbon dioxide will stay in the air.
- A warmer Earth will cause more water to evaporate. More water vapor in the air increases the greenhouse effect. But more water vapor also causes more clouds, which reflect more sunlight away from Earth's surface. It's hard to say which effect will be greater.

☉ People voice their opinions about global warming. What's yours?

⋂ Ice core samples like these can help scientists track how the climate has changed over a long period of time.

A Heated Debate

Not all scientists agree about the causes and effects of global warming. Some suggest that burning fossil fuels may not be the main cause of the rise in temperatures. Studies show that the amount of energy from the sun has changed in a regular pattern. Slight changes in solar energy can cause periods of warmer or cooler weather. These scientists point out that Earth's climate has changed many times in the past with ice ages followed by periods of warmer climates. We may be in between ice ages right now.

14

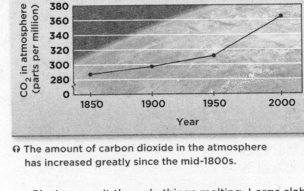

Carbon Dioxide in the Atmosphere

CO_2 in atmosphere (parts per million)

380	
360	
340	
320	
300	
280	
0	

1850   1900   1950   2000

Year

⋂ The amount of carbon dioxide in the atmosphere has increased greatly since the mid-1800s.

Glaciers aren't the only things melting. Large slabs of sea ice in the Arctic Ocean have been noticeably shrinking in recent years. What is causing the glaciers and sea ice to melt? The answer seems to be clear: the climate is warming.

The Arctic's average winter temperature is up 3° to 4° Fahrenheit in the last 100 years. Worldwide the air has warmed by about 1°F since 1850.

The date 1850 is significant. That's about the time factory machines became powered by steam. The steam was made by burning coal to heat water. The inventions of the automobile and the electric power plant in the late 1800s led to an even greater increase in the use of fossil fuels. Our use of fossil fuels and the amount of carbon dioxide in the air have been increasing steadily ever since.

☾ Warmer temperatures are causing Grinnell Glacier to melt.

11

Effects of Global Warming

Does it really matter if Earth warms up a bit? What's one or two degrees here and there? The answers may surprise you because the effects of **global warming** may not always be obvious. For example, in the Arctic, as more sea ice melts, polar bears, seals, and walruses lose places to find food and raise their young. That could lead to a decrease in the populations of these animals. Also, as more ice melts in summer, more of the Arctic Ocean remains uncovered. That allows more water to evaporate, form clouds, and produce more snow or even rain. Thunderstorms that were once rare in northern Alaska are becoming more common.

Coral Bleaching

Researchers are seeing the effects of global warming in the tropics, too. Many of the colorful corals turn white when the water gets too warm. The process is called bleaching. The ocean surface temperature has warmed an average of 1.8°F in the past 100 years, causing more bleaching than ever before. Some corals get back their color and their health. But some stay bleached and die.

The amount of ice covering the Arctic Ocean ↻ has been decreasing for the past 25 years.

What other changes might be on the way? It all depends on how much global warming continues. Some scientists predict an increase of 3° to 11°F worldwide and 15° to 20°F in the Arctic over the next century. The effects of such changes could be enormous. Take a look below at some possible effects.

Global Warming

Parts of the Arctic and Antarctic ice caps would melt.

→ The melting ice would raise sea levels.

→ Cities along the gently sloping coasts of the Atlantic and Gulf of Mexico would become flooded.

Storms such as hurricanes and tornadoes might become more powerful and frequent.

→ Weather patterns might shift. Some places would get more rain than usual; other places would get less rain.

Word Workout

WORDS TO KNOW

civilized	precede	steadfastly	trenches
excavate	prolong	superstitious	utensils

Discovery Words What amazing discovery might we find if we started digging in the yard or school playground? Let's describe what we find. We'll use at least one of the above words in each sentence.

SPELLING WORDS

unknown	outpost	enrich
outfield	proclaim	incredible
independent	enlarge	outlaw
uncommon	superhuman	incomplete
superstar	outstanding	untangle
prolong	enlist	supermarket
outcry	unhook	

Get You Started I'll spell a word without its prefix. Then you can spell the word with the correct prefix.

© Macmillan/McGraw-Hill

(fold here)

Home-School Connection

Dear Family Member:

Some discoveries are expected. Scientists might work for years and discover a new way to treat a disease. Other discoveries are a big surprise. That's what happened in China when three farmers uncovered an amazing army of pottery soldiers. I think these life-size figures are one of the biggest discoveries in the history of archaeology.

While we're reading *The Emperor's Silent Army,* I'm also practicing summarizing. This skill will help me whenever I read. It helps me recall and remember the most important facts in an article or story.

This Week's Skills

Comprehension: summarize

Vocabulary: word parts

Spelling/Phonics: words with prefix

Name _____

Some Are Better Than Others

Whenever you finish reading an article, take a short break. Stop reading and tell yourself what the article is mostly about. Let's read this article. Then we can compare the four summaries. Which one do we think is best? What do we think is "wrong" about the other three?

Is China Chinese?

China is a type of high-quality porcelain. It was first made in China, but that doesn't mean the word *china* comes from that country. In fact, it doesn't! The name of the country China comes from the English spelling of the Chinese word *Qín*. The Qín dynasty ruled in China from 221 to 206 B.C. On the other hand, the word *china* comes from the Persian word *chini*. This word described the high-quality porcelain made in China. So while china was originally made in China, the word was originated in Persia!

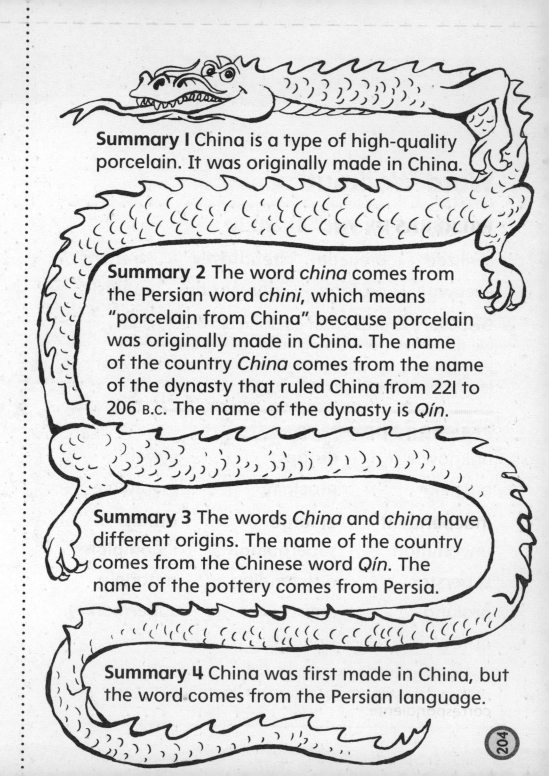

Summary 1 China is a type of high-quality porcelain. It was originally made in China.

Summary 2 The word *china* comes from the Persian word *chini*, which means "porcelain from China" because porcelain was originally made in China. The name of the country *China* comes from the name of the dynasty that ruled China from 221 to 206 B.C. The name of the dynasty is *Qín*.

Summary 3 The words *China* and *china* have different origins. The name of the country comes from the Chinese word *Qín*. The name of the pottery comes from Persia.

Summary 4 China was first made in China, but the word comes from the Persian language.

Ejercicio de palabras

PALABRAS DE VOCABULARIO

civilized	precede	steadfastly	trenches
excavate	prolong	superstitious	utensils

Hablemos de descubrimientos ¿Qué descubrimientos sorprendentes podríamos hacer si excaváramos en el patio o el jardín de la escuela? Vamos a describir lo que encontramos. Tratemos de usar por lo menos una de las palabras de la lista en cada oración.

PALABRAS DE ORTOGRAFÍA

unknown	outpost	enrich
outfield	proclaim	incredible
independent	enlarge	outlaw
uncommon	superhuman	incomplete
superstar	outstanding	untangle
prolong	enlist	supermarket
outcry	unhook	

¿Cómo empieza? Voy a deletrear una palabra sin el prefijo. Tú debes deletrearla agregándole el prefijo correspondiente.

(fold here)

Conexión con el hogar

Queridos familiares:

Algunos descubrimientos son de esperar. A veces los científicos trabajan durante años hasta encontrar una nueva forma de tratar una enfermedad. Otros descubrimientos constituyen una sorpresa total. Eso es lo que pasó en China, cuando tres campesinos descubrieron un maravilloso ejército de soldados de cerámica. Pienso que estas figuras de tamaño real son uno de los descubrimientos más importantes en la historia de la arqueología.

Al leer *The Emperor's Silent Army* también trato de resumir. Esta destreza me ayudará siempre que leo. Me ayuda a recordar los datos más importantes de un artículo o un cuento.

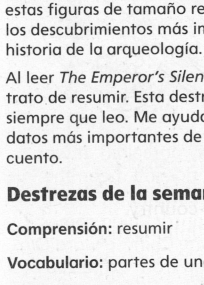

Destrezas de la semana

Comprensión: resumir

Vocabulario: partes de una palabra

Ortografía/Fonética: palabras con prefijos

Nombre _____

¿Cuál es el mejor?

Siempre que termines de leer un artículo, reflexiona brevemente. Deja de leer y piensa de qué trata principalmente el artículo. Vamos a leer el artículo que sigue. Luego podemos comparar los cuatro resúmenes. ¿Cuál nos parece mejor? ¿Qué es lo que no está bien en los otros tres?

Is China Chinese?

China is a type of high-quality porcelain. It was first made in China, but that doesn't mean the word *china* comes from that country. In fact, it doesn't! The name of the country China comes from the English spelling of the Chinese word *Qín*. The Qín dynasty ruled in China from 221 to 206 B.C. On the other hand, the word *china* comes from the Persian word *chini*. This word described the high-quality porcelain made in China. So while china was originally made in China, the word was originated in Persia!

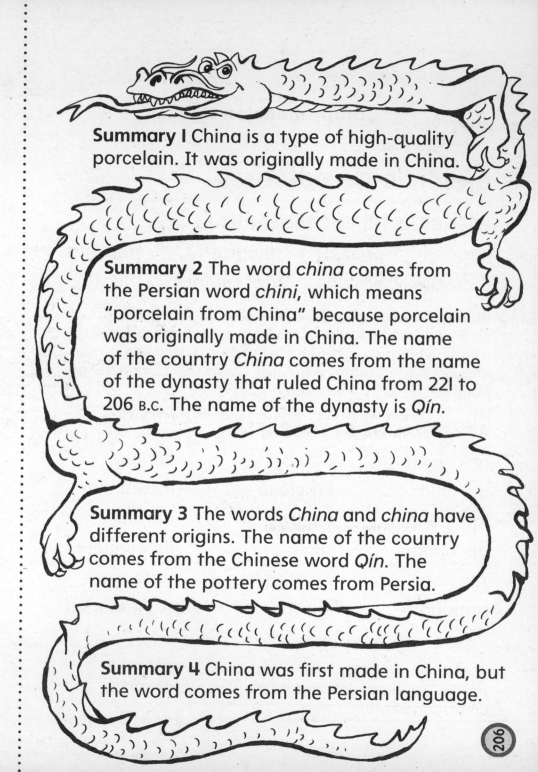

Summary 1 China is a type of high-quality porcelain. It was originally made in China.

Summary 2 The word *china* comes from the Persian word *chini*, which means "porcelain from China" because porcelain was originally made in China. The name of the country *China* comes from the name of the dynasty that ruled China from 221 to 206 B.C. The name of the dynasty is *Qín*.

Summary 3 The words *China* and *china* have different origins. The name of the country comes from the Chinese word *Qín*. The name of the pottery comes from Persia.

Summary 4 China was first made in China, but the word comes from the Persian language.

206

Comprehension Check

Summarize

Use a Summary Chart to help you summarize
Rock Art from the Stone Age.

```
┌─────────────┐
│             │
└─────────────┘
      ↓
┌─────────────┐
│             │
└─────────────┘
      ↓
┌─────────────┐
│             │
└─────────────┘
      ↓
┌─────────────┐
│   Summary   │
└─────────────┘
```

Think and Compare

1. Look back at page 12. What discovery proved to
   archeologists that Stone Age artists were able to paint
   inside caves? What sort of material did this discovery use?
   (Summarize)

2. What if you and your friends accidentally discovered
   a secret cave? Would you try to keep your discovery a
   secret like the four French teenagers did, or would you let
   others know about what you found? Give some reasons
   for your answer. *(Apply)*

3. In 1963 the government of France decided to close
   Lascaux Cave to the general public. What other actions
   could the government have taken to protect the artwork
   inside the cave? *(Evaluate)*

Rock Art from the Stone Age

by George Capaccio

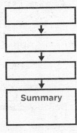

Table of Contents

Introduction

The limestone hills in southwestern France contain many caves. The most famous is in France's Dordogne (dawr-DOHN) River Valley. Its name is Lascaux (lahs-KOH).

Four teenage boys discovered Lascaux Cave by accident on September 12, 1940. They made their discovery while hiking through the woods. Their curiosity soon led them into a stunning and important find. They had discovered a deep underground network of caverns. And on the cave walls were well-preserved paintings that were some 14,000 years old!

Lascaux was not the first cave to be found with examples of **prehistoric** art. But what made this cave so special was the beauty and the large number of the paintings the four boys found. The ancient artists who painted the walls and ceilings of Lascaux Cave have left us clues to our prehistoric past. **Archeologists** studied these ancient paintings. They now consider them the most remarkable of all known prehistoric art. Many people also admire them as great art.

2

Index

23

Glossary

archeologist *(ahr-kee-OL-uh-jist)* a person who studies the way humans lived a long time ago *(page 2)*

carbon-dating *(KAHR-buhn DAYT-ing)* using a formula to figure out how many years have passed since a material was alive *(page 16)*

charcoal *(CHAHR-kohl)* partly burned wood *(page 16)*

culture *(KUL-chuhr)* the arts, beliefs, and customs that make up a way of life for a group of people at a certain time *(page 11)*

Lascaux II *(lahs-KOH)* an exact reproduction of the cave at Lascaux *(page 21)*

Paleolithic period *(PAY-lee-uh-lith-ik PEER-ee-uhd)* the period when stone tools were first used, from about 750,000 to about 15,000 years ago *(page 10)*

pigment *(PIG-ment)* a powder used to make paint *(page 14)*

prehistoric *(pree-his-TAWR-ik)* belonging to a time before people started writing history *(page 2)*

prehistory *(pree-HIS-tawr-ee)* the study of history before written records *(page 7)*

scaffold *(SKAF-old)* temporary raised platform used by workers *(page 13)*

shaman *(SHAH-mun)* a member of a tribe believed to have special powers *(page 19)*

superstitious *(sew-per-STISH-uhs)* believing in the power of good luck charms *(page 18)*

totem *(TOH-tem)* an animal, plant, or object that is the symbol of a family or a group *(page 19)*

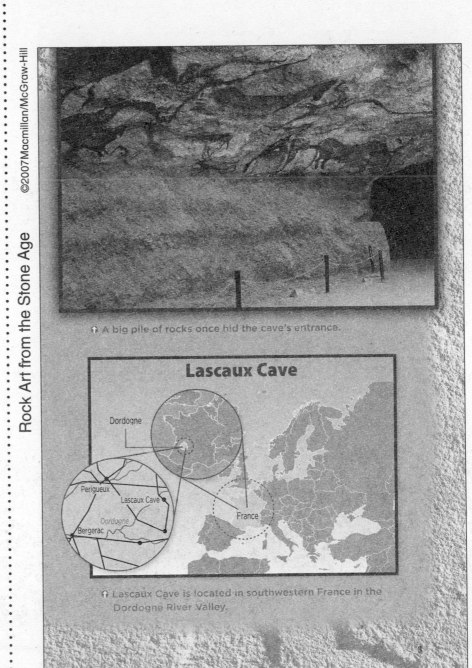

A big pile of rocks once hid the cave's entrance.

Lascaux Cave

Dordogne

Perigueux

Lascaux Cave

Dordogne

Bergerac

France

Lascaux Cave is located in southwestern France in the Dordogne River Valley.

CHAPTER ONE

The Secret Passage

How did those four teenage boys discover Lascaux cave? One story tells how the boys decided to hike to the top of Lascaux hill. It had become their favorite place to explore. The boys' names were Marcel, Jacques, Georges, and Simon. Simon's little dog Robot decided to do his own bit of exploring. When Robot didn't return, the boys began to worry. They soon realized the dog had fallen down an odd hole in the ground.

Rock Art from the Stone Age

↑ Thanks to Lascaux II, people from all over the world are still able to appreciate the artistic wonders found in the original cave.

Lascaux remains closed to the public. Only 20 people a week are given special permits to enter the cave.

But people all over the world wish to visit Lascaux. The French decided to create an exact copy, called **Lascaux II**. Each year about 300,000 tourists visit.

The paintings in the original Lascaux Cave are among people's earliest creations. They deserve to be protected.

Conclusion

The Lascaux Cave was an amazing discovery, and people came from all over to see it. By 1962 the number of visitors had grown to about 1,500 each day!

Tour guides began to notice disturbing changes in the paintings. More than 700 green blotches appeared. Strange white lumps grew on the walls. Experts realized that the lights in the cave were causing algae and bacteria to grow.

The French government believed that the only way to prolong the beauty of the paintings was to close Lascaux. This happened in 1963.

Scientists washed the walls with formaldehyde and antibiotics. The blotches disappeared. Experts still haven't figured out how to remove the white lumps. But the damage has been controlled.

↑ Tour guides noticed that flecks of paint were breaking off.

Jacques Marval was ↻ one of the four boys who first discovered Lascaux. As an adult, he worked as a tour guide in the cave.

Without the right tools, the boys couldn't rescue Robot. They walked back to their village. The next day they returned with pieces of rope, a knife, and an oil lamp.

Another tale says that the dog had nothing to do with the discovery. Instead, one of the boys noticed the hole when he was out in the woods by himself. He shared his secret with his friends. Then the four of them explored the cave together.

↻ Lascaux is located in a lush, green river valley filled with rocky cliffs.

Limestone Caves

The Lascaux Cave is a limestone cave. Limestone is a soft rock that easily dissolves in water. Over thousands of years, underground waterways slowly dissolve the limestone in their path, creating caves like this one.

After enlarging the entrance, the boys squeezed through the hole. One at a time, they tumbled down a big pile of rocks. Safely on their feet again, they passed a series of water-filled basins. Soon they came to a large space, now called the Great Hall of the Bulls. The light from their oil lamp lit the space for the first time in thousands of years. The boys looked in amazement at the paintings that covered the walls. The four friends vowed that this would be their secret hideaway. They would not breathe a word of it to anyone.

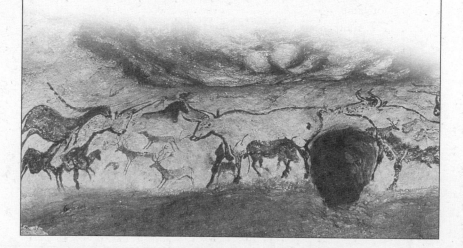

Another idea is that the caves might have been places for special ceremonies. Even today some hunting societies around the world have a certain animal that is the symbol, or **totem**, for the group.

Perhaps young boys about to become men or young girls about to become women were led into the dark cave. There they may have been shown paintings of the tribe's totem animal. If the totem animal were the horse, then the cave might have held many paintings of horses.

Still another theory holds that cave art may have had a healing purpose. Could the artists have been **shamans** (SHAH-munz)? These were special members of the tribe believed to have healing powers. Shamans are said to have special animal helpers. The animal paintings may have stood for these animal helpers.

↻ The lines in front of the cow may represent a trap set by hunters.

19

Stone Age people survived by hunting. Some archeologists think that cave art was meant to bring the hunters luck. If so, then people might have been **superstitious**. For them the art served as a kind of good-luck charm, according to this theory.

Consider the paintings at Lascaux. Could the strange squares stand for traps? Do the lines on the walls stand for arrows? Is the jumping cow leaping over the horses to avoid being caught in a trap?

Here's another mystery. During the time when this art was being made, reindeer was the main prey of the hunters. Yet there are no paintings of reindeer on the cave walls. As a result most scientists now believe that the good-luck-charm theory doesn't stand up.

↷ Abbe Henri Breuil was a leading archeologist of his time.

Some secrets are just too hard to keep. The boys soon told their teacher what they had found. When Monsieur (Meh-SYUR) Laval (La-VAHL) saw the cave, he knew at once that the paintings were very valuable. Soon word spread beyond the village. Some of France's most famous archeologists became interested. Among them was Abbe Henri Breuil (BROYL). Although trained as a priest, Breuil devoted his life to the study of **prehistory**, which is history before written records.

At the time of Lascaux's discovery, World War II was under way. The German army occupied France. Interest in the cave faded as the French people became more concerned with the problems of war. But when the war was over, workers began to excavate the area around the cave. They built a new entrance with metal doors and a staircase to the main chamber. On July 14, 1948, Lascaux Cave officially reopened.

↶ The boys were the first people to enter the Great Hall of the Bulls in thousands of years.

Exploring the Cave

If you could explore Lascaux the way the four French teenagers once did, what do you think it would be like? Where would you start? There are seven different areas in the Lascaux cave with paintings. Let's follow in the footsteps of those four friends.

Begin by visiting the largest and some would say most impressive area—the Hall of the Bulls. On its walls and ceiling are horses, wild cattle, giant bulls, horned deer, and a bear. Near the entrance is a strange animal with long, slender horns.

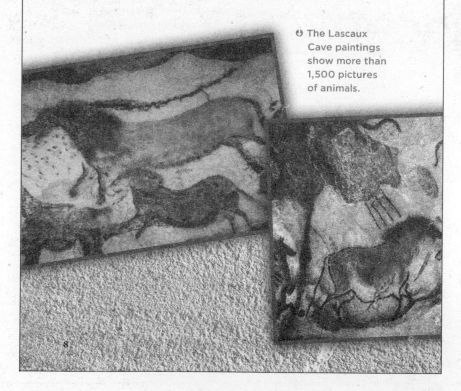

⟳ The Lascaux Cave paintings show more than 1,500 pictures of animals.

Rock Art from the Stone Age

CHAPTER THREE

Mysteries of the Cave

Cave paintings still fascinate archeologists. One question that they are thinking about is what the cave paintings mean. At Lascaux some of the drawings in one part of the cave are completely different in style and subject matter from those found in the rest of the cave. Maybe the paintings served more than one purpose. To answer this question, scientists have a number of different ideas.

⟳ The Lascaux Cave contains about 400 mysterious signs and symbols.

Carbon-Dating

How did archeologists figure out the age of charcoal? They used a scientific method called carbon-dating. Only materials that were once alive, like the wood that was burned to make charcoal, can be carbon-dated. Archeologists use a mathematical formula to figure out how many years have passed since the wood was alive.

Scientists once believed that cave art grew better and better over thousands of years. They thought the cave paintings in Lascaux were the high point of cave art.

But then, in December 1994, three French explorers discovered another cave filled with beautiful paintings. Some of them had been made with **charcoal**. This is partly burned wood that can be **carbon-dated**. Using this method, scientists found that these paintings were at least 30,000 years old. They preceded the paintings at Lascaux.

Scientists now saw that great art did not develop slowly over time. Cave art did not reach its high point at Lascaux. Instead creativity and artistic skill have been important parts of human life from the beginning.

The Axial (AKS-ee-uhl) Gallery lies directly ahead of the Hall of the Bulls. It contains many paintings of horses. There is a cow that seems to be leaping over the horses. Also there are four lines in front of the cow. Could these stand for trenches, used by hunters to trap their prey?

Let's go back to the Hall of the Bulls. This time we'll turn left and enter an area called the Passageway. This will lead us to another area called the Nave. The walls of the Nave are decorated with drawings of horses, buffalo, and other animals. One of the more striking images in the Nave is that of five deer. They appear to be holding their antlers above water while steadfastly crossing a river.

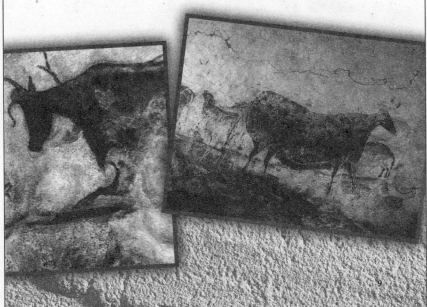

CHAPTER TWO

Prehistoric People

Who created these paintings? How old could they be? Scientists knew that modern humans arrived in Europe about 40,000 years ago. These early people lived in a time known as the **Paleolithic** (PAY-lee-uh-lith-ik) **period**. It began about two million years ago and ended in various places between 40,000 and 10,000 years ago. This period is also called the Stone Age. That's because the people who lived then made and used stone tools.

During the Paleolithic period, many different cultures developed and died out. One of these is called the Magdalenian (MAG-dah-LIN-ee-in) culture. These people lived in southwestern France at a time when the glaciers of the last Ice Age were moving northward.

The cave artists must have been very talented to create such beautiful art. They probably spent a lot of time sharpening their skills. They may have practiced on the walls of cliffs, tree bark, or animal skins.

The artists used color very well. But they had another great skill. They were able to create art that looked realistic and had a sense of depth. Sometimes they used the shape of a wall to create a sense of depth. Sometimes they painted one animal in front of another. This is amazing considering the artists' difficult working conditions.

The artists got their paints from rocks. Some rocks made shades of yellow, red, and brown. Others made black and dark brown and even violet. The artists pounded the rocks into powder. Then they added water or animal fat to make a paste.

For brushes they might have used bits of fur, moss, or even human hair. In some cases they used hollow bone tubes to blow powdered paint onto the walls. Large, flat bones served as a place to mix their paints.

The artists of Lascaux had only one chance to get it right. They couldn't erase a mistake and start over. As soon as the artist applied paint, the **pigment**, or color, chemically bonded with the wall.

Lascaux artists created a sense ⟳ of depth by painting one animal slightly in front of another.

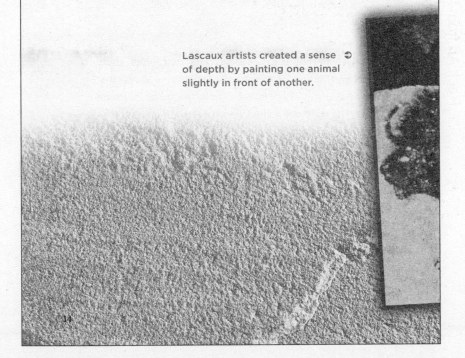

Icy Times in Europe

The paintings found in Lascaux were painted during the last Ice Age, which began around 110,000 years ago. As temperatures dropped, glaciers moved southward. They covered most of northern Europe. During the Magdalenian period, the climate in southwestern France was somewhat milder than in other parts of Europe. Around 10,000 years ago, the glaciers began to melt away. Over time the Magdalenians moved away.

In their daily lives, the Magdalenians used many different tools and utensils. Their tools were far more advanced than those found in earlier **cultures**. They made them from flint, ivory, and bone, and possibly wood, bark, and leather as well. For clothing they wore animal skins sewn together with bone or antler needles. They were highly skilled hunters and fishermen. Their favorite prey was reindeer. They followed the reindeer herds, which moved with the seasons.

The Magdalenians were much more than hunters. They were also a civilized people who valued art. Their most beautiful creations are the paintings at Lascaux.

Long-Ago Artists at Work

Archeologists discovered the first examples of cave art in the early 1800s. In Europe alone Stone Age art appears in hundreds of places. Most are found on rocks. At first some scientists had doubts about the age of this art. They didn't think that Paleolithic people could have invented a way to make light that would allow them to work in pitch-black caves.

Then, around 1900, an archeologist found a decorated piece of sandstone. It had once been used to burn animal fat, creating light. It must have been used as a lamp. This was the first prehistoric lamp ever found.

Early in the 1960s, another French scientist discovered a similar lamp in the Lascaux Cave. Scientists now agree that ancient artists must have used fat-burning lamps while they worked inside the caves.

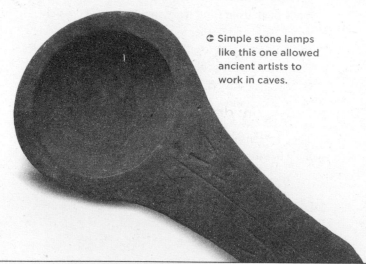

☾ Simple stone lamps like this one allowed ancient artists to work in caves.

Altimira

In 1879 a five-year-old Spanish girl named Maria wandered away from her father. He was an amateur archeologist digging in Altimira cave in northern Spain. When Maria looked up and saw paintings of animals on the cave ceiling, she exclaimed, "Mira, Papa! Bueyes!" (Look, Papa! Bulls!) Maria was the first person in 14,000 years to see the paintings in this cave. Since her discovery, archeologists have explored hundreds of similar caves in France and Spain.

Many of the paintings at Lascaux are high on the walls and ceiling. How were the artists able to reach such out-of-the-way places? Evenly spaced holes found along the walls are a clue. They suggest that the artists built wooden **scaffolds**, or platforms, to stand on while they worked.

Archeologists have also found the remains of rope made from braided plant material. They think Lascaux artists might have tied long poles together with rope to make the scaffold. They then inserted the ends of the poles into holes cut in the cave walls. They packed clay around the poles to keep the scaffolds well anchored.

Word Workout

WORDS TO KNOW

anonymous	charismatic	mimics
sleuthing	array	despondently
significance	sponsoring	

Word Out I'll say a sentence using one of the words but I'll leave out the word. Can you guess the missing word?

SPELLING WORDS

inspire	separate	instruct
react	hesitate	inspiration
separation	instruction	reaction
hesitation	consult	illustrate
observe	connect	represent
consultation	illustration	observation
connection	representation	

Changes I'll read the first word, and you can tell me the word with the ending **ion** or **ation**.

(fold here)

Home-School Connection

Dear Family Member:

Great ideas come when you least expect them. Still, I know that you can't just wait for good ideas. You have to be an active searcher. This week we are reading *The Case of the Phantom Poet*. It's a play about a student who is looking for an idea to write about. I can certainly identify with her because I often have to come up with new ideas for school projects. It will be interesting to see what idea she finally comes up with. In fact, by reading about her solution, I'll be able to draw my own conclusions about inspiration and hard work.

This Week's Skills

Comprehension: draw conclusions

Vocabulary: analogies

Spelling/Phonics: adding **ion** and **ation**

Name _____

Draw Carefully

Benjamin Franklin had advice for getting ahead. Write the answers to the clues. Then write in the puzzle to read Franklin's message.

A. a day before Monday

$\overline{3}$ $\overline{31}$ $\overline{32}$ $\overline{43}$ $\overline{23}$ $\overline{40}$

B. rubber disk used in hockey

$\overline{27}$ $\overline{42}$ $\overline{50}$ $\overline{20}$

C. day after yesterday

$\overline{34}$ $\overline{44}$ $\overline{9}$ $\overline{14}$ $\overline{22}$

D. annoying insect that bites

$\overline{12}$ $\overline{2}$ $\overline{39}$ $\overline{16}$ $\overline{52}$ $\overline{54}$ $\overline{24}$ $\overline{28}$

E. you read them in newspapers and magazines

$\overline{38}$ $\overline{29}$ $\overline{46}$ $\overline{18}$ $\overline{6}$ $\overline{51}$ $\overline{36}$ $\overline{15}$

F. what a butterfly comes out of

$\overline{19}$ $\overline{41}$ $\overline{5}$ $\overline{55}$ $\overset{O}{\overline{}}$ $\overline{49}$

G. the total number of people who live in one place

$\overline{26}$ $\overline{48}$ $\overline{13}$ $\overline{11}$ $\overline{21}$ $\overline{45}$ $\overline{30}$ $\overline{33}$ $\overline{25}$ $\overline{56}$

H. fairness; the legal system

$\overline{10}$ $\overline{17}$ $\overline{57}$ $\overline{1}$ $\overline{35}$ $\overline{47}$ $\overline{7}$

I. employs; utilizes

$\overline{4}$ $\overline{37}$ $\overline{8}$ $\overline{53}$

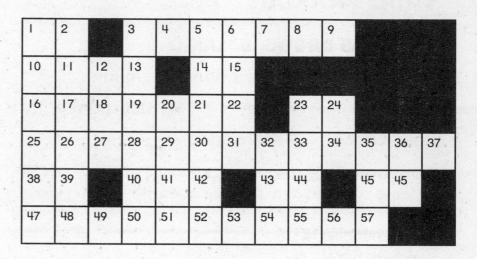

Ejercicio de palabras

PALABRAS DE VOCABULARIO

anonymous	charismatic	mimics
sleuthing	array	despondently
significance	sponsoring	

¿Qué palabra falta? Voy a hacer una oración con una de las palabras de arriba. Te la diré en voz alta sin incluir la palabra escogida. ¿Puedes adivinar la palabra que falta?

PALABRAS DE ORTOGRAFÍA

inspire	separate	instruct
react	hesitate	inspiration
separation	instruction	reaction
hesitation	consult	illustrate
observe	connect	represent
consultation	illustration	observation
connection	representation	

Cambios Voy a leer una palabra. Dímela con la terminación **ion** o **ation** que corresponda.

(fold here)

Conexión con el hogar

Queridos familiares:

Las buenas ideas aparecen cuando uno menos lo espera. Pero sé que no se puede esperar que aparezcan, hay que buscarlas activamente. Esta semana estamos leyendo *The Case of the Phantom Poet*. Es una obra de teatro que trata de una estudiante que necesita una idea para escribir. Puedo identificarme con ella muy fácilmente, porque a menudo necesito ideas nuevas para proyectos de la escuela. Va a ser interesante ver cuál es la idea que finalmente se le ocurre. Al leer sobre la solución que da, podré sacar mis propias conclusiones sobre la inspiración y el empeño.

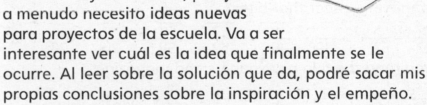

Destrezas de la semana

Comprensión: sacar conclusiones

Vocabulario: analogías

Ortografía/Fonética: palabras terminadas en **ion** y **ation**

Nombre _____

Cómo tener éxito

Uno de los consejos de Benjamin Franklin se refería a cómo lograr éxito. Escribe las respuestas a las pistas. Luego usa los números de las letras para escribirlas en el crucigrama. El resultado será el consejo de Franklin.

A. a day before Monday

$\overline{3}$ $\overline{31}$ $\overline{32}$ $\overline{43}$ $\overline{23}$ $\overline{40}$

B. rubber disk used in hockey

$\overline{27}$ $\overline{42}$ $\overline{50}$ $\overline{20}$

C. day after yesterday

$\overline{34}$ $\overline{44}$ $\overline{9}$ $\overline{14}$ $\overline{22}$

D. annoying insect that bites

$\overline{12}$ $\overline{2}$ $\overline{39}$ $\overline{16}$ $\overline{52}$ $\overline{54}$ $\overline{24}$ $\overline{28}$

E. you read them in newspapers and magazines

$\overline{38}$ $\overline{29}$ $\overline{46}$ $\overline{18}$ $\overline{6}$ $\overline{51}$ $\overline{36}$ $\overline{15}$

F. what a butterfly comes out of

$\overline{19}$ $\overline{41}$ $\overline{5}$ $\overline{55}$ $\overset{O}{}$ $\overline{49}$

G. the total number of people who live in one place

$\overline{26}$ $\overline{48}$ $\overline{13}$ $\overline{11}$ $\overline{21}$ $\overline{45}$ $\overline{30}$ $\overline{33}$ $\overline{25}$ $\overline{56}$

H. fairness; the legal system

$\overline{10}$ $\overline{17}$ $\overline{57}$ $\overline{1}$ $\overline{35}$ $\overline{47}$ $\overline{7}$

I. employs; utilizes

$\overline{4}$ $\overline{37}$ $\overline{8}$ $\overline{53}$

1	2		3	4	5	6	7	8	9			
10	11	12	13		14	15						
16	17	18	19	20	21	22		23	24			
25	26	27	28	29	30	31	32	33	34	35	36	37
38	39		40	41	42		43	44		45	45	
47	48	49	50	51	52	53	54	55	56	57		

Answers: A. Sunday B. puck C. today D. mosquito E. articles F. cocoon G. population H. justice I. uses. To succeed, jump as quickly at opportunities as you do at conclusions.

222

Comprehension Check

Summarize

Use a Conclusions Chart to help you summarize *Will the Show Go On?* What conclusion can you draw about each of the characters in the play?

Text Clues	Conclusion

Think and Compare

1. What kinds of skills does the director of a play need to have? Support your answer with evidence from the text. *(Draw Conclusions)*

2. Have you ever been involved in a school play? How would you feel if you wrote a play but someone really wanted to change it? *(Apply)*

3. Think about a group of people who are working on a common project. What might happen if they stop working together? Explain your answer. *(Synthesize)*

Will the Show Go On?

by **Sarah Glasscock**
illustrated by **Dean Lindberg**

Table of Contents

Characters (in order of appearance)

Erica Nolette, playwright of the school play

Joel Nolette, Erica's twin brother and the lead in the play

Jesse Garza, new student who wants to help with the play

Kasey Doogan, student who wants to help with the play

Coach Linus, baseball coach and science teacher who plays in a jazz band on the weekends

Mr. Wheeler, drama teacher

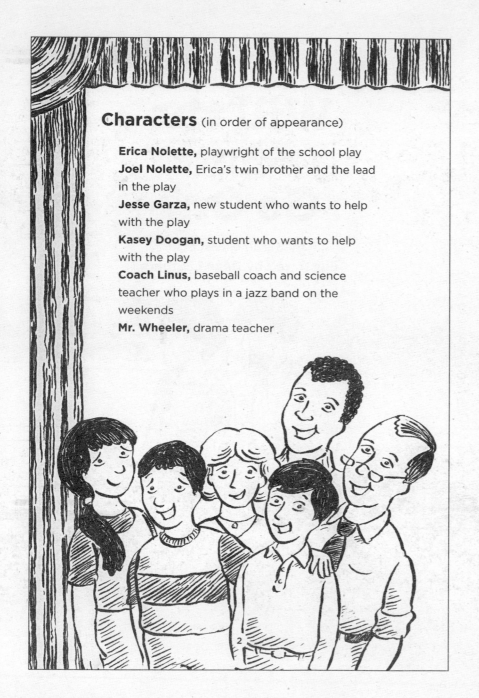

2

Will the Show Go On?

19

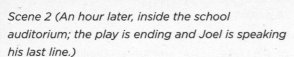

Scene 2 *(An hour later, inside the school auditorium; the play is ending and Joel is speaking his last line.)*

Joel: Remember—there is enough room on this planet for all of us.

(The curtain comes down. Joel and Kasey run offstage. The applause begins.)

Jesse: Listen—they're clapping like crazy.

Coach Linus: We hit a home run!

Joel: We knocked it out of the park!

(Mr. Wheeler appears backstage.)

Mr. Wheeler: What are you all standing around here for? Go out and take your curtain call. You deserve it.

(Joel, Kasey, Erica, and Jesse go onstage and take a bow.)

Mr. Wheeler: Coach, you're a natural at this. We should talk about what our next production is going to be.

Coach Linus: Grrrrr! I'm like Old Teddy. I work better outdoors than indoors.

18

Act One

Break a Leg

(The stage in the school auditorium; Erica reads aloud from a script. Joel practices karate. They are unaware that Jesse is watching them.)

Erica: "Ranger: Old Teddy's going to hurt somebody soon." Joel, say that line despondently so the audience sees how upset you are. Should I write *unhappily* in the stage direction instead of *despondently*?

Joel: I'm feeling despondent about this play. There's not enough action in it. I should be a karate instructor instead of a park ranger.

Erica: It's set in a forest. It's about a bear that gets into campers' stuff. It's about how people have to learn to respect animals' homes.

Joel: I could be a ranger who teaches karate in his spare time. *(He chops the air and kicks one leg to the side.)* Pow! Take that, Old Teddy! Erica, I'm going to make up my own lines.

3

Erica: You're going to ruin my play!

Joel: You're going to ruin my acting career!

Erica: A real actor follows the script and listens to what the director tells him.

Jesse: *(to himself)* This play needs my help.

(Kasey rushes into the auditorium.)

Kasey: Where's Mr. Wheeler? I've got a ton of suggestions about the scenery and the ads, and my mom said she's sponsoring the programs and—

(Jesse enters quietly.)

Jesse: Your mom's going to pay the whole cost of the programs, the design and paper and printing and everything?

Kasey: I haven't really asked her yet, but I'm sure—

Erica: Has anybody seen Mr. Wheeler? He's usually never late.

Kasey: Joel said you've changed the setting to a karate school. I think that's a great idea!

Erica: The setting hasn't changed because nothing in the play has changed.

Joel: We'll just wait and see what Mr. Wheeler thinks about my ideas.

4

(Kasey returns.)

Kasey: He's throwing up!

Coach Linus, Jesse, and Erica: Shhhhh!

Kasey: *(whispering)* Old Teddy is throwing up! His mother thinks he ate some bad pizza. What are we going to do?

Jesse: *(whispering)* Get the bear costume, Kasey—quick!

(Joel panics when Old Teddy doesn't appear on stage.)

Jesse: *(whispering to Joel)* He'll be out in thirty seconds, Joel.

Erica: *(whispering to Joel)* Joel, make up something. It's okay.

Joel: Make up . . . ? Oh, oh, I'd know Old Teddy's footsteps anywhere—and that wasn't him. No, that sounded like . . . like Groucho the Bear. He sounds like Old Teddy, except he's got kind of a limp. Get away from here, Groucho! *(Joel gives a karate chop.)*

(Kasey arrives with the bear suit.)

Jesse: *(whispering)* Put it on, Kasey.

Kasey: What!

Jesse: *(whispering)* You're going to play Old Teddy. Get out there and growl.

17

(Jesse, Erica, Kasey, and Coach Linus step into the wings as the curtain goes up. When the audience claps, Joel freezes.)

Jesse: (whispering) "These are Old Teddy's tracks all right."

Joel: (trying to clear his throat) These . . . tracks . . . all right.

Erica: (whispering) "He's starting to come closer to the campsites."

Joel: Closer and closer . . .

Kasey: (whispering to Erica) At least he's not making up his own lines.

Coach Linus: (whispering to Erica) I've got an ideal (growls loudly) GRRRRRR!

Joel: (jumping) What was that? (recovering himself) Why . . . that sounds like Old Teddy, like he's starting to come closer to the campsites!

Jesse: (whispering to Kasey) Where is Old Teddy?

Kasey: I'll go find out!

(She speeds away.)

Joel: It's been a lean year, and the bears are hungry. Too many campers don't protect their food as they should. They don't realize that they are camping in the bears' backyards.

16

Kasey: Since Mr. Wheeler's late, I'd be glad to step in as director.

Joel: The lead actor should take over as director.

Erica: Joel, where's your script?

Joel: It's in my head.

Kasey: If I take over as director, then, Erica, you can relax and listen to the play. Joel, you can go ahead and act. Nobody has to worry about a thing.

Jesse: What kind of experience have you had?

Kasey: That's not important. What's important is that I want to do it, and I will do a great job!

(Coach Linus strolls into the auditorium, trying to appear confident.)

Coach Linus: Okay, listen up! Mr. Wheeler's had an accident. He'll be out for a few weeks, so you're looking at your new director. Joel and Jesse, you know my method. I don't care if you're about to play baseball, do a science experiment, or act in a play, you need to warm up.

5

Joel: I didn't know you knew anything about plays, Coach.

Coach Linus: Okay, listen up! Form a line, and give me fifty!

Kasey: Give you fifty what?

Joel: Jumping jacks—and hurry, or he'll make it a hundred.

(Joel, Erica, Kasey, and Jesse form a line on stage and do jumping jacks.)

Coach Linus: Active bodies make active minds.

Kasey: So, Coach, what kind of stage experience have you had?

Coach Linus: I'm on stage every weekend playing drums with a jazz band. What are we doing— a musical?

Erica: No music—it's a drama.

Coach Linus: I haven't seen a play yet that wouldn't be better with music.

Joel: Or karate chops! Active bodies make active minds, right, Coach?

Jesse: Maybe you should read through the play first before changing anything.

Coach Linus: Okay, listen up! We'll read through the play, and then we'll start changing it.

6

(Coach Linus enters.)

Coach Linus: The curtain's going up in one minute, Joel. Break a leg!

Joel: Break a leg? Do you think I'm going to break my leg while I'm fighting the bear?

(Jesse and Erica enter.)

Erica: You look a little nervous, brother.

Joel: I should look nervous. I'm about to go out and fight a bear in front of thousands of people— and Mr. Wheeler.

Jesse: Mr. Wheeler's here?

Joel: He's here all right—along with thousands of other people.

Erica: I hope we make him proud of us.

Jesse: How about a pep talk before the curtain goes up, Coach?

Coach Linus: Okay, listen up! I want you to go out there and give it your best. We've trained hard for this, and thanks to Erica and Jesse—we've learned from our mistakes.

15

Act Three

Applause or Boos?

Scene 1 (A week later, inside the school auditorium; Joel peers through the curtain at the array of faces in the audience. Kasey rushes around the set, straightening props.)

Joel: I can't believe the auditorium is completely filled.

Kasey: I'm so nervous I can hardly stand it! How can you be so calm?

Joel: *(takes a deep breath)* Whoa—you'll never believe who's walking down the aisle.

Kasey: Who? Let me see!

Joel: Mr. Wheeler—he's on crutches.

Kasey: Wow, we really have to put on a great show for him! We have to be perfect.

14

7

Act Two

Stage Fright

Scene 1 (A week later, inside an empty classroom; Erica paces as Jesse watches.)

Erica: I can't believe they've turned my play into a kung fu musical! And Joel just mimics what Coach Linus says. *(in a deep voice)* Okay, listen up! Give me fifty!

Jesse: You should still show up for rehearsals.

Erica: My play's turned into a disaster! All I wanted to do was to write a good play about how people should respect animals. I should have known Joel would try to change it. He's as stubborn as a drawer that sticks.

Jesse: That's why we need to act.

Erica: That's very funny, Jesse.

Jesse: I'm serious, I have a plan.

Erica: Everybody has a plan. Joel wants to be an action hero. Coach Linus wants to be a musician. Kasey wants to be in charge of everything, and now you have a plan.

8

Scene 3 (An hour later in the school auditorium; the coach, Joel, and Kasey slump in their seats. Jesse and Erica stand in the background.)

Coach Linus: We can't put on a play like that.

Joel: I'll be laughed out of school.

Kasey: I can write another play tonight!

Jesse: I don't think you understand the significance of the video, Kasey. It's important because it shows how hard it is to write a good play. You had a good script until you started changing it.

Coach Linus: Okay, listen up! Erica, you're off the bench and back in the game. Jesse, I'm going to need your help, too.

Erica and Jesse: *(in unison)* Yes, sir!

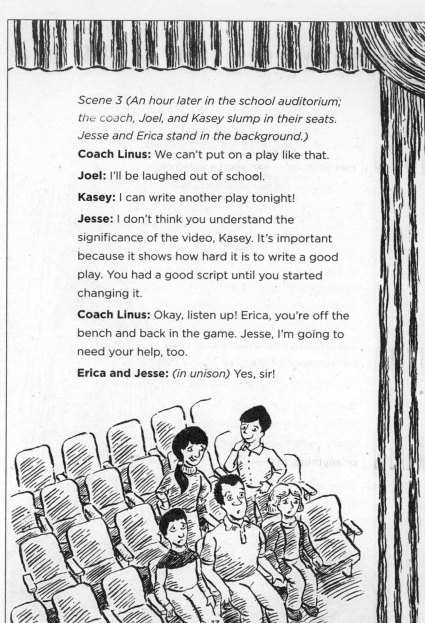

13

Jesse: *(to Erica)* That's our cue. *(to the coach)* Hey, Coach, let's make a video.

Kasey: *(to herself)* Why didn't I think of that?

Joel: Brilliant—I can send a video of my performance to Hollywood!

Coach Linus: How's the sound on that thing? The music is what really pulls this whole thing together.

Jesse: Your wife loaned us your camera. She was afraid you'd want to remain anonymous so no one would know you are directing the play.

Erica: We should do interviews first. Jesse can film while I ask the questions. Then we'll film a performance of the play.

Coach Linus: That's what I call teamwork, and I like teamwork. Joel—step up to the plate!

Kasey: Um, is everybody going to be interviewed? I mean, I know I'm not in the play or anything, but—

Erica: *(firmly)* Everybody gets interviewed.

12

Jesse: I've been doing some sleuthing. I went to see the coach perform.

Erica: Did he make the audience give him fifty jumping jacks before they could listen to the music?

Jesse: He and the band were actually really good.

Erica: I have to admit that the music he wrote for my—for Joel's play—makes me want to do some karate kicks and chops, too. I mean that in a good way. His music makes me want to dance.

Jesse: His wife was filming the band. She said Coach always has his performances filmed. He has all of our baseball games filmed, too.

Erica: What an ego!

Jesse: That's not it. He watches the films to see what he needs to do better.

Erica: If he waits until opening night to film the play, he's going to be in for a big surprise.

Jesse: Exactly.

9

Erica: *(skeptically)* Why are you so interested in what happens to my play? You didn't even try out for a part or anything.

Jesse: I don't want to be an actor.

Erica: Oh, I know—you want to write plays.

Jesse: Are you always so suspicious?

Erica: You want to be a director!

Jesse: Yes. We move a lot because of my dad's job, but everywhere we go, my parents join a community theater group. My mom acts, and my dad helps design and build the sets.

Erica: So you've got the theater in your blood?

Jesse: Sort of. They always take my sister and me with them to rehearsals. *(modestly)* I've picked up some knowledge here and there.

Erica: And you think my play's pretty good?

Jesse: It could use a little polishing here and there, but I think it's a solid play.

Erica: Okay, then—what's your plan?

10

© 2007 Macmillan/McGraw-Hill

Scene 2 (The next day, inside the school auditorium; Joel jumps around the stage as he delivers his lines, and the coach listens to music on headphones.)

Joel: This forest isn't big enough for both of us, Old Teddy!

(Kasey rushes on stage.)

Kasey: The school paper printed the article I wrote about the play!

Joel: If you're not playing a bear, you don't belong on stage.

Kasey: Look, it says right here how charismatic you are, Joel, how charming and magnetic you are on stage.

(Erica and Jesse enter the auditorium. Jesse carries a video camera.)

Joel: Coach, Kasey wrote an article about me and the play.

Coach Linus: Doogan, I don't remember being interviewed by you. The director of a play is like the coach of a team. I also don't remember posing for any photographs. An article should have photographs.

11

Word Workout

WORDS TO KNOW

awesome	guidance	peripheral	summit
deteriorated	maturity	specialists	typical

Challenge Tell me one of the words in a sentence. Challenge me to use the word in a different sentence.

SPELLING WORDS

admit	explain	include	divide
omit	admission	explanation	inclusion
division	omission	permit	exclaim
explode	decide	collide	permission
exclamation	explosion	decision	collision

Mind Your sions and ations I'll give you a word, and you tell me the word with a new ending or without it.

Home-School Connection

Dear Family Member:

We all face tough problems every day. Some people, however, have overcome huge obstacles. *Seeing Things His Own Way* is the true story of Erik Weihenmayer. He climbed the highest mountain in North America. And he is completely blind! As we read, we are looking at the reasons why the author wrote this article. Understanding an author's reason for writing enables me to keep in mind just what the author wants me to know.

This Week's Skills

Comprehension: author's purpose

Vocabulary: synonyms

Spelling/Phonics: word endings **sion** and **ation**

Name _____

Snow Job

All of the writers below talk about snowshoes, but they are writing for different purposes. Let's read them together and then talk about each author's purpose.

How Do Snowshoes Work?

A snowshoe is a type of shoe that makes it easier to walk on snow. Traditional snowshoes are wooden frames with leather lacings. Modern snowshoes are usually made of metal or plastic. However, all snowshoes work on the same principle. They make your feet very wide, so that you do not sink into the snow when you walk. The lacings or openings help prevent snow from sticking to the shoes.

PERCHALL SNOWSHOES

Announcing the brand new XY-3000 Snowshoes

The latest technology brings you the lightest, strongest, sturdiest snowshoe ever made.

They're so comfortable, you'll think you're wearing slippers!

He trudged three miles through the snow
to bring the happy news.
He would have been happier
if he had worn snowshoes.

Which writer is trying to inform?
Which writer hopes to entertain readers?
Which writer wants to persuade?

234

Ejercicio de palabras

PALABRAS DE VOCABULARIO

awesome	guidance	peripheral	summit
deteriorated	maturity	specialists	typical

Desafío Dime una oración que tenga una de las palabras de la lista. Desafíame a usar la misma palabra en una oración diferente.

PALABRAS DE ORTOGRAFÍA

admit	explain	include	divide
omit	admission	explanation	inclusion
division	omission	permit	exclaim
explode	decide	collide	permission
exclamation	explosion	decision	collision

¿Cómo termina? Te daré una palabra. Tú dímela con una nueva terminación o sin ella.

© Macmillan/McGraw-Hill

(fold here)

Conexión con el hogar

Queridos familiares:

Todos los días debemos enfrentar problemas difíciles. Hay personas, sin embargo, que han debido sobreponerse a obstáculos más serios. *Seeing Things His Own Way* es la verdadera historia de Eric Weihenmayer. Eric escaló la montaña más alta de América del Norte. ¡Y es completamente ciego! Mientras leemos, vemos cuál es el motivo del autor para escribir este artículo. Comprender la razón que tiene un autor para escribir algo nos permite enfocarnos específicamente en lo que el autor quiere que el lector sepa.

Destrezas de la semana

Comprensión: el propósito del autor

Vocabulario: sinónimos

Ortografía/Fonética: palabras terminadas en **sion** y **ation**

Nombre_____

Zapatos para nieve

Todos los escritores que presentamos aquí hablan de zapatos para nieve, pero no todos tienen el mismo propósito para escribir. Juntos, vamos a leer cada uno de los textos; después hablaremos del propósito de cada uno de los autores.

How Do Snowshoes Work?

A snowshoe is a type of shoe that makes it easier to walk on snow. Traditional snowshoes are wooden frames with leather lacings. Modern snowshoes are usually made of metal or plastic. However, all snowshoes work on the same principle. They make your feet very wide, so that you do not sink into the snow when you walk. The lacings or openings help prevent snow from sticking to the shoes.

PERCHALL SNOWSHOES

Announcing the brand new XY-3000 Snowshoes

The latest technology brings you the lightest, strongest, sturdiest snowshoe ever made.

They're so comfortable, you'll think you're wearing slippers!

He trudged three miles through the snow
to bring the happy news.
He would have been happier
if he had worn snowshoes.

Which writer is trying to inform?
Which writer hopes to entertain readers?
Which writer wants to persuade?

Comprehension Check

Summarize

What do you think the author's purpose is in writing this book? How do you think the author feels about Marla Runyan? Use the Author's Purpose Chart to support your thinking.

Clues	Author's Purpose

Think and Compare

1. Why do you think the author chose to tell Marla Runyan's story? Find evidence to support your point of view. *(Author's Purpose)*

2. What do you think it would be like to attend school with impaired vision? How would your friends would react? *(Evaluate)*

3. Do you think it is important to have the Paralympic games? Why not just have the Olympics? *(Analyze)*

24

© 2007 Macmillan/McGraw-Hill

MARLA RUNYAN
IN IT FOR THE LONG RUN

by Stephanie Cohen

Table of Contents

INTRODUCTION

Marla Runyan likes to be known as a fast runner. She has been running most of her life. Marla has competed in **sprints**, or short races. She has also run long-distance **marathons**. She holds American records in the 800-meter race and the 5,000-meter race.

In addition to running, Marla has also competed in the high jump, the hurdles, and the **heptathlon**. The heptathlon is a combination of seven track and field events, which require strength, speed, and endurance.

Marla Runyan is a competitive Olympic athlete. She is also **legally blind**. Though you might guess that Marla is very different from other athletes, in most ways she really isn't. She has had injuries and disappointments. She has had victories, too. She has changed coaches and tried new events. She has been good at a lot of things, and awesome at a few. She is stubborn, competitive, and proud.

Today, Marla is confident she can leap any hurdle.

Marla Runyan

Index

Glossary

bioptic *(bigh-OP-tik)* a magnifier used to enhance poor central vision *(page 10)*

braille *(BRAYL)* a system of printing for blind people using raised dots *(page 7)*

deteriorate *(di-TEER-ee-uh-rayt)* to make or become steadily worse *(page 5)*

heptathlon *(hep-TATH-luhn)* a women's athletic competition with seven track and field events *(page 2)*

legally blind *(LEE-guhl-ee BLIGHND)* incomplete loss of vision *(page 2)*

macula *(MAK-yuh-luh)* the center of the retina *(page 6)*

marathon *(MAR-uh-thon)* a race for runners over a course of 26 miles and 385 yards *(page 2)*

peripheral *(puh-RIF-ur-uhl)* located near the side or outer edge *(page 3)*

prosthetic *(prahs-THE-tik)* a device used to replace a missing body part *(page 15)*

retina *(RET-uh-nuh)* a light-sensitive membrane in the inner eye that sends images to the brain *(page 6)*

specialist *(SPESH-uh-list)* an expert in a particular field *(page 5)*

sprint *(SPRINT)* a short, fast race *(page 2)*

Stargardt's Disease *(STAHR-gahrtz di-ZEEZ)* an inherited disease in the center of the retina, or macula, which results in central vision loss *(page 6)*

Marla Runyan

What does make Marla different is that she lacks full vision. She has only **peripheral** vision. This means she can see only the outer edges of what most people normally view. For example, if she looks at a picture of a person, she might see only the top of his head, his fingertips, and his shoes. The rest of his body is a blur of colors.

Marla's vision problems are uncommon in the world of top-notch athletes, but what really makes her different is that she hasn't let poor vision stop her from doing what she loves and doing her best.

LEGALLY BLIND

There is a difference between being blind and being legally blind. A blind person has no vision, but a legally blind person has some limited vision. Normal vision is 20/20. A legally blind person has 20/200 or worse vision that cannot be corrected. This means their distance vision is very poor and details are very hard to see.

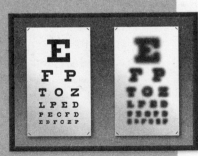

CHAPTER ONE

A VISION PROBLEM

Most fourth grade students have some worries about starting a new school year. Will I like my teacher? How much homework will I have? Marla Runyan was a typical fourth grader in many ways. She loved sports, enjoyed music, and had an awesome big brother and caring parents.

On her first day of fourth grade, Marla had just transferred out of a private school with loose rules and noisy, unorganized classrooms. That was not Marla's style at all. After she pleaded with her parents to get her into a more organized school, she began fourth grade in a traditional public school in her hometown, Camarillo, California. Marla was looking forward to a great year.

↻ Marla went to school in Camarillo, California.

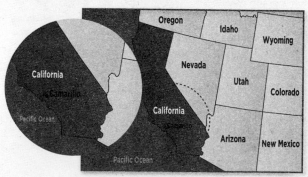

Marla Runyan

CONCLUSION

Marla's awesome accomplishments are well deserved, not just because she is legally blind, but because she works hard and doesn't give up. Marla admits that when she was injured and desperate, "I was very close to saying, 'Why am I even doing this?'" But, in the end, it was all worth it.

Marla still has trouble with everyday tasks like picking broccoli from the salad bar because it looks just like the spinach. But when she sees a runner in her side view take the lead, the race is on! She can't see the clock or the finish line, but she can get there fast.

Marla is written into the history books as the first legally blind Olympic athlete. She would rather just be known as a fast runner who is versatile, hard-working, and happy. Her history is far from over. She'll continue to meet challenges and learn from her mistakes. For her, there is no finish line.

Marla says there is ↪ no finish line. Just keep accepting challenges and moving ahead.

THE NEW YORK CITY MARATHON

The New York City Marathon course meanders through all five New York boroughs. Starting in Staten Island, the course then winds through Brooklyn, Queens, and the Bronx, crossing over five bridges, finally ending in Manhattan's Central Park. The course unites the diverse neighborhoods of New York and challenges thousands of runners who come from around the world each year.

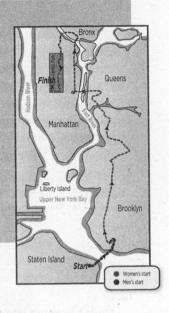

Always looking for a new challenge, Marla broke the indoor 5000-meter record and then began training for the 2002 New York Marathon. She ran in New York and then in the Boston Marathon the following year. She finished among the top five females in both races.

Despite the challenges of running a long, unfamiliar, unpredictable course, Marla kept right on running. With a guide to point out obstacles like potholes and curbs, Marla saw no barriers, only a race to be won.

Marla Runyan

A CHAMPION ATHLETE

Gymnastics was one of Marla's many activities. She admired Olga Korbut, who was the first inductee into the International Gymnastics Hall of Fame in 1988. Korbut's gold medal performances in the 1972 and 1976 Olympics took the gymnastics world by storm.

After school started, Marla discovered a problem. When she looked up at the chalkboard to read the first spelling lesson, Marla couldn't see a word. She couldn't tell if the teacher had written letters, numbers, or a message in Chinese print.

Marla was confused and scared. Though she was unaware of it at the time, Marla had a disease that was causing her eyesight to **deteriorate**, or gradually get much worse. Two weeks after fourth grade began, Marla's vision was so poor that she struggled to read a book two inches in front of her face.

As Marla's vision deteriorated, her parents and teachers became more concerned. She began to visit a variety of **specialists** in hopes of finding out what was wrong.

STARGARDT'S DISEASE

Stargardt's Disease is a common form of macular degeneration. The **macula** is the center of the **retina**, which is the part of the eye responsible for central vision. When the macula degenerates, or becomes damaged, the damage is permanent and can't be corrected with glasses or contact lenses. Central vision gets very blurry, but peripheral, or side, vision stays the same. People with Stargardt's Disease have this kind of limited vision which affects their ability to see details and colors.

Finally, Marla visited Dr. David Boyer. He found that Marla had **Stargardt's Disease**. This diagnosis was both good news and bad news. The bad news was that Marla's vision would continue to deteriorate, so it would become harder and harder for her to see. The good news was that she would not become completely blind. Dr. Boyer told Marla's parents that she would become legally blind but retain her peripheral vision.

Looking back now, Marla remembers that she had always been sensitive to bright light. She had headaches all the time and often felt tired. She didn't know these symptoms were part of a bigger problem. None of that ever stopped her from getting out into the California sunshine to dance and run and play the sports that she loved.

Marla Runyan

ENDORSEMENTS

Sell. Sell. Sell. Are they athletes or shoe salesmen? Michael Jordan sells shoes. Serena Williams sells shoes. Tiger Woods sells shoes. As you read this page, somewhere in the world an athlete is signing an endorsement contract. Why? Because consumers want to use the products their heroes use. Whose shoes are you wearing?

Suddenly everyone wanted to know Marla's story. One year earlier she had been desperate to recover from her injuries and resume her training. Now she was closing in on the summit of her career.

Marla continued to compete in the 1500 as the 2000 Olympic trials approached. As she crossed the finish line at the Olympic trials, Marla made history. She had qualified to run 1500 meters in the Olympics. She became the first legally blind Olympian.

Marla made it all the way to the finals in the 1500 at the 2000 Olympics and to the semifinals in both the 1500 and 5000 at the 2004 Olympics.

CHAPTER FOUR

THERE IS NO FINISH LINE

Marla got a new coach and continued her recovery. After a surprisingly fast run in a 1500-meter race that Marla entered on impulse, she was faced with a problem. Should she continue to run the 800 without much room for improvement, or should she grab onto a new challenge and go for the 1500? Her coach flipped a coin. Marla got the answer she wanted.

At the 1999 Pan Am Games, Marla faced international competition in her fourth ever 1500 race. It was a photo finish. Unable to see the replay or results, Marla asked, "Who won?" The second-place finisher looked up at the posted times and panted, "You did."

◑ Marla and Leah Pells ran to a photo finish at the Pan Am Games. Marla didn't know she'd won until Leah congratulated her.

18

Though other parents might have gone into a complete state of panic, all Marla's parents could hear was the good news that she wouldn't become completely blind. With her family behind her, Marla went back to school.

Being back in school was not easy. Marla did not yet understand how to deal with her limitations. She was embarrassed and stubborn and didn't want people to think she was "special" because of her failing eyesight. This was the beginning of a long struggle for Marla as she began to accept that she was different in a world of people who could see.

◑ People whose vision is impaired or are blind often read **braille**, a special system of writing.

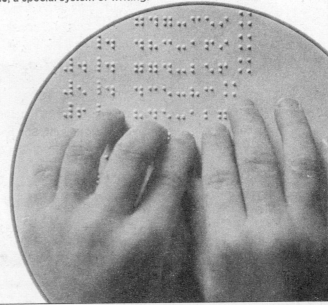

CHAPTER TWO

LIVING WITH A DISABILITY

Marla attempted to live her life exactly as she had before, but she couldn't see standard-size print, she could no longer follow a soccer ball, and bright lights were literally blinding to her. To make matters worse, she refused to ask for help.

Things became a little easier in junior high school when she began to learn how to use more resources for visually impaired students. She learned to use a Closed Caption Television (CCTV) that converted regular-size print from her textbooks into large print projected onto a TV screen. Marla could get up close to this super-size print and read her assignments slowly but independently.

This student ⟳ is using CCTV.

⋒ Marla runs with her husband, Matt Lonergan.

Marla began training with a new coach but was soon sidelined by a series of injuries. She had knee surgery followed by a difficult recovery.

Waiting to regain her strength and speed was hard for Marla. She couldn't wait any longer and began to take short hikes. She experienced more pain and had another surgery, this time on her foot. She became frustrated with slow walks and longed to run the beautiful, challenging trails that Oregon was famous for. But Marla couldn't run.

Her next obstacle was torn muscles in her foot. Marla was discouraged and in need of a new coach. Then something good happened. A physical therapist named Matt Lonergan offered to help with her recovery. Matt and Marla would later marry.

Marla Runyan

8

17

Marla continued to compete in national and international competitions. Sometimes she competed against disabled athletes, and sometimes she was in a field of athletes without disabilities. She began to feel that she was overextending herself and decided to reevaluate her goals. Marla resolved to focus her future efforts on qualifying for the Olympics.

Because her unrelenting schedule left Marla no time to recover and refocus, she did not do as well as she had hoped at the 1996 Olympic heptathlon trials. She did, however, set a track record when she ran the 800-meter race. Maybe it was time to consider long-distance races. She moved to Oregon to train for the 800-meter race.

Marla runs a ↻ victory lap at the 1992 Paralympics.

Marla Runyan

WORDS OF WISDOM

In her autobiography, Marla wrote:
"It became a matter of pride with me to prove that I could do anything, to seek out those things that ought to be most difficult, and to show that I could master them. Track was one of them. High jumping was another—even though I couldn't see the bar."

Marla soon realized that there was one place where her vision problems didn't matter—on the track. Though she felt self-conscious about her vision at school, she felt "normal" when she was at the track. She could see enough on the edges of her field of vision to follow a path and avoid bumping other runners.

Marla also became interested in the high jump. Her father built a makeshift high-jump pit in their backyard. There Marla taught herself to count off the steps and leap at the right moment as the bar flashed into her side view. She excelled at the high jump in high school. Her parents continued to believe that there were no limits to Marla's potential.

That was until Marla decided to learn how to drive. She was intent on taking interesting trips and did not want to walk everywhere for the rest of her life!

Marla had heard of a doctor who was able to help visually impaired people learn to drive with the aid of a high-powered magnifier called a **bioptic**. Marla was familiar with the bioptic. Before her vision became very poor, she played the violin in grade school. She wore a bioptic to help her read sheet music.

Reading music is hard, even with ↻ perfect vision!

© 2007 Macmillan/McGraw-Hill

Marla Runyan

THE PARALYMPICS

The Paralympics are the Olympic Games for athletes with disabilities. Competitors include athletes with **prosthetics**, or artificial limbs, with vision or hearing loss, and those in wheelchairs.

Only 400 athletes participated in the first Paralympic games held in 1960. Today more than 5,000 elite athletes with disabilities compete in 21 sports in both the Summer and Winter games combined. Disabled athletes have a genuine Olympic experience, using world-class facilities, attending events, competing, winning, and losing with pride.

In 1992 Marla participated in the Paralympics for the first time. She went to Barcelona, Spain, to compete. Marla saw many extraordinary athletes there, each one with the determination to win. She even watched an athlete without arms swim the breaststroke. Over the course of 17 days, Marla won gold medals in the 100-, 200-, and 400-meter races, and in the long jump.

Marla remembered, "All of us were there to show the world that we were athletes first, disabled second." She was discouraged by the media always labeling the athletes as "courageous" or "inspirational." Why couldn't they just see that she was fast?

Marla continued to attend school, working toward her master's degree in teaching students with visual and hearing difficulties.

Marla also began to attend athletic competitions for disabled athletes. She was relieved to be in a group where she wasn't an oddity but was considered one of the crowd because of her disability. She gratefully accepted special accommodations because no one expected her to see. She could be herself.

WORDS OF WISDOM

"Don't allow others to discourage you. Don't listen to negative influences. Believe in yourself and show others what you can do. Only you can find your potential."
—Marla Runyan

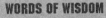

THE BIOPTIC

The bioptic is a magnifier, similar to a telescope, mounted on a pair of eyeglasses. A visually impaired person with good peripheral vision can wear one to improve his or her field of vision, but the higher the magnification, the smaller the field of vision. For Marla it was like looking through a tube.

The benefits of her first bioptic didn't last long. Marla found her vision was becoming too limited and learning new sheet music was too time-consuming. It's easy to see why her parents were skeptical, not to mention terrified, of imagining Marla behind the wheel of a car.

In typical Marla style, she was not deterred. With her mother's help, she got a new bioptic and passed her road test. No sooner was Marla a licensed driver than she whirled through the local fast food drive-thru and considered her next move. And move she did.

CHAPTER THREE

ON HER OWN

After years of living under the guidance of her parents, Marla wanted to be independent. She enrolled at San Diego State College. She lived on her own for the first time in a place that made few accommodations for visually impaired students.

Marla had enough maturity now to realize she needed to ask for help. She found a student to take notes for her and readers to make tapes of her reading assignments. The workload was grueling and the help was sometimes unreliable.

↻ Marla struggled to keep up at San Diego State College.

A TRACK AND FIELD STAR

Jackie Joyner-Kersee broke scoring records throughout her long professional career as the finest heptathlete in history. She is regarded as the best all-around female athlete in the world. She has won several Olympic medals in the heptathlon, two of them gold. Jackie was inspired to take on the challenging variety of heptathlon events by another all-around female star athlete, Babe Didrikson.

Marla again found comfort at the track. Though she could see only the outer edges of her surroundings, some colors, movement, and a lot of feet, she still felt strong, fast, and capable when she was running.

Marla began to broaden her skills by setting records in high jump and running on the relay team. In the summer of 1988, Marla was fascinated by American Olympic athlete Jackie Joyner-Kersee as she broke the world record in the **heptathlon**. The heptathlon is a seven-event track and field competition. The events are 100-meter hurdles, shot put, javelin, high jump, long jump, 200-meter race, and 800-meter race. The competition requires superior athletic versatility and stamina. It got Marla thinking about her next challenge. She decided to train for the heptathlon.

Word Workout

WORDS TO KNOW

hovering   clockwise   formations   severed

edgy   interior   intact   wreckage

Around We Go Can we create sentences that link two of the above words in the order in which they are shown?

SPELLING WORDS

vocalize   storage   criticize   advantage

wreckage   explosive   modernize   organize

attractive   specialize   recognize   positive

creative   percentage   sympathize   passage

negative   realize   emphasize   secretive

All's Well That Ends Well I'll give you one of the spelling words. Give me a word with the same ending. It can be one of the words above or any other word with the same ending. You can give me the words a second time around.

(fold here)

Home-School Connection

Dear Family Member:

Reading about people with interesting careers helps me imagine different ways I might make a living after graduation. This week we're reading about Robert D. Ballard, a researcher who went with his team to the depths of the ocean to explore the remains of the *Titanic*.

In *Exploring the Titanic*, Ballard tells what happened in his own words. Much of the information is factual. However, one of the great things about reading someone's story is that you also learn about his or her opinions.

This Week's Skills

Comprehension: fact and opinion

Vocabulary: adding **ive, age,** and **ize**

Spelling/Phonics: words with **ive, age,** and **ize**

Name _____

Face the Facts

Can you separate which statements are facts and which are opinions? All the facts are true.

Let's write **F** next to every fact and **O** next to every opinion. Then we can count to see whether there are more facts or opinions.

 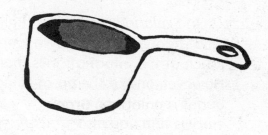

The *R.M.S. Titanic* was built in 1911.

Out of 2,223 passengers, only 706 survived.

The word *titanic* means "huge."

Many people at the time believed that the *Titanic* was "virtually unsinkable."

The sinking of the *Titanic* was the greatest tragedy in the history of navigation.

The luxurious interiors of the *Titanic* were breathtakingly beautiful.

In 1985, Robert D. Ballard and his team discovered the remains of the *Titanic*.

When you look at these photographs, you can't help but feel sad for the people who died.

The *Titanic* struck an iceberg and sank on its first voyage, in 1912.

The best version of the film was the 1997 blockbuster starring Leonardo DiCaprio.

Photographs of the sunken ship are magnificent but a little frightening, too.

There are _____ facts.

There are _____ opinions.

Ejercicio de palabras

PALABRAS DE VOCABULARIO

hovering   clockwise   formations   severed

edgy   interior   intact   wreckage

De a dos ¿Podremos crear oraciones que tengan dos de las palabras de arriba en el mismo orden en el que están en la lista?

PALABRAS DE ORTOGRAFÍA

vocalize	storage	criticize	advantage
wreckage	explosive	modernize	organize
attractive	specialize	recognize	positive
creative	percentage	sympathize	passage
negative	realize	emphasize	secretive

Un mismo final Te daré una de las palabras de la lista. Dime una palabra que tenga la misma terminación. Puede ser una de las palabras de arriba o cualquier otra palabra con la misma terminación. Repitamos el juego. Esta vez las terminaciones me las darás tú.

(fold here)

© Macmillan/McGraw-Hill

Queridos familiares:

Leer acerca de personas que tienen carreras interesantes me ayuda a imaginar diversas formas en que podré ganarme la vida después de graduarme. Esta semana estamos leyendo sobre Robert D. Ballard, un investigador que fue con su equipo hasta las profundidades del océano para explorar los restos del Titanic.

En *Exploring the Titanic*, Ballard cuenta lo que pasó en sus propias palabras. Gran parte de la información está basada en hechos. Sin embargo, una de las ventajas de leer un relato hecho por alguien es que también lees sus opiniones.

Destrezas de la semana

Comprensión: hecho y opinión

Vocabulario: las terminaciones **ive, age, ize**

Ortografía/Fonética: palabras con **ive, age, ize**

Nombre _____

Frente a los hechos

¿Puedes separar los enunciados que son hechos y los que son opiniones? Todos los hechos son verdaderos.

Let's write **F** next to every fact and **O** next to every opinion. Then we can count to see whether there are more facts or opinions.

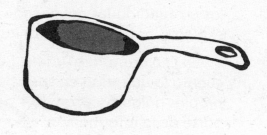

The *R.M.S. Titanic* was built in 1911.

Out of 2,223 passengers, only 706 survived.

The word *titanic* means "huge."

Many people at the time believed that the *Titanic* was "virtually unsinkable."

The sinking of the *Titanic* was the greatest tragedy in the history of navigation.

The luxurious interiors of the *Titanic* were breathtakingly beautiful.

In 1985, Robert D. Ballard and his team discovered the remains of the *Titanic*.

When you look at these photographs, you can't help but feel sad for the people who died.

The *Titanic* struck an iceberg and sank on its first voyage, in 1912.

The best version of the film was the 1997 blockbuster starring Leonardo DiCaprio.

Photographs of the sunken ship are magnificent but a little frightening, too.

There are _____ facts.

There are _____ opinions.

252

Comprehension Check

Summarize

Jacques Cousteau has been called the greatest underwater explorer. Use the Fact and Opinion Chart to support that claim. List both facts and opinions.

Fact	Opinion

Think and Compare

1. Turn to page 18. Cousteau describes how his view of the ocean changed. What in his statements is fact and what is opinion? *(Identify Fact and Opinion)*

2. If you could devote your life to exploring a part of the world, what part would you choose? Explain your answer. *(Analyze)*

3. Do you think that exploring the ocean and its inhabitants is worthwhile? Why is it important to understand ocean life? *(Synthesize)*

Jacques Cousteau

by E. C. Hill

Table of Contents

Introduction

Humans have a long history of exploring the sea. Boats have skimmed across its dark surface for thousands of years. Sailors could explore the seas, but they could not penetrate that surface with their gaze. They could only wonder what secrets the sea held. Did the depths hide monsters? When would the sea's mood change? Would storm-tossed waves swallow the ship?

The sea still holds many mysteries. Yet there has been a revolution in our understanding of the ocean in recent years. Few people have done more to make this revolution happen than Jacques Cousteau (ZHOK koo-STOH) has. Through his inventions, explorations, writings, and television programs, Cousteau has opened the eyes of millions of people to the complex life of the undersea world.

Jacques Cousteau

Index

Glossary

algae *(AL-jee)* small plants without roots or stems that grow in water *(page 5)*

aqualung *(AK-wuh-lung)* a breathing apparatus for diving *(page 9)*

artifact *(ART-i-fakt)* an object, often old, made by humans *(page 12)*

coral reef *(KAWR-uhl REEF)* an underwater strip of rocklike material made up of the skeletons of tiny sea creatures *(page 15)*

ecology *(ee-KOL-uh-gee)* the relationship between living things and their surroundings *(page 18)*

environment *(en-VYE-ruhn-mehnt)* the natural world of the land, sea, and air *(page 21)*

extinction *(eks-TINK-shuhn)* death of a species of plant or animal *(page 20)*

goggles *(GOG-uhlz)* tight-fitting protective eyeglasses *(page 4)*

mammal *(MAM-uhl)* a warm-blooded animal with a backbone. Female mammals produce milk to feed their young. *(page 19)*

pollution *(pol-EW-shuhn)* harmful materials that damage the air, water, and soil *(page 20)*

snorkel *(SNORK-uhl)* a J-shaped tube that allows swimmers to breath underwater the water *(page 4)*

troika *(TROY-kuh)* a sledlike machine used to explore the ocean floor *(page 16)*

zoologist *(zoh-OL-uh-jist)* a scientist who studies animal life *(page 20)*

© 2007 Macmillan/McGraw-Hill

Jacques Cousteau

Chapter 1

Lure of the Silent World

Jacques Cousteau did not begin his life near the sea. He was born in 1910 in France. His hometown of St.-André-de-Cubzac (sant on-DRAY duh koob-ZOK) is set along a river.

Jacques was often sick as a boy so he did not spend as much time outside as his adventurous spirit would have liked. Most of his adventures came from his reading. Jacques loved books about pirates, pearl divers, and distant seas.

Jacques had another habit during childhood. He loved inventions and toying with all kinds of machinery. He saved his allowance to buy one of the first movie cameras sold in France. He taught himself to take it apart and put it back together. When he was 13, he used the camera to shoot his first film.

⌒ Jacques Cousteau has been called the "Father of Oceanography."

When he was a young man, Cousteau joined the navy. As he traveled around the world, he became more and more interested in the sea. One bright weekend morning in 1936, the young sailor waded into the waters of the Mediterranean Sea.

This outing was different from the usual swim for Cousteau. The salt water of the sea always burned his eyes on such swims. This time he came prepared. He pulled a pair of **goggles** over his head and secured them tightly in place over his eyes. Then he waded deeper and lowered his head into the water to test his new eyewear. In that moment, his life changed forever.

◔ Goggles, **snorkel**, and flippers help divers explore the ocean.

Conclusion

Cousteau believed that people could help restore the **environment**. He encouraged plans to protect endangered species. He noted that many species returned to their optimum number when given the chance. "Each time a species of marine [sea] mammal has been protected, it has made a dramatic comeback."

Jacques Cousteau's long adventure with life ended in 1997, when he died at the age of 87. By that time he was recognized as a hero by millions of people. United States President Bill Clinton admired Cousteau. "While we mourn his death, it is far more important that we celebrate his remarkable life and the gifts he gave to us all."

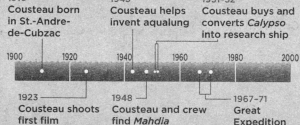

Jacques Cousteau's Life

1910
Cousteau born in St.-Andre-de-Cubzac

1943
Cousteau helps invent aqualung

1951–52
Cousteau buys and converts *Calypso* into research ship

1900   1920   1940   1960   1980   2000

1923
Cousteau shoots first film

1948
Cousteau and crew find *Mahdia*

1967–71
Great Expedition

Cousteau saw close up the damage caused by human activities. "Assumption Island, isolated in the Indian Ocean, north of Madagascar (mad-uh-GAS-car), was one of the richest underwater sanctuaries I ever visited. But when I came back 13 years later, I found that damage had already been done to the coral fringe of the island. . . ."

He believed that heavy fishing or **pollution** had caused the damage. The sea's ecology was not only complex; it could be fragile. As he saw more and more signs of the ocean's damaged health, Cousteau began to speak out in defense of the sea and the creatures that lived there. He reminded his audience that humans had hunted hundreds of species to **extinction**. **Zoologists** think that 94 percent of whales had been killed by the 1970s. Cousteau warned that humans were destroying the oceans.

⟁ Cousteau worried that the blue whale, the largest animal on Earth, would be hunted to extinction.

Jacques Cousteau

⟁ Although Cousteau traveled the world, the Mediterranean was his home base for much of his career.

His goggles helped Cousteau see things he had never seen before. "I was astounded by what I saw," he said. "Rocks covered by green, brown, and silver forests of **algae**, and fishes unknown to me." He looked back over his shoulder toward shore. He saw people, light poles, and a trolley car. He turned away from the crowded scene and plunged his head back into the translucent water again.

"Sometimes we are lucky enough to know that our lives have been changed," he said. "It happened to me . . . on that summer's day, when my eyes were opened on the sea."

Chapter 2

Free in the Sea

Now that Cousteau had glimpsed the richness of the sea's life, he swam and dived whenever he could. He was not the only one in the area with a passion for diving. Cousteau heard stories of other divers and their underwater feats. He sought them out. These divers had no way to breathe underwater, so they practiced holding their breath as long as possible.

One was Frédéric Dumas (fray-day-REEK doo-MAH). Everyone called him Didi. Didi Dumas was known as one of the best divers in France in the early 1940s. He could dive to 60 feet below the surface on a single breath.

Cousteau was concerned with the health of ocean mammals, such as dolphins.

The more he traveled, however, and the more he saw, the more Cousteau's beliefs began to change. He came to admire the rich life found in places like coral reefs even more. Cousteau became deeply devoted to the health of the sea and the creatures that lived there. He had a special affection for the **mammals** of the sea, such as dolphins and whales. He believed that they are intelligent and can communicate. He believed that they can even show qualities like faithfulness, tenderness, and friendliness.

Chapter 5

Speaking Out for the Sea

Year after year, Cousteau sailed *Calypso* across the ocean. His knowledge of the sea and its **ecology** grew with each voyage. The plants and animals of the sea live in a complex balance with each other and with their surroundings. Millions of viewers learned to share Cousteau's respect for the sea. The series continued after the Great Expedition and ended in 1973.

Cousteau learned that life is precious in part because it is rare. Early in his career he did not understand that. "At the time, I was convinced that the oceans were immense, teeming with life, rich in resources of all kinds." After many voyages, however, he found that belief colliding with reality. "I had to face the evidence: the blue waters appeared to be, most of the time, a discouraging desert."

⟲ These butterfly fish live in coral reefs.

Cousteau and Didi Dumas met another diver named Philippe Taillez (fi-LEEP ty-YAY). Dumas described seeing Taillez for the first time. "I am out on the rocks when I see a real manfish," he recalled fondly. "He never lifts his head to breathe, and after a surface dive, water spouts out of a tube in his mouth." The tube was a snorkel. In these early years, Didi Dumas had not yet seen many snorkels. The three men became the heart of a team that stayed together for years.

Simone (see-MOAN) Cousteau, Jacques's wife, was another member of the team. She, too, loved the sea and accompanied her husband on many dives. In time their family grew to include sons Jean-Michel (zhan mee-SHEL) and Philippe. When they were old enough, they would also join Jacques's team of divers.

How Deep?

How deep can people dive safely? Cousteau met a sponge diver who could swim down to 130 feet below the surface without any extra source of air or special equipment. The diver stayed submerged for up to two and one half minutes.

Cousteau and his fellow divers loved diving, but they were frustrated, too. They were limited to underwater swims that they could make on a single breath. They dreamed of finding a way to breathe underwater so they could better explore the world that fascinated them so completely.

Inventors tried to help. One inventor used an on-board pump and some tubing to get fresh air to underwater divers. Yet Cousteau found this system difficult to use and sometimes dangerous. Even when it worked well, divers were still tethered to the boat that hovered above. And if the tubing was severed, the diver would be in danger.

Late in 1942, Cousteau began to experiment. He wanted to find a way for divers to carry a supply of air with them.

Early diving suits allowed ⟲ divers to explore deeper in the ocean.

Jacques Cousteau

⌒ Whale sharks are the biggest of all fish, but they are not dangerous.

In 1967 the team began "the Great Expedition." This adventure lasted almost four years. Cousteau had planned the journey to be the basis for a new television show known as *The Undersea World of Jacques Cousteau.*

Cousteau filmed amazing things including the rare whale shark. Two of these giants came near the *Calypso.* The larger one was about 50 feet long.

Two of the divers quickly joined the sharks. One grasped a shark tail fin for a ride as the other diver filmed the scene. Edgy events like this thrilled television audiences.

⟲ Cousteau helped to design the troika, a useful ocean-exploring vessel.

Cousteau and the *Calypso* made many similar voyages in the next few years. Scientists came along on every trip. Cousteau and the crew continued to build their knowledge of the sea.

Cousteau also helped design other inventions for exploring the sea. One was called the **troika**, (TROY-kuh), which means "three." It was named after a Russian sled. The troika could be lowered to as much as 25,000 feet below the sea's surface. As a ship dragged it along, the troika took pictures of the sea floor.

© 2007 Macmillan/McGraw-Hill

Jacques Cousteau

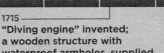

Within half a year, Cousteau and his friends had created the **aqualung**. The prefix *aqua–* means "water." The device acted as a kind of lung for underwater breathing.

The aqualung was made of tanks filled with compressed air that the diver wore on his or her back. Flexible tubes led from the tanks to a special mouthpiece. The diver swam with a mouthpiece set in the mouth and breathed air from the tank. The aqualung was heavy when it was out of water but seemed weightless when the diver submerged.

Best of all, the aqualung allowed divers to swim freely on long dives. Cousteau and his divers were thrilled. The aqualung was one of the most important inventions in the history of sea exploration.

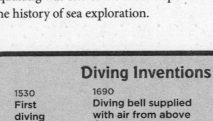

⊙ The diving bell held a bubble of air in its bell-like shape. Divers could breathe that air while they stood inside.

Diving Inventions

1530 First diving bell

1690 Diving bell supplied with air from above

1943 Aqualung invented

1500   1600   1700   1800   1900   2000

1715 "Diving engine" invented; a wooden structure with waterproof armholes, supplied with air from above

1837 First sealed rubber diving suit, with air supplied from above

© 2007 Macmillan/McGraw-Hill

Chapter 3

Explorations

"That first summer in the sea with the aqualung, . . . we [recorded] 500 dives," Cousteau wrote. They practiced to see how far down humans could safely swim. As divers go deeper, the pressure of the surrounding water grows. It presses in from all sides, even squeezing air out of the lungs. If divers dive too far down or stay underwater for too long, the pressure can cause severe physical problems.

Cousteau also added something new to his underwater explorations. He began to take cameras with him on the dives.

↻ Ships have been sinking in the Mediterranean Sea since people began sailing there.

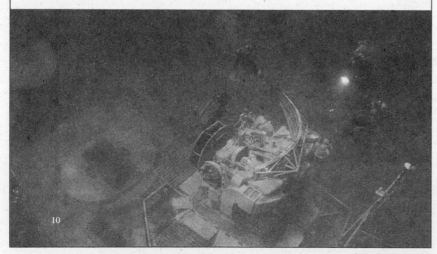

10

Over the course of his years of diving, Cousteau was developing a philosophy. "We must go and see for ourselves," he said. Cousteau's first voyage with *Calypso* was memorable. They cruised east across the Mediterranean to the Red Sea. In the Red Sea were some of the world's largest **coral reef** formations

The trip was a great success. With scientists on board to help, the team identified several unknown species of plants and animals. Some of these species were named after Cousteau and his teammates. One species was even named for the *Calypso*.

This journey on the *Calypso* marked a turning point for Cousteau. "What had gone before in our underwater adventure was adolescence," he said. "The big years were ahead."

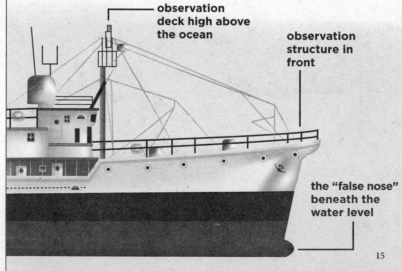

observation deck high above the ocean

observation structure in front

the "false nose" beneath the water level

15

Chapter 4

The Big Years

The aqualung gave Cousteau and his divers the opportunity to explore the sea with new freedom. Then in the summer of 1951, Cousteau bought a nine-year-old ferry boat and renamed it *Calypso* (kuh-LIP-so). Over the next year, Cousteau worked to transform the ship into a world-class ocean research vessel. One feature he added was the "false nose." This was a bulb-shaped structure built into the front of the ship. The bulb had eight sturdy windows built into it. The crew could lie in the space and watch activity in the water.

↻ The interior rooms of the *Calypso* included science labs.

crane for moving troika and other heavy objects into and out of the water

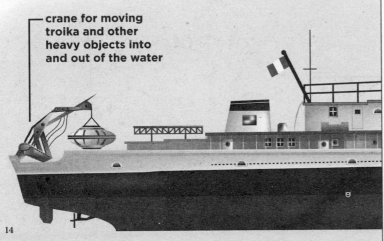

© 2007 Macmillan/McGraw-Hill

Jacques Cousteau

Mahdia Wreckage

⌒ Cousteau had to search a wide area to find the *Mahdia* wreck.

Cousteau and his team began to go on dives to explore shipwrecks. In 1948, they heard the story of the wreck of a ship called the *Mahdia* (MAH-dee-uh). One of the largest of the known ancient shipwrecks, it had been partly explored 35 years earlier. Then it was abandoned and nearly forgotten. The ship was Roman. Experts believed it had sunk around 80 B.C.E.

Cousteau called the Mediterranean Sea "the mother of civilization" because many ancient cultures grew along its shores. If you traveled clockwise around the edge of the sea, you would find the remains of many ancient civilizations, including these two Mediterranean civilizations.

- The Greek civilization reached a peak during the fifth century B.C.E.

- The Roman civilization had its center in Rome on the Italian peninsula. According to tradition, Rome was founded in 753 B.C.E. and reached its height between 100 and 200 C.E.

Nobody was sure how to find the ship. Cousteau and his crew got help from local residents who remembered the earlier dives. Still, divers found no trace of the wreckage through five long, frustrating days.

On the sixth day, Philippe Taillez went down to try again. Cousteau and the others watched and waited as Taillez explored. Suddenly, a small orange marker bobbed to the surface. The crew knew that this was Taillez's signal that he had found something.

After a few tense minutes, Taillez burst to the surface and yanked out his mouthpiece. "A column!" he shouted, "I found a column." This was a sure sign they had found the *Mahdia* wreck. Marble columns were part of the cargo that the ship carried when it sank. Cousteau called the wreck "a drowned museum" because of all the **artifacts** they found in the ship. These artifacts included columns and well-preserved parts of the ship, many of them intact.

The *Mahdia* was loaded with goods taken from Athens, the center of Greek civilization.

Jacques Cousteau

Word Workout

WORDS TO KNOW

accessible	hamper	prohibit
bewildering	moderate	

Meaning Mystery Let's talk about the words and come up with a topic for which we can use them. Then let's discuss the topic using the words.

SPELLING WORDS

unfairness	discouragement	reminder
unevenly	designer	disgraceful
incorrectly	enclosure	unsucessful
disapproval	departure	outlandish
enforcement	unselfish	disappointment
unhappiness	outsider	delightful
repayment	enjoyment	

One Letter at a Time Let's keep choosing a word and take turns spelling the word letter by letter.

(fold here)

Home-School Connection

Dear Family Member:

We all need help sometimes. No one can live without it. In *Saving Grace*, we are reading articles about people who really help out. Their stories are an inspiration to help others. They show me different ways I might decide to give back to our community.

As we are reading, we are also practicing comparing and contrasting information. This skill helps me understand many topics by looking at how things are similar and how they are different.

This Week's Skills

Comprehension: compare and contrast

Vocabulary: homographs: words spelled the same but with different meanings

Spelling/Phonics: prefixes, suffixes, and base words

Name _____

A New View

These three students at P.S. 99 have different ideas about how to improve the community garden. We can read what each student has to say and then talk about how their ideas are similar and how they are different.

The garden is big enough to be split into two parts—half as a garden, with lots of flowers and vegetables, half as a dog run. Our neighborhood really needs a dog run. Right now there's nowhere for our dogs to play.

I think a long row of tall sunflowers would look great along the back wall of the garden. The rest should be vegetables that we can harvest and donate to local food shelters.

Why not divide the garden into two parts? Half can be used for fruits and vegetables and half for flowers, such as roses and daisies. I like sunflowers, too.

What do these plans have in common?

Do you have ideas for a garden plan? How is your idea different? How is it the same?

Ejercicio de palabras

PALABRAS DE VOCABULARIO

accessible   hamper   prohibit

bewildering   moderate

Un tema especial Hablemos de las palabras de la lista y pensemos en un tema en que podamos usarlas a todas. Luego hablemos sobre el tema usando las palabras.

PALABRAS DE ORTOGRAFÍA

unfairness   discouragement   reminder

unevenly   designer   disgraceful

incorrectly   enclosure   unsucessful

disapproval   departure   outlandish

enforcement   unselfish   disappointment

unhappiness   outsider   delightful

repayment   enjoyment

Una letra por vez Vamos a elegir palabras por palabra y a turnarnos par deletrearlas.

(fold here)

Conexión con el hogar

Queridos familiares:

Todos necesitamos ayuda en algún momento. Nadie puede vivir sin ella. En *Saving Grace*, estamos leyendo artículos sobre personas que realmente ayudan a los demás. Sus historias son una fuente de inspiración. Me sugieren diversas alternativas que podría escoger para ser útil en nuestra comunidad.

En la lectura estamos practicando comparar y contrastar información. Esta destreza me ayuda a comprender muchos temas al observar en qué se parecen y en que se diferencian las cosas.

Destrezas de la semana

Comprensión: comparar y contrastar

Vocabulario: homógrafos: palabras que se escriben igual, pero tienen diferente significado

Ortografía/Fonética: prefijos, sufijos y palabras base

Nombre _____

Perspectivas diferentes

Estos tres estudiantes de la Escuela Pública 99 tienen diferentes ideas para mejorar el jardín de su comunidad. Podemos leer lo que cada uno tiene que decir, y después platicaremos sobre cómo se parecen y cómo se diferencian sus ideas.

The garden is big enough to be split into two parts—half as a garden, with lots of flowers and vegetables, half as a dog run. Our neighborhood really needs a dog run. Right now there's nowhere for our dogs to play.

I think a long row of tall sunflowers would look great along the back wall of the garden. The rest should be vegetables that we can harvest and donate to local food shelters.

Why not divide the garden into two parts? Half can be used for fruits and vegetables and half for flowers, such as roses and daisies. I like sunflowers, too.

What do these plans have in common?

Do you have ideas for a garden plan? How is your idea different? How is it the same?

Comprehension Check

Summarize

Compare and contrast the first school Mary McLeod Bethune opened with the college she ran much later.

Think and Compare

1. Look back at page 5. How was young Mary McLeod's life the same or different from the lives of the children her mother worked for? *(Compare and Contrast)*

2. Think about a time when someone told you that you couldn't do something because you weren't big enough, smart enough, or some other excuse that you believed was unreasonable. How did you feel? What did you do? *(Analyze/Synthesize)*

3. How have civil rights activists such as Mary McLeod Bethune changed the world? *(Evaluate)*

24

Achievements in Education

Mary McLeod Bethune

by Barbara A. Donovan

Table of Contents

Introduction

In the hundred years between the **Civil War** and the **civil rights** movement, life in the South for many African Americans was filled with frustrated promise. Though no longer enslaved, they had few rights and even fewer opportunities. Few schools were open for African Americans. Even then it was the rare family that could spare a child for school.

Without an education, African Americans found it nearly impossible to get ahead. For those children who could go to school, there was hope of a better life. And if the child came to school armed with a thirst to learn, then who knew what heights that child might achieve. Such was the case with Mary McLeod Bethune.

ᕤ Mary's parents, Samuel and Patsy McLeod, were formerly enslaved people. They saved the money they earned to buy five acres of their own farmland.

© 2007 Macmillan/McGraw-Hill

Achievements in Education: Mary McLeod Bethune

Index

Glossary

aerobics *(ayr-OH-biks)* exercises that help the body to take in and use more oxygen; they can strengthen the heart and lungs. *(page 7)*

amateur *(AM-uh-chur)* a person who does something for the pleasure of doing it, not for pay *(page 9)*

chemotherapy *(kee-moh-THER-uh-pee)* the use of chemical substances to treat diseases, such as cancer *(page 14)*

Olympian *(oh-LIM-pee-uhn)* an athlete who has competed in the Olympic Games *(page 6)*

professional *(pruh-FESH-uh-nuhl)* a person who works for money doing something that other people do for fun *(page 2)*

pro circuit *(PROH SUR-kit)* short for professional circuit; the races in which professional athletes compete *(page 10)*

rank *(RANGK)* to have a certain position or grade *(page 11)*

stage *(STAYJ)* in cycling, to stop at a designated place in the course of a race *(page 11)*

survivor *(suhr-VIGH-vur)* someone who lives through a life-threatening challenge *(page 6)*

therapy *(THE-ruh-pee)* treatment for a disability, injury, or illness *(page 15)*

triathlete *(trigh-ATH-leet)* someone who competes in a triathlon *(page 7)*

triathlon *(trigh-ATH-lon)* an athletic contest in which participants compete without stopping in three successive events, usually long-distance swimming, bicycling, and running *(page 7)*

♫ Mary McLeod Bethune was among the influential African American leaders whom President Harry Truman consulted for advice.

Mary grabbed with both hands at her chance to go to school. She was determined to get her education. And she succeeded. She became a teacher because she believed that education was the path out of poverty.

Mary McLeod Bethune was a born leader who was able to make friends among the rich and the powerful. Throughout her life, she spoke out on education, **democracy**, and issues facing African Americans. Some of the most powerful people in the country, including presidents of the United States, came to her for advice. Mary McLeod Bethune's life is a study in achievement.

Chapter One

The Education of Mary McLeod Bethune

Those first ten years after the Civil War were a time of rebuilding in the South. To some, **Reconstruction** meant rebuilding homes and farms destroyed by war. For the McLeod family of Maysville, South Carolina, it meant rebuilding their lives. Many of their children had been sold to other slave holders. Once freed they found their way back into the arms of their parents, Samuel and Patsy. They worked, and they saved. Finally, the family had enough money to buy five acres of farmland. They built a log cabin there and began working the land.

↻ Mary McLeod's parents worked in cotton fields.

© 2007 Macmillan/McGraw-Hill

Conclusion

Throughout her life, Mary McLeod Bethune worked to make the lives of African Americans better. No task was too small or too hard for her to handle. Mary McLeod Bethune believed that education was the path to freedom. It still is.

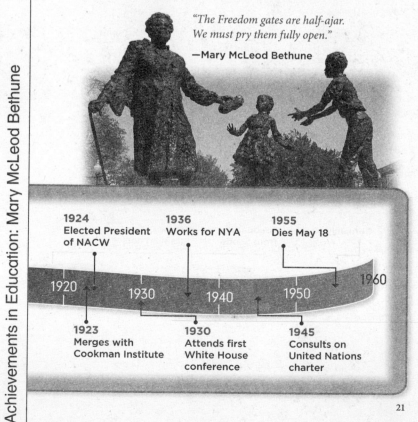

"The Freedom gates are half-ajar. We must pry them fully open."

—Mary McLeod Bethune

1924
Elected President of NACW

1936
Works for NYA

1955
Dies May 18

1920   1930   1940   1950   1960

1923
Merges with Cookman Institute

1930
Attends first White House conference

1945
Consults on United Nations charter

In 1939 Mary McLeod Bethune became a director of the NYA. She also had the President's ear. She advised him on issues important to African American people.

Once her job at the NYA ended, she continued to work for her country and her people. When President Truman asked her to work on the charter for the newly formed United Nations, she went. In 1953 Mary McLeod Bethune gave her home and possessions to a foundation that she created. She hoped that future generations would use them for research. She wanted her foundation to bring the races together and to teach others. Mary McLeod Bethune died in 1955.

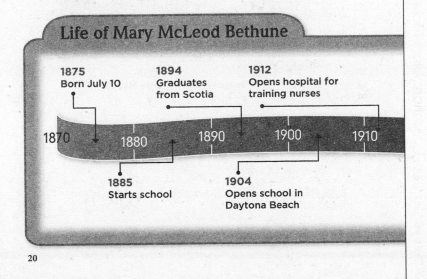

Life of Mary McLeod Bethune

1875
Born July 10

1894
Graduates from Scotia

1912
Opens hospital for training nurses

1870 1880 1890 1900 1910

1885
Starts school

1904
Opens school in Daytona Beach

⋒ Mary McLeod was born in the log cabin her father and brothers had built.

Mary was the fifteenth of seventeen McLeod children. She was one of the few born into **freedom**. Young Mary worked the cotton and corn fields. She learned the value of hard work, yet she was unsatisfied. She saw the opportunities that the white children had. They went to school while she worked. Mary ached for a better life.

Mary's mother worked for a white family. One day Mary went into the playhouse where the children did their schoolwork. When Mary began to look at a book, one of the girls took it away from her. She said that Mary couldn't read, so she couldn't have that book. Instead she handed Mary a picture book. With a heavy heart, Mary looked at the pictures. After a while, her hurt hardened into a fierce resolve. She *would* learn to read. No one could stop her.

After the Civil War, there were still two worlds in the South. Education was not accessible to everyone. Many whites did not think that blacks needed to read or write. But Mary knew that she must learn to read to get a better life.

Mary's education began at age 10 in a **segregated** mission school just outside of Maysville. By her own account, she was a fairly average student. But she was a natural leader. The **work ethic** that she'd learned working on her family's farm drove her to study. At home she taught other children as well as adults who had that same hunger for learning that she had.

Segregated Schools

During most of Mary McLeod's life, there were laws to prohibit mixing of races in schools. Schools for whites and blacks were separate and unequal. In 1954 the United States Supreme Court changed these laws. Children of all races could attend the same good schools. Their education had to be equal.

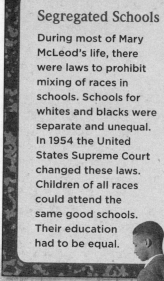

⟲ The first school that Mary McLeod attended was a Presbyterian Mission School.

Achievements in Education: Mary McLeod Bethune

Mary McLeod Bethune's work on behalf of children and on issues facing African Americans began to get noticed. In 1928 President Calvin Coolidge invited her to add her voice to the National Child Welfare Commission. She became friends with many powerful people in Washington.

Beginning in 1929, the Great Depression swept the country. It wiped out the savings of most Americans. Tension between the races flared. By the time Franklin D. Roosevelt (FDR) took office in 1933, people needed a change. FDR began creating organizations that could help people in need. One was the National Youth Administration (NYA). Through the NYA, America's youths would get education and training. And when they were ready, they'd be placed in much needed jobs.

In 1936 FDR asked for Mary McLeod Bethune's help. He needed an advisor at the NYA. He needed someone who understood the needs of minorities and could talk to government workers about those needs. So for the next eight years, Mary McLeod Bethune worked for the NYA. Through her efforts, African Americans had the chance to work at NYA jobs.

⟲ Mary McLeod Bethune and Eleanor Roosevelt became good friends.

18

Scotia Seminary was located in Concord, North Carolina. In the late 1800s, Concord was a bustling mill town.

Mary soaked up all the learning she could in her years at school. One October day when she was about fifteen, her life changed. Mary and her family were working in a field. A man from the community and her teacher, Miss Wilson, came up to them with a remarkable offer. There was a scholarship to Scotia Seminary, a high school, for a girl who would use such an education well. They believed that Mary McLeod was just such a girl. Would she like to go? Mary was thrilled. She packed her few belongings into boxes. Neighbors gave her dresses. Soon she was off on her first bewildering train ride to Concord, North Carolina. She had never traveled outside her hometown.

7

When Mary McLeod arrived at Scotia Seminary, she couldn't believe her eyes. It was the first time she lived in a big town. She had a lot to get used to. At school she learned subjects such as English and math. She associated with girls from cities and towns.

While at Scotia, Mary had little time to rest. To keep the school's costs down, the students helped out around the school. Mary worked in the laundry, scrubbed floors, stoked the coal stoves, and did the rest of the work she was assigned. She sang with the chorus and joined the debate team. Even with the chores, going to school was a joy. She was ever grateful for her education.

In 1893 Mary McLeod graduated from Scotia with the dream of being a missionary. She wanted to travel to faraway places and teach people who weren't able to go to school. She studied at the Moody Bible Institute in Chicago.

⏾ When Mary McLeod Bethune opened her own college, she had her students learn practical skills like laundry.

© 2007 Macmillan/McGraw-Hill

Achievements in Education: Mary McLeod Bethune

Mary McLeod Bethune believed the power for change was in the hands of women like her. She became an active member of the National Association of Colored Women's Clubs (NACW). By 1924 she was its president. She wanted African American women to unite. She wanted them to use their voices to make changes.

Voting Rights

Two Constitutional amendments (fifteenth and nineteenth) gave African American men and women the right to vote. Most, however, never got the chance to vote. Poll taxes kept out the poor. Literacy tests kept out those who couldn't read. Violence kept out many more. With the Voting Rights Act of 1965, such barriers to voting became illegal.

Mary McLeod Bethune ➔ began another politically active organization in 1935, the National Council of Negro Women (NCNW).

Chapter Three

The Education of a Nation

Education was not the only issue Mary McLeod Bethune felt strongly about. Mary McLeod Bethune also believed in democracy. She especially believed in the power of the vote. To her, voting was the key to equality.

In 1920 women at last had the right to vote. Now even Mary McLeod Bethune could vote, and vote she would! She also worked to get African Americans registered to vote. She went door-to-door, collecting money to pay the **poll taxes**. This was a tax on each adult citizen who wanted to vote. She taught adults to read so they could pass the **literacy test**. Then the night before the election, a group of white men visited her. They warned her against bringing out the black vote. But they didn't count on her backbone. She refused to back down. The next day she proudly walked to her polling place to vote. And she brought a hundred other Africans Americans along with her. They all voted for the very first time. This was the power of democracy.

Word got out that Mary McLeod Bethune had not backed down. She earned a reputation as a fighter for her people. Soon she was speaking around the country. And she spoke from her heart. For the next three decades, she spoke out against unfair and unsafe housing. She spoke for the need for color-blind health care and education.

© 2007 Macmillan/McGraw-Hill

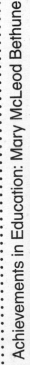

Achievements in Education: Mary McLeod Bethune

Despite the prejudices of other people, Mary McLeod had never let the color of her skin hold her back. She knew that her accomplishments would speak for her. Yet at the end of the term, she was prohibited from becoming a missionary.

Mary did not let this hamper her. She set her sights on a new dream. She headed back to Maysville and became her former teacher's assistant. Yet Mary McLeod was restless. She moved from place to place. In 1898 she married Albertus Bethune. A year later they had a son. She stayed at home to care for her family.

When Mary McLeod Bethune was offered the chance to start a school in Florida, she moved her family there. Then in 1904 they moved to Daytona Beach. Here she established her second school. It was the start of her lasting **legacy**.

"I would not exchange my color for all the wealth in the world, for had I been born white I might not have been able to do all that I have done or yet hope to do."

— Mary McLeod Bethune

Chapter Two

The Education of Children

When Mary McLeod Bethune chose Daytona Beach for her school, she was just about out of money. Unlike schools for white children that got money from the government, Mary had to find her own funding.

According to her stories, she only had $1.50 to start her school. She rented a house for her school on credit. She got boxes and crates to use as desks and chairs. She borrowed the other supplies that she needed. In 1904 she opened The Daytona Literary and Industrial School for Training Negro Girls. This was an elementary school. She had five girls and her son as pupils.

↻ Mary McLeod Bethune leads her students to school.

↺ Mary McLeod Bethune returned as president to Bethune-Cookman College for a year.

In 1931 she reached another goal. Her one-room schoolhouse was now a junior college named Bethune-Cookman College. Many more students went there. They could choose from a wide variety of different courses. Graduates got good jobs, such as teaching. Mary McLeod Bethune was becoming a well-known educator. Still she spent much of her time trying to raise money to keep her dream alive. She guided her college through the **Depression**. She kept it afloat through hurricanes. But being president of the college was more than her health could bear. Finally in 1942, she resigned. She handed over her dream to the care of others.

By 1923 the school was growing by leaps and bounds. It owned a farm. It also had 315 students and 25 teachers. Its campus had several buildings. Still, raising money to run the school was an almost daily chore. At the same time, Mary McLeod Bethune was ready to push her students up the academic ladder.

Florida needed African American teachers. So Bethune began to coordinate her school's curriculum. She wanted it to become a junior college to train teachers. In 1923 she took the first step. Her school joined with the Cookman Institute. This new high school served both boys and girls. The changes had begun.

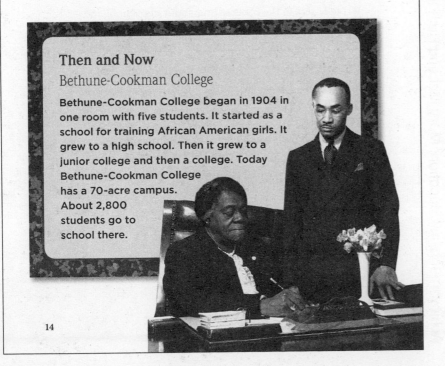

Then and Now
Bethune-Cookman College

Bethune-Cookman College began in 1904 in one room with five students. It started as a school for training African American girls. It grew to a high school. Then it grew to a junior college and then a college. Today Bethune-Cookman College has a 70-acre campus. About 2,800 students go to school there.

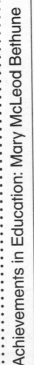
Mary McLeod Bethune planned to teach her students just as she'd been taught. They'd learn reading, writing, and other school subjects. They'd also learn to cook and sew and do laundry. These were practical skills they could use later. Mary McLeod Bethune believed it was the best way for African Americans to get ahead.

Little by little the school grew. More students enrolled. She hired teachers and found a bigger home for her school. She added more academic classes. She added upper grades. Soon Mary McLeod Bethune was running a high school. And it was still growing.

Booker T. Washington

Booker T. Washington was born into slavery. Like Mary he hungered for an education. Once freed he worked days as a janitor. At night he went to school to become a teacher. In 1881 he became the president of a new school for African Americans. Today it's known as Tuskegee University. Washington influenced Mary McLeod Bethune's ideas about education.

Daytona Educational and Industrial Training School for Negro Girls		
	Day pupils	Boarding pupils
Entrance fee	$2.00	$2.00
Tuition (per month):		
Under age 12	$1.50	$10.00
Above age 12	$1.50	$9.00
Vocal music lessons	Free	Free
Instrumental music lessons (per month)	$3.00	$2.00

These were the student costs for 1910–1911.

Despite her success, there was never enough money to run the school. Tuition from her students helped but didn't come close to covering her costs. Mary McLeod Bethune relied on donations to keep her school going. Community members helped out when they could. They fixed the roof. They gave her dishes. Men whom she taught to read paid her as they got paid. But Mary needed big money for her big dreams.

Many wealthy white people had homes in Daytona Beach. Mary knew this when she started her school there. Armed with her positive attitude and the power of her personality, she set out to convince them to give to her school. She'd make the rich and powerful believe in her dream, too.

James N. Gamble of Proctor and Gamble was one of the first people who agreed to help her. When she asked him to be a school trustee, he looked at her few students. He looked at the boxes and crates they used as tables and benches. Then he asked her what she wanted him to be trustee of. Mary McLeod Bethune told him that she wanted him to be the trustee of her school as she planned it for the future. Mr. Gamble trusted Mary and her dream. For the next twenty years, he was chairman of the school's Trustee Board.

Mary McLeod Bethune needed people like James N. Gamble. They wrote and donated money and supplies to the school. But the school's expenses never seemed to end. So Mary had to press other people for money. She wrote letters to the press telling about her school and the need for money. She wrote to local newspapers and the *New York Times* alike. Her struggle for money was constant.

As her school experienced moderate success, Mary McLeod Bethune put more focus on traditional academic skills and less on homemaking skills, such as sewing.

13

Word Workout

WORDS TO KNOW

adept	demonstration	maneuvered
prominent	collective	luxury
prevail	spectators	

Word Race How many of these words can we use in a conversation in just one minute? Let's start talking—right now!

SPELLING WORDS

compete	competition	moment	momentous
reside	resident	ignite	ignition
final	finality	metal	metallic
nation	nationality	crime	criminal
origin	original	refer	reference

Strange Changes I'll say a word and you say the other form of the word. Notice how the sound of the vowel changes. Spell the other form aloud.

© Macmillan/McGraw-Hill

·······(fold here)·······

Home-School Connection

Dear Family Member:

Few people in 1891 could afford a bicycle. That's why it was even more surprising that Marshall Taylor, an African-American boy, became one of the greatest cyclists of his time. This week we're reading a biography—*Major Taylor, Champion Cyclist*—that tells about Taylor's extraordinary accomplishments. The facts of the story speak for themselves. I am really impressed by Taylor's skill, but also by his determination. As I read, I can form my own opinions about this American athlete. I can also learn to recognize which of the writer's statements are facts and which are opinions.

This Week's Skills

Comprehension: fact and opinion

Vocabulary: analogies

Spelling/Phonics: vowels

Name _____

When Facts Are Few

It's a good idea to back up your opinions with facts. However, people don't always have good reasons for their opinions. This puzzle ends with a secret quotation about this topic.

Read the clues and circle the twelve words that complete the sentences below. From the puzzle, write the letters that are not circled to find the quotation.

1. A fact is something that can be _____.

2. When _____ knocks, be ready to answer.

3. The course of a bicycle race can be called the _____. It rhymes with toot.

4. You need a _____ to drive a car.

5. The opposite of oldest is _____.

6. A bicycle has two _____.

7. The first bicycles did not have _____ you can shift.

8. The opposite of exterior is _____.

9. Someone who rides a bicycle is called a _____.

10. You use the _____ to stop a bicycle you are riding.

11. A _____ is someone who gives a speech.

12. Alpha Centauri is a _____.

T	H	O	P	P	O	R	T	U	N	I	T	Y
E	L	F	R	E	W	O	E	C	R	N	T	O
B	I	H	O	E	F	U	A	Y	C	T	T	U
R	C	S	V	T	H	T	G	C	E	E	S	N
A	E	T	E	W	H	E	E	L	S	R	R	G
K	N	O	D	N	G	E	A	I	R	I	T	E
E	S	P	E	A	K	E	R	S	H	O	E	S
O	E	P	I	N	I	O	S	T	A	R	N	T

___ ___ ___   ___ ___ ___ ___ ___

___ ___ ___   ___ ___ ___ ___ ___ ___'

___ ___ ___

___ ___ ___ ___ ___ ___ ___

___ ___ ___

___ ___ ___ ___ ___ ___ ___ ___.

—Arnold Glasow

Ejercicio de palabras

PALABRAS DE VOCABULARIO

adept	demonstration	maneuvered
prominent	collective	luxury
prevail	spectators	

Carrera de palabras ¿Cuántas de las palabras de arriba podemos usar en una conversación de sólo un minuto? Comencemos a hablar... ¡ahora mismo!

PALABRAS DE ORTOGRAFÍA

compete	competition	moment	momentous
reside	resident	ignite	ignition
final	finality	metal	metallic
nation	nationality	crime	criminal
origin	original	refer	reference

Cambios extraños Te voy a decir una palabra y tú dirás la otra forma de la palabra. Observa cómo cambia el sonido de la vocal. Deletrea en voz alta la otra forma de la palabra.

(fold here)

© Macmillan/McGraw-Hill

Conexión con el hogar

Queridos familiares:

No había muchas personas en 1891 que pudieran comprarse una bicicleta. Por eso es tan sorprendente que Marshall Taylor, un joven afroamericano, llegara a ser uno de los más grandes ciclistas de todos los tiempos. Esta semana estamos leyendo una biografía —*Major Taylor, Champion Cyclist*— que habla de los logros extraordinarios de Taylor. Los hechos de esta historia hablan por sí mismos. Me impresiona mucho la destreza de Taylor, pero también su determinación. Mientras leo, puedo formarme mi propia opinión sobre este atleta estadounidense. También puedo aprender a reconocer cuáles de los enunciados del autor son hechos y cuáles son opiniones.

Destrezas de la semana

Comprensión: hecho y opinión

Vocabulario: analogías

Ortografía/Fonética: vocales

Nombre _____

Cuando los hechos son pocos

Es una buena idea basar tus opiniones en hechos. Pero la gente no siempre tiene una buena razón para sus opiniones. Este acertijo termina con una cita sobre el tema.

Read the clues and circle the twelve words that complete the sentences below. From the puzzle, write the letters that are not circled to find the quotation.

1. A fact is something that can be _____ .

2. When _____ knocks, be ready to answer.

3. The course of a bicycle race can be called the _____ . It rhymes with toot.

4. You need a _____ to drive a car.

5. The opposite of oldest is _____ .

6. A bicycle has two _____ .

7. The first bicycles did not have _____ you can shift.

8. The opposite of exterior is _____ .

9. Someone who rides a bicycle is called a _____ .

10. You use the _____ to stop a bicycle you are riding.

11. A _____ is someone who gives a speech.

12. Alpha Centauri is a _____ .

```
T H O P P O R T U N I T Y
E L F R E W O E C R N T O
B I H O E F U A Y C T T U
R C S V T H T G C E E S N
A E T E W H E E L S R R G
K N O D N G E A I R I T E
E S P E A K E R S H O E S
O E P I N I O S T A R N T
```

___ ___ ___ ___ ___ ___ ___

___ ___ ___ ___ ___ ___ ___ ___ ,

___ ___ ___

___ ___ ___ ___ ___ ___ ___

___ ___ ___

___ ___ ___ ___ ___ ___ ___ .

—Arnold Glasow

284

Comprehension Check

Summarize

Use a Fact and Opinion Chart to help you retell key events in Lance Armstrong's life. Then use your chart to give a short oral report on Lance Armstrong. How will you use the author's opinions in your report?

Fact	Opinion

Think and Compare

1. Look at pages 6–7. Think about how the author describes Lance Armstrong. Identify which of the author's statements are facts and which are opinions. Why doesn't the author use only facts in writing this book? *(Author's Purpose)*

2. People's attitudes towards bikes have changed over the years. How do you think a champion like Lance Armstrong influences people's attitudes towards cycling? How has he influenced your attitude toward cycling? *(Evaluate/Apply)*

3. Cycling helps the environment as well as people's health. Do you think that more people should use bikes as a method of transportation? Why or why not? Use the text to support your opinions. *(Analyze)*

Lance Armstrong
Racing into Bicycling History

by Karen M. Howard

Table of Contents

Introduction

Did you know that the first bicycles were for sport and pleasure? Some of the earliest bikes were luxury toys for the rich. Today people ride bikes for many different reasons. Children ride bikes for fun. Your mom or dad may ride to work or to the store. Some people, such as bicycle messengers, even use bikes to do their job.

The **professional** cyclist made the sport of cycling popular. These athletes spend their time training and competing in national and international cycling events. They appear on television. They are front-page news in newspapers. Some have become the new athletes of the year in sports magazines.

© 2007 Macmillan/McGraw-Hill   Lance Armstrong Racing into Bicycling History

Index

Glossary

aerobics *(ayr-OH-biks)* exercises that help the body to take in and use more oxygen; they can strengthen the heart and lungs. *(page 7)*

amateur *(AM-uh-chur)* a person who does something for the pleasure of doing it, not for pay *(page 9)*

chemotherapy *(kee-moh-THER-uh-pee)* the use of chemical substances to treat diseases, such as cancer *(page 14)*

Olympian *(oh-LIM-pee-uhn)* an athlete who has competed in the Olympic Games *(page 6)*

professional *(pruh-FESH-uh-nuhl)* a person who works for money doing something that other people do for fun *(page 2)*

pro circuit *(PROH SUR-kit)* short for professional circuit; the races in which professional athletes compete *(page 10)*

rank *(RANGK)* to have a certain position or grade *(page 11)*

stage *(STAYJ)* in cycling, to stop at a designated place in the course of a race *(page 11)*

survivor *(suhr-VIGH-vur)* someone who lives through a life-threatening challenge *(page 6)*

therapy *(THE-ruh-pee)* treatment for a disability, injury, or illness *(page 15)*

triathlete *(trigh-ATH-leet)* someone who competes in a triathlon *(page 7)*

triathlon *(trigh-ATH-lon)* an athletic contest in which participants compete without stopping in three successive events, usually long-distance swimming, bicycling, and running *(page 7)*

© 2007 Macmillan/McGraw-Hill

Lance Armstrong Racing into Bicycling History

But there is one professional cyclist who changed cycling history. He is Lance Armstrong. He won the Tour de France six times. The Tour de France is the greatest race in cycling. No one has ever won this race so many times. But there's more. In the midst of his cycling career, Lance had to overcome cancer. As a cancer survivor, Mr. Armstrong made the greatest comeback in cycling history.

History of Cycling

Most of Lance's racing bikes are sleek and incredibly lightweight. This is quite a dramatic change from early bicycles.

In 1817 Baron von Drais invented a walking machine to help him move at the swift speed of 8 miles per hour (mph) around the gardens of Baden, Germany. This machine was known as the Draisienne, or hobby horse. It was one of the earliest bicycles.

Then, in 1865, a French mechanic named Pierre Michaux produced a wooden vehicle that riders could pedal, called a "boneshaker."

Boneshakers were very popular. But they were painful to ride on bumpy streets. Indoor tracks, much like skating rinks today, were better for riding boneshakers. Then, in 1870, the speedy high-wheel bicycle was invented. Designs continued to change over the years because riders wanted fast, comfortable bikes.

© 2007 Macmillan/McGraw-Hill

Lance Armstrong Racing into Bicycling History

Cancer was the shadow over Lance's career, but it also changed Lance's life. Coming close to dying gave him a new will to live. Armstrong made a decision to train the right way. He had a new zeal for life, and life for Lance was racing. His family and friends told him he could do it. To the amazement of all, Lance beat his cancer. Wanting to help others, he founded the Lance Armstrong Foundation (LAF) in 1997. The LAF provides services for cancer survivors and funds cancer research.

Six-time winner of the Tour de France, Lance would be the first to say that his winning the race against cancer made him a true champion.

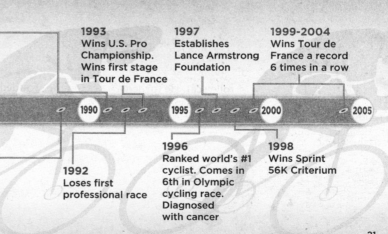

1993 Wins U.S. Pro Championship. Wins first stage in Tour de France

1997 Establishes Lance Armstrong Foundation

1999-2004 Wins Tour de France a record 6 times in a row

1990   1995   2000   2005

1992 Loses first professional race

1996 Ranked world's #1 cyclist. Comes in 6th in Olympic cycling race. Diagnosed with cancer

1998 Wins Sprint 56K Criterium

Conclusion

Bicycle racing has a long history, but one racer stands above the rest. Lance Armstrong became a champion at an early age. He worked hard to be named the king of racing. Good training and a determined spirit made him unbeatable. Lance chose his battles. The one battle he did not choose was the toughest to win.

Lance Armstrong's Life

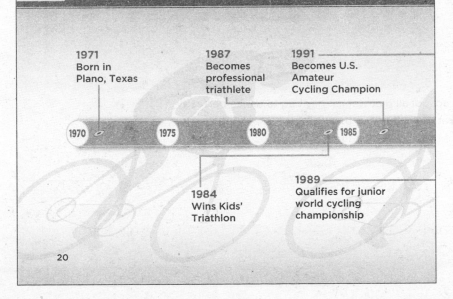

1971
Born in Plano, Texas

1987
Becomes professional triathlete

1991
Becomes U.S. Amateur Cycling Champion

1970   1975   1980   1985

1984
Wins Kids' Triathlon

1989
Qualifies for junior world cycling championship

Lance Armstrong Racing into Bicycling History

CHAPTER 1

Meet Lance Armstrong

Bicycling has been a sport for over 150 years. There have been many winning racers. But none of them has captured the world's attention like Lance Armstrong. Armstrong's record in national and world cycling events is unbeaten. Lance is a two-time **Olympian** champion. He is a cancer **survivor** and a role model. He is the prominent six-time winner of the Tour de France. His demonstration of superb athletic ability and courage in facing a terrible illness has won him legions of fans.

6

19

Lance began preparing for the Tour. An American, Greg LeMond, had won three times riding with the French. But Lance's team (USPS) was the first American team to make winning the Tour a goal.

Lance resumed his tough training schedule, strict diet, and four to five hours a day of riding. Training for the Tour also meant entering various races. He chose only the events that would groom him for victory. Lance felt renewed. He had gained back much of his strength and was training even harder than he had before his illness. Early morning training included breakfast, weight lifting, and aerobics. In the afternoon, Lance would ride four to five hours over steep hills and across flat land.

Lance's hard work paid off. He rode across the finish line in Paris a winner. He beat his nearest competitor by seven minutes. This win was not only a great victory for Lance Armstrong, it was a triumph for cancer survivors all over the world. Lance continued to win many races. He conquered the Tour de France five more times, making him the greatest athlete in the sport of cycling.

Lance crosses the victory line for ↻ the Tour de France in Paris, 2004.

Lance Armstrong was born on September 18, 1971, in Plano, Texas. His mother, Linda, loved him dearly, but he was a difficult child. He had his own opinions about things and went his own way. He was a very active boy. Lance's mother encouraged her son to try many sports.

Lance got his first bike when he was seven. He loved to ride. Lance has said that he was "born to race bikes." Lance was a good swimmer, too. By age 13, he had won the Kids' Triathlon. A **triathlon** is an event that includes biking, running, and swimming. Lance became a professional **triathlete** at 16.

In 1987 Lance went to the Cooper Institute in Dallas, Texas. This research center was one of the first to explore the bond between fitness and **aerobics**. Everyone uses oxygen to break down food into energy. The more oxygen you use, the faster you can run, ride, or swim. Lance was given a test to measure how much oxygen he used when he worked out. The results were shocking. His scores ranked him number one, above everyone who had ever taken the test!

Eventually, Lance chose cycling over swimming and running. While he was in high school, many people wanted to sponsor him in racing events. His fast-growing career as a cyclist was taking over his life.

King Harald V of Norway congratulates Lance after a big win.

During Lance's senior year, most of his classmates were preparing for the prom and graduation. Not Lance! He was training with the U.S. Olympic Development Team. Lance almost did not graduate from high school because of his busy schedule. He had to have private lessons late in his senior year to get his high school diploma.

Lance was a talented cyclist. He had a strong heart. Armstrong's thighbones were very long, which made applying pressure to the pedal easy for him. He was not easy to train, though. His coach complained that Lance did not eat right and did not keep to his schedule. He started training for his races too late. He was still able to win one-day races, but he wore down too early in longer trials. He was rude and thought he knew all he needed to know about biking.

Tour de France

UK   GERMANY

Paris

Alps

FRANCE

Atlantic Ocean

SPAIN   Pyrenees   Mediterranean Sea

- - - - -
Tour de France Route

Did You Know?

- The Tour de France has 20 stages.

- The race covers more than 2,000 miles.

- The mountain stage through the Pyrenees was added in 1910.

- The mountain stage through the Alps was added in 1911.

- Team leaders started wearing yellow jerseys in 1919 so spectators could see which team was winning.

Tour de France

The first Tour de France was held in 1903. *L'Auto*, a French newspaper, wanted to attract more readers. One of the writers suggested a bicycle race. This race would be different because it would not take place on a track. Instead the riders maneuvered their bikes through towns and along roads in the countryside. Maurice Garin won the first Tour with 20,000 spectators greeting him in Paris. He won more than $3,000, a lot of money in those days, and *L'Auto* got 100,000 new readers.

CHAPTER 3

The Tour de France

Lance made a comeback to U.S. cycling in 1998 when he won the Sprint 56K Criterium in the streets of downtown Austin, Texas. Riding for the U.S. Postal Service (USPS) pro-cycling team, Lance entered the Paris-Nice Tour. The cold, rainy weather reminded him of his first professional race, which he had lost. Feeling defeated, Lance pulled over to the side of the road and gave up. Lance thought his pro-cycling career was over.

But his teammates and friends would not let Lance quit. They knew there was one goal that Lance still had to achieve: to win the Tour de France. In 1999 Lance made the decision that he and the USPS team would enter the Tour de France.

16

Lance left Plano after high school to go to Moscow, Russia. He had qualified for the 1989 junior world championship. The shy Texan boy was a long way from home. But Armstrong was beginning to meet people who could help him in the cycling world. His cycling career continued to grow. By 1991 he was the U.S. Amateur Champion. His short **amateur** career would end the following year at the Olympic Games in Barcelona.

Olympic Bicycle Racing

The first cycling event in the Olympics was road racing. In 1896 cyclists raced about 54 miles over two laps. Today the Olympic bicycle road-racing program has four events.

9

Until now Lance had easily won his amateur races. However, professional cycling would prove much more challenging. On a cold, rainy day in Spain, Lance lost his first professional race. The year was 1992. Lance crossed the finish line 27 minutes too late. Crushed, Lance wanted to end his professional career that day. As an amateur Lance had always won. He was not used to defeat. His mother encouraged him to stay on the **pro circuit**. Lance learned an important lesson that day, which was never to quit.

Lance did prevail the following year. He won 10 titles, including the U.S. Pro Championship.

© 2007 Macmillan/McGraw-Hill

Lance Armstrong Racing into Bicycling History

Cancer left Lance's body in poor physical shape. He briefly lost his passion for cycling. Then, a mere five months after being sick, Lance tried riding his bike again. It was hard, but Lance said getting cancer was ". . . the best thing that ever happened to me." Cancer gave Lance a second chance to appreciate good health, family, and friends.

What Is Chemotherapy?

Chemotherapy uses drugs to treat cancer. Cancer cells divide quickly in your body. The drugs stop cancer cells from dividing and kills them. A doctor puts the patient on a course of drugs. A full course of drug **therapy** can be four to eight cycles, which can take weeks or months. The treatment can make you sick to your stomach, cause hair loss, and leave you very tired. Once the cancer cells are dead and the chemotherapy is completed, you slowly begin to feel better.

Lance was now at the top of his game. No one could doubt that he was a gifted athlete. But his good fortune was about to change. A month after turning 25, Lance didn't feel well. Parts of his body were sore. One evening while talking to a friend, he had a metallic taste in the back of his throat. He coughed into the bathroom sink. He splattered the sink with blood. Lance learned that he had a cancer common to men. Doctors told him that it had spread to his lungs and brain. Lance was seriously ill. His only hope was to undergo an aggressive form of **chemotherapy**, a drug treatment called chemo for short.

Lance underwent two operations in two weeks, one to remove the cancerous lump and the other on his brain. The collective, or group, opinion of the medical experts was that Lance had a 40–60 percent chance of living. The chemo made him very weak. The drugs sapped his strength and left burns on his body. However, with the support of his family and friends, Lance held onto a lesson his mother had taught him. Do not quit!

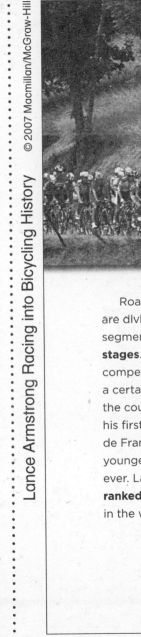

Lance cycles to raise money ↻ for cancer survivors.

Road races are divided into segments, called **stages**. Riders compete to arrive at a certain point along the course. Lance won his first stage in the Tour de France. That made him the youngest road-racing champion ever. Lance's Team Motorola was **ranked** as one of the top five teams in the world.

Team Motorola was the first United States ↻ team to rank in the top five.

CHAPTER 2

Training a Champion

Champions as adept as Lance do not simply appear in a race and win overnight. Lance began training in November for the Tour de France in July 1994. He had a training coach who helped him prepare for the race. Lance trained from Monday through Saturday. He rode two to five hours per day. Lifting weights was part of his program. Aerobic exercises helped to strengthen his heart and lungs. Lance learned the hard way that in order to be a champion, you have to follow a strict training schedule.

By 1996 Lance Armstrong was the world's number one cyclist. He raced with the U.S. cycling team in the summer Olympic Games that year. He was America's best cyclist, finishing the 32-mile cycling race in sixth place.

His ongoing success led the French Cofidis racing team to give Lance a $2 million contract to race with them. Lance wanted to use this money to give his mother something. After two years of planning, Lance moved his mother into a new home that he had bought for her in Austin, Texas. He called it "Casa Linda" in her honor.

Lance's Typical Weekly Training Schedule

MONDAY
Morning: weight workout
1-hour ride to and from weight workout. Stay seated on all hills. Include 4–5 power starts of 10 seconds each on ride home.

TUESDAY
3-hour ride at moderate pace. Stay seated on all hills.

WEDNESDAY
Weight workout only

THURSDAY
3-hour ride at moderate pace. Stay seated on all hills.

FRIDAY
Morning: weight workout
1-hour ride to and from weight workout. Stay seated on all hills. Include 4–5 power starts of 10 seconds each on ride home.

SATURDAY
4-hour ride at moderate pace. Stay seated on all hills.

SUNDAY
Day off

Word Workout

WORDS TO KNOW

arid	ceramics	derision	furrowed
benefit	deftly	eaves	symmetry

A Word to the Wise Choose a word. Give me one-word clues until I guess the word. How many clues will I need? Then we'll swap places.

SPELLING WORDS

crumb	solemn	reject	public
magic	crumble	solemnity	rejection
publicity	magician	design	muscle
create	prejudice	office	designate
muscular	creation	prejudicial	official

Additional Words We can use math symbols to write spelling sentences. For example: *prejudice* + *ial* = *prejudicial*. How many math sentences do we need to include all of the list words?

© Macmillan/McGraw-Hill

(fold here)

Home-School Connection

Dear Family Member:

I know that to achieve a goal I have to work and focus my energy. That is exactly what the hero of *A Single Shard* does. He is an orphan living in Korea in the twelfth century. More than anything, he wants to become a potter. It is a difficult goal and I hope he can reach it.

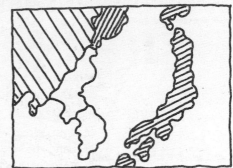

As we read this story, we're learning to think about the author's perspective. The writer's point of view is reflected in many different elements of the story.

This Week's Skills

Comprehension: author's perspective

Vocabulary: homophones

Spelling/Phonics: consonant alternation

Name _____

Attitude Check

When we read two articles about the same topic, differences in the authors' perspectives can be very clear. Let's read these articles together. Then we'll use the questions to compare them.

The Potter's Wheel

No one knows for sure where the potter's wheel was first developed. Many experts think that it was invented in Mesopotamia, while others claim that it happened in China or Egypt. No matter where it began, we are lucky that this marvelous invention has stood the test of time. Early potter's wheels were powered by the potter's feet. Some potter's today still enjoy the control and energy of foot-powered wheels. Others take the easy way out and use a motorized wheel.

The Potter's Wheel

The earliest potters used pottery wheels that were foot-powered. You used your feet to turn the wheel. As a modern potter, you have a choice. Some people still like to use foot-powered wheels. Others take advantage of electronic technology and use a motorized pottery wheel. The choice is personal, but in the end, surprisingly minor. Whether you use your feet or a motor, you still need to learn the same skills to create beautiful, functional pottery using a wheel.

If these two authors met, what do you think they might agree about? What might they argue about?

Ejercicio de palabras

PALABRAS DE VOCABULARIO

arid	ceramics	derision	furrowed
benefit	deftly	eaves	symmetry

Una palabra Escoge una palabra. Dame pistas de una sola palabra hasta que adivine cuál escogiste. ¿Cuántas pistas voy a necesitar? Después adivinas tú.

PALABRAS DE ORTOGRAFÍA

crumb	solemn	reject	public
magic	crumble	solemnity	rejection
publicity	magician	design	muscle
create	prejudice	office	designate
muscular	creation	prejudicial	official

Oraciones matemáticas Podemos usar símbolos matemáticos para escribir oraciones. Por ejemplo: *prejudice + ial = prejudicial.* ¿Cuántas oraciones matemáticas necesitamos para incluir todas las palabras de la lista?

© Macmillan/McGraw-Hill

(fold here)

Conexión con el hogar

Queridos familiares:

Sé que para alcanzar una meta, debo trabajar y concentrar mi energía. Eso es exactamente lo que hace el protagonista de *A Single Shard*. Se trata de un huérfano que vive en Corea en el Siglo XII. Lo que más quiere es ser alfarero. Es una meta difícil y espero que pueda lograrla.

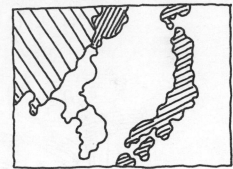

Mientras leemos este relato, aprendemos a considerar la perspectiva del autor. El punto de vista del escritor se refleja en muchos elementos del cuento.

Destrezas de la semana

Comprensión: perspectiva del autor

Vocabulario: homófonos

Ortografía/Fonética: alternación de consonantes

Nombre _____

Control de actitud

Cuando leemos dos artículos sobre el mismo tema, las diferencias entre las perspectivas de los autores pueden ser muy claras. Vamos a leer estos artículos juntos. Luego los compararemos por medio de las preguntas.

The Potter's Wheel

No one knows for sure where the potter's wheel was first developed. Many experts think that it was invented in Mesopotamia, while others claim that it happened in China or Egypt. No matter where it began, we are lucky that this marvelous invention has stood the test of time. Early potter's wheels were powered by the potter's feet. Some potter's today still enjoy the control and energy of foot-powered wheels. Others take the easy way out and use a motorized wheel.

The Potter's Wheel

The earliest potters used pottery wheels that were foot-powered. You used your feet to turn the wheel. As a modern potter, you have a choice. Some people still like to use foot-powered wheels. Others take advantage of electronic technology and use a motorized pottery wheel. The choice is personal, but in the end, surprisingly minor. Whether you use your feet or a motor, you still need to learn the same skills to create beautiful, functional pottery using a wheel.

If these two authors met, what do you think they might agree about? What might they argue about?

Comprehension Check

Summarize

Use an Author's Perspective Web to summarize the main idea of each chapter of *Crafts in Medieval Europe*.

Think and Compare

1. Look back at page 4. What is the author's perspective on life and work in a medieval town? What does the author want the reader to understand about this way of life? **(Author's Perspective)**

2. Do you know or would you like to learn a craft such as carpentry or pottery-making? Why or why not? **(Apply)**

3. Today machines make many of the things that individual craftspeople once made. What do you think are the good and bad aspects of this change? **(Evaluate)**

24

CRAFTS IN MEDIEVAL EUROPE

by Barbara Brooks Simon

Table of Contents

INTRODUCTION

During the Middle Ages, most people in Europe were farmers. They lived in villages on the estate of a noble. They grew crops and tended animals. They provided food for themselves and others. They also had to make by hand everything they wore or used. There were no machines.

At the same time, many men and women were skilled in various crafts. One person in a village, for instance, might be a weaver. Other villagers went to him or her for wool and linen cloth to make into clothing. Villagers also needed a carpenter to build their houses. They needed a blacksmith to make iron tools and nails.

2

Index

23

Glossary

apprentice *(uh-PREN-tis)* a young person bound by an agreement to work for a master for a certain time in return for learning a craft *(page 4)*

artisan *(AHR-tuh-zuhn)* a worker with skill in a specific craft *(page 4)*

barbarian *(bahr-BAYR-ee-uhn)* a person who belongs to a tribe or a people that is uncivilized *(page 3)*

guild *(GILD)* a professional association of craftspeople or merchants *(page 7)*

journeyman *(JUR-nee-muhn)* a worker who has completed an apprenticeship and works for a daily wage *(page 9)*

manor *(MAN-ur)* in the Middle Ages, the estate of a lord or knight, including the village and surrounding lands *(page 3)*

master *(MAS-tur)* a person who has great skill or knowledge about something *(page 8)*

medieval *(mee-dee-EE-vuhl)* related to the Middle Ages (A.D. 500–A.D. 1500) *(page 3)*

noble *(NOH-buhl)* a person of high rank *(page 3)*

solar *(SOH-lahr)* private family living quarters in a castle or manor *(page 15)*

tapestry *(TAP-uh-stree)* a heavy fabric with a woven design *(page 15)*

textile *(TEKS-tighl)* a woven or knitted fabric *(page 16)*

wage *(WAYJ)* the money a person is paid for work *(page 7)*

As time passed, more people needed the things made by these craftspeople, such as cloth and tools. So some people stopped farming and worked at their craft. People began to depend on the work of skilled craftspeople. The craftspeople became more specialized, and the number of different crafts grew. Medieval craftspeople made everything from arrows and armor to wheels and woolen cloth.

THE MIDDLE AGES

The Middle Ages in Europe lasted from about A.D. 500 to A.D. 1500. In many places, this was a time of war and lawlessness. **Barbarians** invaded by land and sea. To defend themselves and keep order in society, powerful lords and **nobles** built castles and **manor** houses. Ordinary people looked to these lords for protection. In exchange, they promised the lords loyalty and labor. The term **medieval** means "related to the Middle Ages."

Chapter 1

MEDIEVAL CRAFTSPEOPLE

I f you could stroll down the narrow streets of a medieval town, you would see the hundreds of crafts that medieval men and women practiced. Many craftspeople, or **artisans**, sold goods out of their workshops. Other people opened shops that sold other artisans' handiwork. Mercers and drapers, for instance, sold cloth made by home weavers.

On your walk down the medieval street, you'd pass the shops of a carpenter and a cutler, who made knives. On the next street, you could buy loaves of bread from the woman who baked them.

You might stop for a minute at the shop of the joiner. He is a woodworker who makes chests, beds, and beautiful paneling. An **apprentice** is carefully smoothing the surface of an oak chest with a plane. The master himself is drawing a pattern for the carved decorations on a bed.

Walking on, you stroll off the street and into a yard where people are dyeing woolen cloth. Medieval people loved bright-colored clothing. Lengths of finished cloth—green, blue, scarlet—are hanging out to dry.

On a medieval street, shoppers could ↻ find almost anything they might need.

Crafts in Medieval Europe

CONCLUSION

Everything that the people of the Middle Ages used or wore had to be made by a craftsperson. Today you can often buy nearly everything you want in a single store. Just imagine having to go to five separate artisans' shops to buy everyday items such as nails, buttons, shoes, gloves, or chairs.

Making cloth, for instance, took the work of at least five or six different craft guilds. Some artisans were self-taught, but many went through a long and difficult course of apprenticeship with a master. They had simple tools but great skill.

At the same time, medieval craftspeople worked to make things that were beautiful as well as useful. These "pieces from the past," such as rich tapestries, still give people pleasure today.

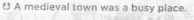

↻ A medieval town was a busy place.

🔊 This panel from the Bayeux Tapestry shows the soldiers sailing to England.

One of the most famous pieces of medieval needlework is the *Bayeux* (bigh-YEW) *Tapestry*. It is not really a tapestry but a 230-foot-long piece of embroidered linen. It includes 58 panels like those in a comic strip. They tell the story of the Norman Conquest of England in 1066. Above each scene, a caption explains what is happening. Borders at the top and bottom picture camels, lions, birds, dragons, and other fantastic animals.

The tapestry was probably made soon after the Norman Conquest. The women who embroidered it used eight vivid colors of wool yarn: blues, reds, yellow, green, black, and dove-gray. They are still bright after more than 900 years.

One scholar counted the creatures in the tapestry. He found 202 horses and mules, 55 dogs, and more than 500 other animals! Scenes of everyday life form the background for battles. Today the tapestry is on display at a museum in Bayeux, France.

© 2007 Macmillan/McGraw-Hill

⑤

Remember that *someone* made everything people used or wore. Most clothing was sewn at home. But before making clothes, you had to visit several different craftspeople. First, people bought linen, wool, or silk cloth from weavers or drapers. Then they bought needles, thread, buttons, and ribbons or lace from all the different artisans who made them. They went to a cobbler or leather-worker for shoes and boots.

All of the dishes you used were made by hand, too. Potters made jugs and pitchers. Some made fine ceramic dishes. Families displayed them on a sideboard. This showed that they could afford beautiful things. Others made decorative tiles for floors and fireplaces.

WHAT'S IN A NAME?

The last names of families in England often came from their craft. It's easy to identify the work of people named *Baker*, *Weaver*, or *Carpenter*. Do you know anyone with these names?

• A *Smith* was anyone who worked with metal.

• A *Fletcher* made arrows.

• A *Thatcher* made thatched roofs with wide eaves using straw or reeds.

• A *Cooper* made wooden tubs or barrels.

© 2007 Macmillan/McGraw-Hill

Weavers used wool thread for most tapestries. But they also used silk and linen thread to create different textures or special effects. In tapestries for kings and nobles, weavers added richness with glittering gold and silver threads.

Today you can view many beautiful old tapestries in museums. Museums hang their tapestries on walls in the same manner that medieval lords hung them on their castle walls.

One American museum, the Cloisters, is part of the Metropolitan Museum of Art in New York. Some of its most popular attractions are two famous sets of tapestries. They are the *Unicorn Tapestries* and the *Nine Heroes Tapestries*.

The myth of the unicorn fascinated medieval artisans and artists. Unicorns often appear in their work. The *Unicorn Tapestries* are thought to have been designed in France and probably made in Belgium. The seven tapestries portray different scenes from various unicorn myths. The tapestries may have belonged to Anne of Brittany, who was twice queen of France, but no one is sure. The *Nine Heroes Tapestries* show heroes from history, including King Arthur. They were probably made in the 1300s.

↻ The Cloisters in New York houses over 5,000 works of art from medieval Europe. The pieces date from A.D. 300 to the 1400s.

⊙ Displaying pottery showed wealth.

⊙ Tailors made clothes. Each garment was made individually to fit the person.

As the Middle Ages went on, trade increased. People in towns had more money to buy the work of craftspeople. The number of crafts grew, too. Craftsmen and merchants formed organizations called **guilds**. By the 1400s, most large towns in Europe had craft guilds. Most of the members were men. Guilds became very important and powerful.

Guilds set the hours when shops could be open. They agreed on the **wages** that workers would get and how much a craftsman could charge for work. They also helped members who were sick and looked after the families of masters who had died. In some ways guilds were like today's labor unions.

ARTISAN'S TOOLS

Tools were very precious to medieval artisans. In a fifteenth-century poem, carpenter's tools were the characters. Here is a speech from a wimble—a sharp-pointed tool for boring holes in wood:

Yes, yes, said the wimble,

I am as round as a thimble;

My master's work I will remember,

I shall creep fast into the timber.

Getting into the guild was hard. But many young people tried. They studied and trained with an older, skilled teacher, or **master**. They got the benefit of the teacher's knowledge.

The first step was to become an apprentice. The apprentice had to find a master. A master was a well-established member of the guild. The apprentice became a part of the master's household. He did the worst jobs, such as sweeping the workshop or making the fires in a pottery kiln.

Apprentices started at about 13 or 14 years old. They grew up with the master's family, not their own. While learning his craft, the apprentice also learned proper manners and behavior. The apprentices were not paid for their work.

This journeyman helps create a sword. ↪
Sword smithing was an important craft.

© 2007 Macmillan/McGraw-Hill

Crafts in Medieval Europe

Tapestries were both beautiful and practical. Castles and manor houses were built of stone. Whether they stood on an arid heath or in a green valley, they were cold and drafty. In winter a fire blazed on a hearth in the center of the Great Hall. But it was not enough to warm the cold stone walls and floor.

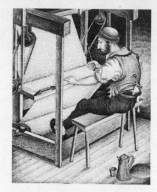

↩ A weaver works at his craft.

Often the women of the manor wove tapestries to hang on the walls. They kept in the heat from the fires in the room and blocked cold air from the outside. Sometimes noble families ordered a set of tapestries from a weaving workshop.

Weaving tapestries took a special technique and great skill. Usually a painter made a sketch of the design. Patterns had color and symmetry. Often the background was full of charming animals, flowers, trees, and shrubs. Weavers followed the artist's sketch, but they added their own ideas and creativity.

↩ Tapestries told stories. Unicorn myths were a common subject.

Chapter 3

TEXTILES AND TAPESTRIES

Making **textiles**—woven or knitted fabrics—was an important craft in medieval Europe. A special kind of weaving technique created tapestries. These thick, woven wall hangings show scenes or geometric patterns. Tapestries were often designed in sets of several panels. They were woven to fit the walls of a room. Each set followed a theme or told a story from history or mythology. Many famous tapestries illustrate Greek myths.

16

An apprentice worked for about seven years. Then he became a **journeyman**. Now, at last, he was getting paid for his work!

Many craftsmen stayed journeymen for their entire lives. Others took the next step toward becoming a master. They created and presented a masterpiece or well-made piece of work.

The masters of the guild judged the journeyman's work. If it failed, he might face the scorn and derision of his fellow craftsmen. If it passed, the journeyman became a master. Now he could own tools. He could hire apprentices and open his own shop.

9

Chapter 2

WOMEN AT WORK

Women in the towns worked in almost every craft field. They were barbers, butchers, goldsmiths, and glove-makers. In the working classes, both married and single women had to work to earn a living. They made up half the working world. Many women worked as servants in upper-class households. Others were skilled craftspeople.

Because most artisans had their workrooms at home, many women took part in a family business. A craftsman's wife and daughters helped him in the workshop, along with his apprentices and journeymen.

10

Outside the towns, the center of economic life was the manor. A manor was the estate of a medieval lord or noble. The lord owned the village and all the surrounding fields and forests. The manor was a small world all its own. Its people grew or made almost everything that the lord and lady, their family, and the villagers needed.

Women on the manor needed many skills. The lady of the manor, her daughters, and female servants spun wool or linen fibers into thread. Then they wove fabric for clothing and household linens and dyed it with natural colors. Then they sewed shirts, trousers, jackets, and dresses. They also made their own soap, candles, cosmetics, and medicines.

The women of the household also wove woolen **tapestries** and painted linen wall hangings. These hung on the cold stone walls of the Great Hall and the **solar**. The solar was the family's private living quarters. On cold winter evenings, wall hangings made these rooms brighter and more comfortable.

15

LIFE ON A MEDIEVAL MANOR

The lord's stone manor house or castle was the center of life on the manor. A village, a church, and craftsmen's workshops clustered around it. Roads between towns were muddy and deeply furrowed. Travel was slow and difficult. As a result almost everything the manor needed—even large chests and beds—was made there. Usually a carpenter and a blacksmith lived in the village. There was usually a mill where the grain was ground into flour. Ordinary people seldom traveled far from their home village on the manor.

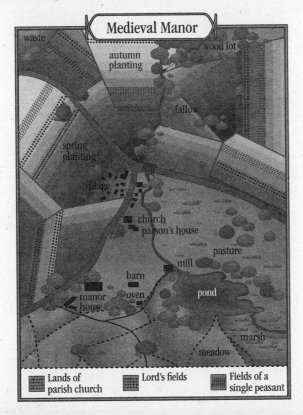

Medieval Manor

waste

autumn planting

wood lot

fallow

spring planting

village

church
parson's house

pasture

mill

barn
oven

manor
house

pond

marsh

meadow

| ▨ Lands of parish church | ▦ Lord's fields | ▨ Fields of a single peasant |

© 2007 Macmillan/McGraw-Hill

Crafts in Medieval Europe

MEDIEVAL BOOKS

Like everything else in the Middle Ages, books were made by hand. Many of the artisans in this field were women, often those who lived in convents, or religious communities. Scribes made copies of the text of a book. Another artisan made the ink. Artists painted colorful designs and pictures in the borders or on the pages. Female artisans also made elaborate embroidered cloth or leather book covers.

In a weaver's family, for instance, one of his daughters might design patterns. Then she would choose colors and buy colored wool from the dyer. Another daughter would card, or comb, wool fibers. She would deftly spin them into thread with a hand-held spindle. Other women in the household might be skillful weavers.

☢ Women sold meat, fish, and farm produce in the markets.

Other women—both married and single—set up their own businesses. Often these crafts related to food and clothing. Women made hats, gloves, purses, and caps. They were butchers and bakers, or "baxters." Female "brewsters" made beer. The women who brewed beer often were bakers as well. Bread and beer or ale were the basics of almost every medieval meal.

Women also made cloth. In England unmarried women called "spinsters" spun almost all linen thread and woolen yarn.

Female craftspeople also took and trained apprentices. Sometimes a father left money in his will to make sure that his daughters learned a trade or craft. Girls were mostly apprenticed to craftswomen.

In spite of all the work they did, few women were full members of the craft guilds. Most women who were listed as guild members were probably the widows of masters who had died. Still, a master's widow not only inherited the business. She also taught the apprentices and journeymen and kept the business running.

Women "websters" were ↻ prominent in the weaving industry.

Crafts in Medieval Europe

Word Workout

WORDS TO KNOW

illegally	mistreated	ruptured
migrant	reputation	uttered

Word Minute Let's improvise sentences for each word in one minute. How many times can we use each word in different sentences in that time?

SPELLING WORDS

lesson	isle	pane	vane	idle
lessen	navel	miner	vein	idol
aisle	naval	minor	principal	sheer
I'll	pain	vain	principle	shear

Hearing and Seeing These words are tricky because they sound the same but have different spellings. Give me a sentence with each word so I know which meaning you are using. Then I will spell the word.

© Macmillan/McGraw-Hill · (fold here)

Home-School Connection

Dear Family Member:

Moving to a new place can be difficult. Learning a new language adds to these challenges. This week, we are reading *Breaking Through*, a true story about a boy who moved to the United States from Mexico. He grew up to be a writer, but it was hard work for him learning to write in English. I think his story is inspiring for anyone. It gives me hope and makes me want to look for reading and writing opportunities I will enjoy. It also reinforced the knowledge I had about not giving up a goal. I bet the author would be happy with my response.

This Week's Skills

Comprehension: author's purpose

Vocabulary: word parts

Spelling/Phonics: homophones

Name _____

On Purpose

We can describe the different forms of writing we think each author will use. We can choose from the forms listed here or think of other forms a writer might use to create our own writing about Mexico.

Writing Forms

Article	Poem
Essay	Story
Letter	Biography
Editorial	Autobiography

• I want to persuade people to visit Mexico. It's an interesting and beautiful place to visit.

• Grandmother told me wonderful stories when I was growing up in Mexico. I want to share these exciting tales.

• There are differences between living in Mexico and living in the United States. I want to help people in both countries understand each other better.

• I have so many strong memories about the people and places I remember in Mexico. I would like to pay tribute to these memories.

An example

An author who wants to persuade people to visit Mexico might write an illustrated article for a travel magazine. The captions, text, and photos would all work together to show why readers should vacation there.

Ejercicio de palabras

PALABRAS DE VOCABULARIO

illegally   mistreated   ruptured

migrant   reputation   uttered

En un minuto Vamos a improvisar oraciones para cada palabra en sólo un minuto. ¿Cuántas veces podemos usar cada palabra en diferentes oraciones en ese período de tiempo?

PALABRAS DE ORTOGRAFÍA

lesson	isle	pane	vane	idle
lessen	navel	miner	vein	idol
aisle	naval	minor	principal	sheer
I'll	pain	vain	principle	shear

Clasifica y deletrea Estas palabras son engañosas porque suenan igual pero se escriben de forma diferente. Dame una oración con cada palabra para que yo sepa cuál es el significado que estás usando. Luego yo deletrearé la palabra.

······(fold here)······

Conexión con el hogar

Queridos familiares:

Mudarse a un lugar nuevo puede resultar difícil. Aprender otro idioma es un desafío más. Esta semana estamos leyendo *Breaking Through*, la verdadera historia de un niño que se mudó a Estados Unidos desde México. Cuando creció llegó a ser escritor, pero aprender a escribir en inglés no fue para él una tarea fácil. Pienso que su historia es motivo de inspiración para todos. Me da esperanzas y me impulsa a buscar diversas oportunidades para leer y escribir. También refuerza algo que yo ya sabía sobre no desistir cuando se tiene una meta. Me parece que el autor se alegraría al saber mi reacción.

Destrezas de la semana

Comprensión: propósito del autor

Vocabulario: partes de una palabra

Ortografía/Fonética: homófonos

Nombre_____

¿Qué propósito tiene?

¿Por qué escriben los escritores? Pueden tener muchísimas razones diferentes. Vamos a hablar de ellas. Para describir el tipo de texto que creemos que cada autor va a escribir podemos escoger entre los tipos mencionados aquí o pensar en otros.

Writing Forms

Article	Poem
Essay	Story
Letter	Biography
Editorial	Autobiography

- I want to persuade people to visit Mexico. It's an interesting and beautiful place to visit.
- Grandmother told me wonderful stories when I was growing up in Mexico. I want to share these exciting tales.

- There are differences between living in Mexico and living in the United States. I want to help people in both countries understand each other better.
- I have so many strong memories about the people and places I remember in Mexico. I would like to pay tribute to these memories.

An example

The author who wants to persuade people to visit Mexico might write an illustrated article for a travel magazine. The captions, text, and photos would all work together to show why readers should vacation there.

Comprehension Check

Summarize

What is the author's purpose in telling us this story? List clues from the story on your Author's Purpose Chart to support your ideas.

Clues	Author's Purpose

Think and Compare

1. Turn to page 17. Why do you think Mica chose this event to write about? Did you get to know Mica better by hearing her story? *(Evaluate Author's Purpose)*

2. Have you ever moved to another city and changed schools? If so, what did you do to get used to your new school? If not, how do you think you would adjust? *(Synthesize)*

3. How can a club like the one at Micaela's school help people make friends at a new school? *(Analyze)*

20

Micaela Moves

by Claudia M. Lee
illustrated by Chris Vallo

Table of Contents

CHAPTER ONE

Micaela's Last Week

Micaela was crushed when she heard the news. She knew that her life had changed forever. All she could do was sob and cry. After she had finally managed to calm down a little, she picked up the phone and dialed the number that she knew by heart. After a quick ring, she heard Mariana's voice, "Hello?"

All Micaela could do was cry when she heard her friend's voice.

"What's wrong, Mica?" Mariana asked.

Micaela finally managed to break the news to her friend between sniffles. Mariana didn't say a word at first. Micaela could hear Mariana sniffling too.

"So when are you moving?" Mariana asked.

"A week from tomorrow," Micaela replied.

Micaela's father had worked for the same company since he and his wife arrived from Mexico 15 years earlier. Now, the company was moving to another city.

When the other performances ended, Mica went out and gave her old friend and her parents a big hug. Mica introduced Margarita to Mariana. Peggy and Ruthie walked up to them. They told Mica how much they liked the dance that she and Margarita did. "Hey, could you show us how to dance like that?" Ruthie asked.

Mariana, Margarita, and Mica smiled at each other. Mica felt like the coolest girl in the world. It wasn't because Ruthie wanted to learn how to dance, but because she had her two best friends by her side.

The two women spent almost the entire week making the dresses, as well as chatting over coffee. They got along well and they had a lot in common. Both women were proud of their heritage and knew that life in another country wasn't easy.

The dresses were ready just in time for Saturday. Mica's mother brought them to the gym for the girls during their final rehearsal before the festival. The dresses fit perfectly and the girls looked beautiful.

The school auditorium was full of people waiting for the show to begin. This year the dance club was first. Mica was nervous. The music started and the curtain went up. The girls started twirling and gliding to the rhythm of the music. As the music quickened, so did the girls' movements. Mica had tried not to look at the audience because she was afraid that she would get nervous. But when she decided to look, she saw some familiar faces in the crowd.

Mariana and her parents were in the audience. Mica was so happy to have her old friend there to watch her dance. The music stopped and the audience cheered and cheered. Mica spotted her parents who were standing and applauding. Mica even saw Peggy and Ruthie, the two "cool" girls, cheering for her.

© 2007 Macmillan/McGraw-Hill

Micaela's father was a hard worker, and he was proud of his family's Mexican heritage. "Other people might try to hide who they are, but not the Flores family," he would say proudly. He believed that you could do anything if you worked hard enough for it. Just before Micaela was born, her parents had moved into their apartment. It was a total mess; there were ruptured water pipes, the kitchen cabinets were falling apart, and work was needed everywhere.

Mr. Flores and his wife worked hard fixing the place up. And Micaela helped, too. Over the years, they had worked as a family to fix their home. Now they were packing their things as a family, too.

Micaela was upset because her parents had waited so long to tell her. She was about to start middle school. Now, instead of starting school together with her best friend, Mariana, she would be all by herself.

"Don't worry, *hija*, you're going to make new friends at your new school," Mrs. Flores said.

"It's not fair, *mami*," Micaela replied. "My life is ruined!"

Mrs. Flores explained that she had felt the same way when she and Mr. Flores immigrated from Mexico.

Mica felt a little better. But she needed to spend as much time with Mariana as possible before the move.

4

"Mica." Ms. Powell said. "We'd like to hear your story now."

Mica took a deep breath and read her story out loud to the class:

My summer was ruined when I heard the bad news. After living my whole life on Charles Street, my parents told me we were going to move. All I wanted to do was cry. I had to leave all my friends behind and start over again. How could my parents ask me to do that?

When I got here, I was lonely and I just wanted to fit in. For a while I felt like I was all by myself. Then I met a great person. I didn't think I would ever meet anyone like my best friend back home, but now I know I was wrong. She has made starting over easy for me.

When Mica finished reading, Ms. Powell passed by to collect her story. Then Mica looked over at Margarita, who was smiling at her. After the bell rang and everyone rushed out into the hall, Margarita told Mica how much she liked her story.

The dance club had extra long practices after school all that week. They had to dance perfectly at the culture fair that Saturday. Since Margarita's mother made traditional Mexican dresses and Mrs. Flores loved to sew, too, they volunteered to make the girls' dresses for the performance.

17

© 2007 Macmillan/McGraw-Hill

CHAPTER FOUR

The Big Day

The next morning, Maggie ran into Mica's room screaming, "Get up, get up, get up!" Mica got up quickly, kicked Maggie out, and got ready for school. Then the girls went downstairs to say good-bye to their father before he left for work. The girls ate their breakfast quickly, got in the car, and their mother dropped them off at school.

The morning flew by and then it was time for English class. Mica and Margarita walked in together as usual and sat down next to each other. The teacher came in, took attendance, and then started to call on people to read their stories.

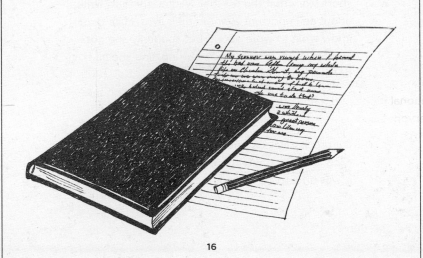

The rest of that week, while her parents packed for the move, Mica spent almost every day with Mariana. Before, they would sit around listening to music, reading magazines or playing video games, but now it was different. The whole week Mica and Mariana talked about how their lives would be different when school started. Both girls were nervous about starting middle school, but they were excited, too. Middle school would be awesome!

Even with the excitement of middle school, Mica and Mariana still felt sad. They promised each other that they would keep in touch and that they would both make as many friends as they could at their new schools.

"Don't make too many new friends, Mica," Mariana joked. "Then you'll forget that I exist."

That last week flew by so fast that the day of the move came before Micaela knew it. The day of the move, Mica and Mariana talked while a couple of Mr. Flores' friends helped load the last few things into the moving van. Then the time to say goodbye had arrived. The girls hugged and hugged each other until Mica's dad shouted, "Come on, Mica. We have to go. The van is parked illegally and we'll get a ticket."

CHAPTER TWO

The New House

Mica's first day in the new house was terrible. She hated it. She wanted to go back and be with Mariana. The only good thing about the new house was that she didn't have to share a room with Maggie anymore. Maggie was only six years old, but she thought she was Mica's age. She would do everything Mica did. She would borrow Mica's clothes and belongings without permission. But not anymore: Mica could just lock Maggie out anytime she wanted.

During that first week, neighbor after neighbor came over to welcome the Flores family to the neighborhood. There were lots of neighbors, but Mica didn't see anyone her age. This made her even more depressed. She began to wonder what her new school would be like. She would find out the next day.

Mica didn't want to get up the next morning. She was excited about her first day of middle school, but she didn't know what to expect. Then Mica slowly rolled out of bed after her mother had yelled for the fifth time for her to get up. Mica locked her door and started to get ready.

6

Mica started her English homework. It was a short story that the teacher wanted them to write about an important event in their lives. Mica didn't know what to write about, but suddenly she got an idea. Mica couldn't stop writing, and she had her story finished before dinner.

After dinner, Mica talked with Mariana on the phone as she did on most Sunday nights. Mica told her old friend about the dance club, the culture festival, and her new friends. Mariana told Mica about her new friends at middle school. Then it was time to go to bed.

15

Mica's parents watched as the two girls put on their show. Mica's mother looked at her husband with a big smile. Mr. Flores began to sing to the music, which he knew by heart. After the girls had finished, Mr. and Mrs. Flores cheered and applauded.

"I feel like I'm back in Mexico," Mr. Flores said. That's when he told the story of his father. Grandfather Flores was a migrant worker, moving from state to state in southern Mexico. But he was also a musician, and his favorite music was *charro* music. Every April, no matter where grandfather Flores was, he would drop everything and go to Aguascalientes for the fair. There he would play his music with a small band. The people cheered and always wanted more.

"You know, I met Mrs. Flores at one of those fairs about twenty years ago. . . ." Mr. Flores told Margarita. Mica grabbed Margarita by the arm and tugged her away as they waved goodbye. She knew her father's stories were good, but he would keep going all night. The culture festival was next weekend and they needed more practice.

On Sunday afternoon, Margarita went home. Mica had such a good time that weekend.

Micaela Moves

Mica and her sister finally made their way downstairs for breakfast. Their father was just finishing his coffee and was on his way out. Before he left, he gave his girls a big hug and a kiss like he always did, and then he wished them good luck on their first day of school.

Breakfast ended when Mrs. Flores looked at her watch and shouted, "*Vámonos, niñas!* We're going to be late." They hurried out the door and got into the car. A few minutes later, they were in front of Mica's new school. Her mother leaned over to give Mica a kiss on the cheek. Mica leaned away and uttered, "*Mami!* Not here." Mrs. Flores understood. She had forgotten that her little girl was now a teenager. She wished Mica luck and drove off on her way to Maggie's school.

Micaela walked slowly toward the building and up the stairs. She noticed right away that this school was a lot bigger than her old one. There were big groups of kids standing around and talking. Everyone was staring at her. She felt like she had a sign around her neck saying, "Hi. I'm the new girl."

She went to the main office just like she had been told to do. There one of the secretaries, Ms. Harriet, welcomed Mica to the school, gave her a copy of her schedule, and explained how to find her homeroom. Micaela started down the hall to find her homeroom.

Micaela got lost a few minutes later. She was so nervous that she couldn't remember Ms. Harriet's directions and took a wrong turn. Finally, she found room 121 and slowly opened the door.

"Well, Ms. Flores! Glad you could join us," Mr. Brick joked. Mr. Brick, the homeroom teacher, thought it was funny, but Mica wasn't laughing.

8

Mica and Margarita went to dance practice every day after school. After practice, one of their mothers would pick the girls up and bring them home. One Friday, after getting in the car with Margarita, Mica begged her mother, "*Mami*, can Margarita stay for the weekend? Please."

"When we get to her house, she can ask her parents if it's all right," her mother replied. The girls were excited. This was the first time that Margarita would spend the night at Mica's house since they had been friends.

That night, the girls practiced their dance. Then they ran downstairs and rushed into the living room where Mica's parents were watching TV.

"We want to show you our dance," Mica told her parents. Mr. Flores turned off the TV and put on a CD. The sounds of guitars and trumpets began to fill the room.

13

One day during study hall, Margarita asked Mica if she wanted to go to dance practice with her after school. Margarita explained that there was a group of girls that got together to practice Mexican folk dance. Mica was excited; she loved to dance, especially to traditional Mexican music. "I'd love to!" Mica replied.

After school that day, Mica and Margarita went to the gym for dance practice. There were already a lot of other people there when the girls arrived. Mica and Margarita walked up to a girl who was stretching in the corner of the gym.

"Hey, Laura. This is Micaela. She's new here."

"Hi, Micaela. I'm Laura Ríos. Nice to meet you."

Laura Ríos was the leader of the dance club. She was a little bit older than Mica and Margarita. Laura was an eighth-grader and all the girls wanted to be like her. And Mica did too.

"You know, Mica, you can dance with us if you want," Laura said. She explained that the club was practicing for the culture festival that the school has every year. This year the club was going to do a traditional Mexican dance to *charro* music from Guadalajara. Mica looked at her new friend and smiled. Mica felt like she was really starting to fit in.

© 2007 Macmillan/McGraw-Hill

"It was a joke, Ms. Flores. I have a reputation for making jokes. Welcome, have a seat," Mr. Brick said, only half apologizing. Mica felt uncomfortable as she took a seat because two girls in the front row were looking her over from head to toe. She sat down at the back of the room. Every few minutes the two girls from the front row would look back at Mica and whisper quietly to each other.

Finally, the bell rang. Everyone started to get up. Mr. Brick stepped in front of the door and joked again, "If you're going to Ms. Potter's class now, don't be late or you'll feel her wrath."

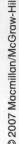

The rest of the morning was pretty boring. The teachers gave long speeches about the classroom rules, handed out textbooks, and gave the homework assignments for that night. Mica noticed that the same girl that she had sat next to in homeroom was in most of the same classes with her.

In history class, Mica was listening to the teacher when she heard a voice from behind her, "Psssst. Hey, *amiga!*" Mica turned around to see the same girl from homeroom smiling at her and passing her a folded piece of paper. Mica unfolded the paper and read, "*Amiga!* I'll see you at lunch."

Mica was happy to meet someone else who liked to speak Spanish. Suddenly, Mica remembered how she and Mariana would speak Spanish all the time. Mica was wondering how Mariana was doing in her new school.

10

CHAPTER THREE

The Dance Club

Mica was fidgeting with her locker trying to get it open when she heard a voice say, "*Lista?*"

"Yeah, I'm ready," Mica answered.

"By the way, I'm Margarita," the girl said. Mica smiled and introduced herself. Then the two girls walked toward the school cafeteria.

Mica and Margarita got their lunch and sat down at a table with some other girls. Margarita introduced Mica to everyone. As they ate and talked, the two girls from homeroom walked by, staring at Mica and giggling.

"That's Peggy and Ruthie. Don't worry about them. They mistreat everyone," Margarita explained. She added that they were supposed to be the "cool" girls in the class.

"The cool girls at my old school weren't like that," Mica thought to herself.

Besides getting homework on the first day of school, there were a lot of other things that Mica would have to get used to in middle school.

11

Word Workout

WORDS TO KNOW

anticipated encounter nourishing participate

dejectedly grimaced ordeals victorious

Two by Two Let's choose two words and use them both in one sentence. Then let's choose two more. When we have paired all the words, we can begin again with different pairs and different sentences.

SPELLING WORDS

aerial	biography	hydrant
microscope	hydrogen	aerospace
biology	grammar	microphone
dialogue	autobiography	diagram
catalog	chronic	thermos
paragraph	microwave	thermometer
program	symphony	

From a Word Long Ago I'll give you a word to spell. Then, let's see if we can determine the root part of the word and what it means.

(fold here)

Dear Family Member:

No two family members are exactly alike. Being in a family means you share some traits and ideas, but not others. We are reading a short story about a girl who grows up as a Kaw Indian in our time. She has a very different idea about what it means to be a Kaw than her grandfather. While we read *Ta-Na-E-Ka*, we're comparing and contrasting important characters and ideas in this story.

This Week's Skills

Comprehension: compare and contrast

Vocabulary: word parts

Spelling/Phonics: Greek roots

Name _____

And the Topics Are...

Let's see if we can solve these puzzles. With a little logical thinking, we can figure out what things are being compared.

Each of these Venn diagrams compares and contrasts two things. Let's try to write the missing labels to tell what is being compared and contrasted.

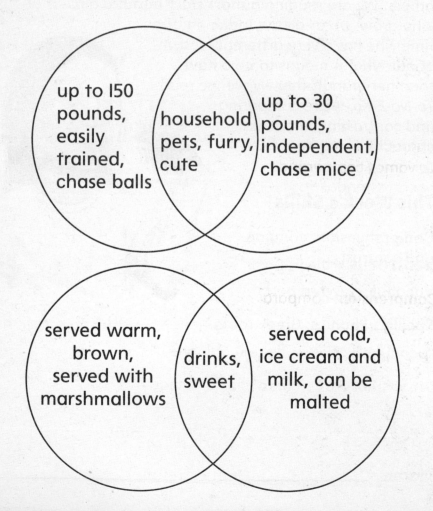

up to 150 pounds, easily trained, chase balls

household pets, furry, cute

up to 30 pounds, independent, chase mice

served warm, brown, served with marshmallows

drinks, sweet

served cold, ice cream and milk, can be malted

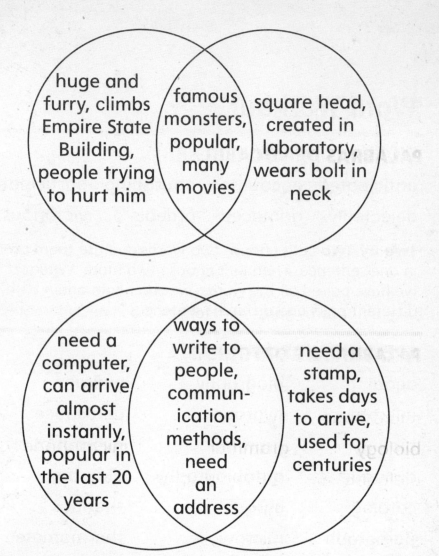

huge and furry, climbs Empire State Building, people trying to hurt him

famous monsters, popular, many movies

square head, created in laboratory, wears bolt in neck

need a computer, can arrive almost instantly, popular in the last 20 years

ways to write to people, communication methods, need an address

need a stamp, takes days to arrive, used for centuries

Ejercicio de palabras

PALABRAS DE VOCABULARIO

anticipated   encounter   nourishing   participate

dejectedly   grimaced   ordeals   victorious

De a dos Vamos a escoger dos palabras y a usarlas en una oración. Después escogeremos dos más. Cuando hayamos formado pares con todas las palabras, elegiremos otros pares para formar oraciones diferentes.

PALABRAS DE ORTOGRAFÍA

aerial	biography	hydrant
microscope	hydrogen	aerospace
biology	grammar	microphone
dialogue	autobiography	diagram
catalog	chronic	thermos
paragraph	microwave	thermometer
program	symphony	

De una antigua palabra Te voy a dar una palabra para deletrear. Después vamos a ver si podemos determinar cuál es la raíz de la palabra y qué significa.

······ (fold here) ······

Queridos familiares:

En una misma familia no hay dos miembros que sean exactamente iguales. Cuando se pertenece a una familia, se comparten algunas características e ideas, pero no otras. Estamos leyendo un cuento sobre una niña de nuestra época, que crece entre los indios Kaw. La idea que ella tiene de lo que significa ser una india Kaw es muy diferente a la que tiene su abuelo. Al leer *Ta-Na-E-Ka* vamos comparando y contrastando ideas y personajes importantes del cuento.

Destrezas de la semana

Comprensión: comparar y contrastar

Vocabulario: partes de una palabra

Ortografía/ Fonética: raíces del griego

Nombre_____

Y los temas son...

Vamos a ver si podemos resolver estos acertijos. Si usamos un poco el pensamiento lógico podremos adivinar qué es lo que se compara.

En cada uno de estos diagramas de Venn se comparan y contrastan dos cosas. Intentemos escribir los rótulos que faltan para indicar qué es lo que se compara y se contrasta.

up to 150 pounds, easily trained, chase balls

household pets, furry, cute

up to 30 pounds, independent, chase mice

served warm, brown, served with marshmallows

drinks, sweet

served cold, ice cream and milk, can be malted

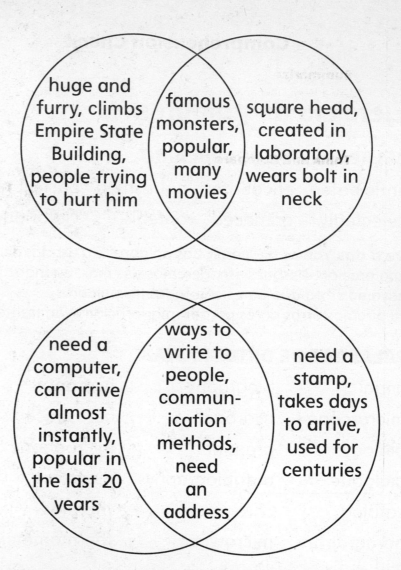

huge and furry, climbs Empire State Building, people trying to hurt him

famous monsters, popular, many movies

square head, created in laboratory, wears bolt in neck

need a computer, can arrive almost instantly, popular in the last 20 years

ways to write to people, communication methods, need an address

need a stamp, takes days to arrive, used for centuries

Comprehension Check

Summarize

Use a Venn Diagram to compare and contrast the two activities Stacey wants to participate in.

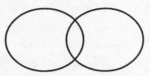

Think and Compare

1. How is Stacey the same as the rest of the Fearsome Foursome? How is she different? Support your answer with examples from the story. *(Compare and Contrast)*

2. What activities do you participate in at school? Which ones are your favorites? Have you ever experienced a situation like Stacey? How did you handle it? *(Apply)*

3. Do you think every problem in life requires a compromise to solve it? Why or why not? Explain. *(Evaluate)*

20

Stacey's Winning Move

by Nan Walker
illustrated by Mark Weber

Table of Contents

CHAPTER ONE

"Think Fast!"

Most kids would fall flat on their faces if they tried to read while walking quickly, but not Stacey Taylor. She stepped nimbly over sidewalk cracks, veered around a tricycle some little kid had left out, and even gave her neighbor's poodle a pat on the head—all without ever lifting her nose from the book in her hands.

The book was the true story of an amazing reporter named Nellie Bly. Back in the late 1800s, most people thought that only men should be reporters. But Nellie Bly did daring things that male reporters were afraid to do. No adventure was too bold for her, no ordeal too severe. She had herself locked up in an insane asylum and wrote about how badly the inmates were treated. She traveled around the world by boat, train, and even rickshaw.

© 2007 Macmillan/McGraw-Hill

Stacey's Winning Move

Jonathan said, "You know, I really love soccer, and when I was in sixth grade I wished I could be on the team. Since I couldn't play, I guess I could have given up on soccer completely. Instead, I thought of being the team manager."

"So you're saying I should pick soccer instead of the newspaper?" Stacey asked.

"No," he said, "I'm saying if you think creatively, maybe you can come up with a compromise that will make you happy."

All that day, Stacey thought about her encounter with Jonathan and what he'd said. But it wasn't until halfway through English that she hit on her solution.

Two weeks later, the soccer team had just won their first game of the season, and Mandy, Darrell, Luis, and Lila were jumping all over each other and pounding each other on the back. Then Mandy said, "Hey, look, you guys, here comes our favorite sports reporter!"

Stacey was wearing the team colors, blue and gold, and she was carrying a pencil and a little notebook. "I hope you are all ready to be interviewed," she told her friends, "because I have a feeling this is going to be a terrific story."

The bell rang, and the crowd of students scattered, leaving Stacey there alone. She looked at the list and saw her name. She saw Lila's name, too, at the top of a shorter list that said "alternates." That meant that if someone didn't join the team, Lila would have a place.

Slumping to the floor, Stacey leaned against the wall and closed her eyes. Lila deserved that place; she really wanted to be on the soccer team.

"Didn't make the team, huh?" said a boy's voice.

Stacey opened her eyes and saw Jonathan, the team manager, looking down at her sympathetically. "Actually, I did," she said.

Pulling himself closer, he asked, "How come you look so rejected and dejected, then?"

Stacey felt a little awkward talking to an eighth-grader she didn't even know, especially someone who was practically in charge of the whole soccer team. But he seemed so nice that she soon found herself explaining her situation.

18

Wow, thought Stacey. Wouldn't it be great to be a reporter like Nellie Bly? She tried to think of something daring she could do. Maybe she could discover what horrific secret ingredients were in the cafeteria food.

Of course, for all she knew, the cafeteria served nourishing, delicious food cooked by a gourmet chef. In fact, there were a lot of things Stacey didn't know about Walker Middle School. Today was the first day of the school year, and she was just starting sixth grade.

Stacey felt excited and a little nervous about starting middle school. She wasn't too nervous, though, because she knew her three best friends would be there with her.

All through elementary school, Mandy, Darrell, Luis, and Stacey had been known as the Fearsome Foursome. They staked out the best seats at the back of the bus. At lunch they sat together at "their" table. In gym, they always picked each other first for teams—and any time all four of them were on one team, that team was sure to win.

As long as the Fearsome Foursome stuck together, Stacey thought, how bad could middle school possibly be?

3

CHAPTER FOUR

A Terrific Story

Coach Stevens had said that the results of the soccer tryouts would be posted outside the gym first thing on Monday morning. And so, for the first time ever, the Fearsome Foursome rode at the front of the bus—Mandy's idea, so they could get off before anyone else. When they arrived at school, Mandy, Luis, and Darrell raced to the gym, Stacey lagging behind.

By the time she reached the gym, the others were already jumping up and down and hugging each other. When Mandy saw Stacey, she shouted, "We made the team!"

"All of us?" Stacey asked.

"Of course, all of us—would we look so happy if you hadn't made it too?"

Spotting Lila on the field, Stacey waved and went over to see her. "I didn't know that you played soccer," she said.

"I love to play, but I'm not very good," Lila said. "I probably won't get on the team, but it would be fantastic if I did!"

Lila wasn't bad, actually, Stacey decided as the tryouts started. But she wasn't as good as the Fearsome Foursome: Mandy and Luis, fast and aggressive; Darrell the goalie, never letting in a shot; and Stacey, moving gracefully and often passing the ball to her friends.

Once, after Stacey set up a shot for Mandy to make the goal, she saw Jonathan point toward them and say something to Coach Edwards. She hoped he had been noticing Luis and Darrell, too.

All four played hard, and when tryouts ended, they wrapped their arms around each other's shoulders and headed off the field.

Darrell's mother took them out for ice cream sundaes afterward. Licking whipped cream off her spoon, Stacey listened to her friends laughing and joking and tried to share in the good time. But her dilemma felt like a big dark cloud above her head.

Suppose she made the team . . . then what?

© 2007 Macmillan/McGraw-Hill

Stacey continued reading until she heard a voice from above.

"Think fast!"

Before Stacey even had a chance to look up, a soccer ball came whizzing down at her from the sky. She stepped back and let it bounce onto the sidewalk, then trapped it neatly with her feet.

A tall girl with long braids swung out of a tree, dropping lightly to the sidewalk. Stacey passed the ball to her. "Hey, Mandy."

Mandy rolled the ball onto the top of her foot and kicked it into the air, then bounced it off her knees a few times. "Got your schedule yet?"

As Stacey dug in her backpack, a small, slender boy came running up behind Mandy. He stole the soccer ball and dribbled it away. Laughing, Mandy ran after him. "Give it back, Luis!"

"Come and get it," he called over his shoulder.

Just then, Stacey spotted a bright flash of yellow coming around the corner at the far end of the street. "The bus is here!" she yelled, but Mandy and Luis paid no attention as they ran the other way—and where was Darrell? They were all going to miss the bus.

The school bus pulled up, and Mandy and Luis ran back, passing the ball between them until they climbed aboard. Stacey hung back, holding the rail.

Giving one last glance over her shoulder, she saw Darrell standing right behind her, grinning. She was so relieved she wasn't even annoyed at him for showing up at the last possible moment, as usual.

Stacey and Darrell walked to the back of the bus, where Mandy and Luis were already sitting together. As they squeezed onto the long seat next to their friends, an older boy wearing an earring turned and scowled at them.

"What do you think you're doing?" he said. "Only eighth graders sit back here, you miniature morons."

Stacey felt the warmth creep up her face. They hadn't even reached the school yet, and already they had managed to do something wrong. Luis started to get up, but Mandy grabbed him by the wrist and held him down. Staring at the older boy, she said, "You mean only eighth-graders *used* to sit back here."

The boy shrugged disgustedly and turned away. Mandy smiled, victorious. "Okay, guys," she said, "let's see those schedules."

While Darrell and Luis searched in their backpacks, Stacey unfolded her schedule and studied it. They had two elective classes, language and music, and she knew Mandy had chosen Spanish and chorus, just like her.

The soccer field was crowded with kids—kids tying on their cleats, kids heading soccer balls, kids dribbling and passing and guarding the goal. Some of them were pretty good, and Stacey realized that the tryouts might not be as easy as she had anticipated. What if she didn't make the team? She wasn't sure if she'd be disappointed or relieved.

An eighth-grade boy in a wheelchair was helping Coach Edwards run the tryouts. Darrell said that he was the team manager, Jonathan. "My brother says Jonathan knows everything there is to know about soccer—more than the coach," he added.

15

SOCCER   NEWSPAPER

be with my friends	be a reporter like Nellie Bly

It wasn't much of a list, Stacey thought, staring at the page. She tried to think what other points might be significant. Playing soccer would be healthy—she'd get lots of exercise and fresh air. On the other hand, writing for the paper would be educational and exercise her mind.

In reality, though, she knew it was not a complicated choice. She could stay with her friends and give up the activity she really wanted to do, or she could trade in the Fearsome Foursome for the Lonesome Onesome.

Stacey's choice was simple—simply awful.

The next morning, Darrell's mother drove all four of them to the soccer tryouts. Stacey squeezed into the back seat between Mandy and Luis, who was wearing a strange, floppy hat she'd never seen before. "It's a beret," Luis explained, adding, "It's French."

"How come you didn't sign up for Spanish like the rest of us?" Mandy was asking Luis.

"*Hablo español perfectamente,*" he said, "so I thought it would be more *interesante* to learn French."

Darrell had picked orchestra instead of chorus; of course, he had been playing the cello for years and years, so that was not a big surprise.

Then, as she looked at the schedules spread out across Mandy's lap, Stacey saw something that she hadn't noticed right away. The Fearsome Foursome were all in the same English, science, math, and social studies classes—all but Stacey. She had been assigned to the accelerated track.

It was the first day of middle school, and she was all alone.

CHAPTER TWO

Just Like Nellie Bly

Stacey slumped dejectedly behind her desk, watching her new English teacher write the first week's assignments on the board. She had to admit that Mr. Ling seemed really nice. Still, she'd like the class a whole lot better if her friends were there to whisper to her and pass notes—classroom activities that Mandy always defended as "exercises in written and oral communication."

As Mr. Ling scribbled, the girl sitting in front of Stacey twisted around. "Aren't you glad we're starting with an autobiography?" she asked. "Some of my favorite books are about real people—maybe because I'm one." Stacey laughed, and the girl said, "I'm Lila."

Lila had short hair, but something in her outgoing manner reminded Stacey a little of Mandy. Smiling back, she was about to say her own name, but Mr. Ling called for their attention.

8

Stacey grimaced. "I've been trying, but I don't know how."

He thought for a moment. "Sometimes, when I have to make a tough decision, I divide a sheet of paper down the middle and summarize the main points on each side. Seeing it right in front of me like that can really help me clarify the situation."

At this point, Stacey thought, she would try anything. She thanked her father and went back up to her room, where she flopped down on her bed with a pen and a spiral notebook. Flipping to an empty page, she wrote SOCCER on one side and NEWSPAPER on the other, then drew a line down the middle.

CHAPTER THREE

Simply Awful

As Saturday drew closer, Stacey thought she knew how Nellie Bly must have felt as the heavy doors of the asylum slammed behind her, and she realized there was no way out.

On Friday, Stacey gathered her courage and stayed after class to talk to Mr. Ling. But Mr. Ling felt just as strongly about newspaper meetings as Coach Edwards did about soccer practice. He even used the word "commitment," too.

That night, she knocked on the door of her father's study. Stacey's father was a judge, and he often went to his study after dinner to look up questions and think about important cases. But he never seemed to mind if Stacey interrupted, as long as she had a good reason.

Her father listened attentively as she poured out her story. When she finished, he leaned back and looked at her, then said, "It appears that you have a decision to make."

© 2007 Macmillan/McGraw-Hill

"As some of you may be aware," he said, "I wear two hats at Walker Middle School."

"Doesn't the school have central heating?" a boy called out, and everyone laughed.

Mr. Ling smiled and went on, "Not only do I teach sixth-grade English, but I am also the adviser to the school newspaper. So, if I may switch to that hat—speaking metaphorically, of course," he added, looking at the boy who had called out, "I'd like to take this opportunity to invite anyone who is interested in writing for the paper to attend our first meeting after school next Tuesday."

Writing for the paper! Stacey felt a tiny thrill run up her spine. This was her chance to learn to be a real reporter, just like Nellie Bly. She was definitely going to be at that meeting.

When the bell rang, Stacey hurried toward the gym—her one class so far that was easy to find, because the entire sixth grade had gym together.

Entering the gym, Stacey spotted Mandy, Darrell, and Luis sitting high up at the very top of the bleachers.

"*Bonjour!*" Luis said as Stacey joined her friends. "That's French for 'hello.'"

Before Stacey could reply, a giant voice boomed out, "Okay, everyone, listen up! I'm Coach Edwards, and I have a few announcements."

Coach Edwards told them that the school had a wide range of sports they could participate in, and tryouts were starting soon. They listened as the coach read through the list. When she announced that tryouts for the coed soccer team would be on Saturday, Mandy cheered, and Darrell and Luis slapped hands.

Stacey was happy, too. She didn't love soccer as much as the others did, but she felt pretty certain she could make the team. The Fearsome Foursome would be reunited on the soccer field.

Wrapped up in her thoughts, she almost didn't hear the next thing the coach said. Stacey leaned over and whispered to Mandy, "What did she say?"

"She said soccer practice is every Tuesday and Thursday after school," Mandy whispered back. "Why, what's wrong?"

© 2007 Macmillan/McGraw-Hill

Stacey's Winning Move

Stacey hesitated. "I have something else I really need to do on Tuesday."

"Can't you skip it, whatever it is?" asked Mandy.

Stacey felt sick to her stomach. "I don't know," she said. "Probably not."

Before she realized what was happening, Mandy's hand had shot up as she called out, "Coach Edwards, can I ask a question?" The coach nodded, and Mandy asked, "If we play soccer, do we have to be at all the practices?"

"Excellent question," boomed the coach, "and I have an excellent answer: only if you want to stay on the team." Some of the kids looked in their direction, laughing, and Stacey sank lower on the bench. Coach Edwards went on, "Playing a team sport is all about commitment—to the sport, to your team, and to yourself. If you're not committed, you don't belong on the playing field."

Wherever her friends were, Stacey thought, that was where she belonged. But what about her dream of being a reporter?

Word Workout

WORDS TO KNOW

chronology   debut   periodic

continuous   economists

Where and When? Name a word and tell me where and when you might see this word. For example, if you saw the word actor, you might say that it is in a review of a movie.

SPELLING WORDS

audience	reduce	incredible	introduce
inject	benefit	credit	structure
prediction	reflection	factory	dictionary
insect	flexible	objection	destruction
section	audio	education	dejected

Stop Me I'll begin spelling one of the list words. See how many letters I spell before you break in and spell the rest of the word.

(fold here)

Home-School Connection

Dear Family Member:

Did you ever take a really close look at the bills and coins we use every day? This week we're reading "Money Matters," a collection of articles about currency. One in-depth article is about the euro, a currency used by many of the countries in Europe. Many countries opposed the currency. Supporters used persuasion to convince others to join their side. Today, the euro is a success, helping countries of Europe compete economically.

This Week's Skills

Comprehension: persuasion

Vocabulary: word parts

Spelling/Phonics: Latin Roots

Name _____

Persuasive Points

People try to persuade us every day. Whenever we see an ad, read an editorial, or listen to a political speech, someone wants us to get the message. All of the quotations below tell how to go about persuading people. Let's talk about each quote and what it means. How does the writer feel about persuasion?

> We persuade others by being in earnest ourselves.
>
> —William Hazlitt, essayist

> I sit here all day trying to persuade people to do the things they ought to have sense enough to do without my persuading them.
>
> —Harry S Truman, U.S. President

> If you would win a man to your cause, first convince him that you are his sincere friend. Therein is a drop of honey that catches his heart, which, say what you will, is the great high-road to his reason.
>
> —Abraham Lincoln, U.S. President

> One of the best ways to persuade others is with your ears—by listening to them.
>
> —Dean Rusk, author

> The shepherd always tries to persuade the sheep that their interests and his own are the same.
>
> —Stendhal, novelist

> A man convinced against his will is not convinced.
>
> —Laurence J. Peter, author

> Leadership appears to be the art of getting others to want to do something you are convinced should be done.
>
> —Vance Packard, nonfiction writer

Which quotes are respectful of persuasion as a goal? Which of the quotes have a more cynical tone?

Ejercicio de palabras

PALABRAS DE VOCABULARIO

chronology   debut   periodic

continuous   economists

¿Dónde y cuándo? Escoge una de las palabras y dime dónde y cuándo puedes verla. Por ejemplo, si dijeras la palabra *actor*, podrías decir que aparece en la crítica de una película.

PALABRAS DE ORTOGRAFÍA

audience	reduce	incredible	introduce
inject	benefit	credit	structure
prediction	reflection	factory	dictionary
insect	flexible	objection	destruction
section	audio	education	dejected

Interrúmpeme Comenzaré a deletrear una de las palabras de la lista. Cuando sepas de qué palabra se trata, interrúmpeme y continúa deletreándola. Veamos cuántas letras dije antes de que me interrumpieras.

(fold here)

© Macmillan/McGraw-Hill

Conexión con el hogar

Queridos familiares:

¿Han mirado alguna vez con detención los billetes y las monedas que usamos todos los días? Esta semana estamos leyendo *Money Matters*, una serie de artículos sobre la moneda circulante. Uno de los artículos trata a fondo del euro, la unidad monetaria usada en muchos países europeos. Muchos países se oponían a un cambio en su moneda. Los que apoyaban el cambio usaron la persuasión para convencer a los demás de que se les unieran. Hoy, el euro tiene éxito y ayuda a los países de Europa a competir económicamente.

Destrezas de la semana

Comprensión: persuasión

Vocabulario: partes de una palabra

Ortografía/Fonética: raíces del latín

Nombre _____

Puntos de persuasión

Todos los días la gente trata de persuadirnos. Cada vez que vemos un anuncio, leemos un artículo editorial o escuchamos un discurso político, alguien quiere convencernos de su punto de vista. Todas las citas de abajo hablan de cómo proceder para persuadir. Vamos a hablar de cada cita y de lo que significa. ¿Qué piensa de la persuasión cada autor?

> We persuade others by being in earnest ourselves.
>
> —William Hazlitt, essayist

> I sit here all day trying to persuade people to do the things they ought to have sense enough to do without my persuading them.
>
> —Harry S Truman, U.S. President

> If you would win a man to your cause, first convince him that you are his sincere friend. Therein is a drop of honey that catches his heart, which, say what you will, is the great high-road to his reason.
>
> —Abraham Lincoln, U.S. President

> One of the best ways to persuade others is with your ears—by listening to them.
>
> —Dean Rusk, author

> The shepherd always tries to persuade the sheep that their interests and his own are the same.
>
> —Stendhal, novelist

> A man convinced against his will is not convinced.
>
> —Laurence J. Peter, author

> Leadership appears to be the art of getting others to want to do something you are convinced should be done.
>
> —Vance Packard, nonfiction writer

Which quotes are respectful of persuasion as a goal? Which of the quotes have a more cynical tone?

344

Comprehension Check

Summarize

How does the author argue that the Department of the Treasury is important? Use evidence from the text to support your answer.

Think and Compare

1. Look back through the text to find the important jobs that the Treasury Department does. Then list them. Tell which ones you think are most important. *(Evaluate)*

2. The Treasury Department does some unpopular jobs. For example, it collects taxes and watches over banks. If you had one of these jobs, how would you persuade people to follow the law? Use evidence from the text to support your arguments. *(Synthesize)*

3. Do you think it is important for the United States to give money to other countries in need? Why or why not? *(Evaluate)*

BEHIND THE SCENES AT THE TREASURY

BY DANIEL ROSEN

Table of Contents

INTRODUCTION

In 1789 the United States was a new country. The Americans had just defeated Great Britain. They were now free and independent. The people had voted for President. They elected George Washington. He was our first President.

The government went to work. Laws were passed. On September 2, 1789, Congress passed an important law. That law set up the Department of the Treasury. The department was to be headed by an officer called the Secretary of the Treasury.

This is the seal of the Department of the Treasury. It has been in use since 1789. The 13 stars represent the original 13 states.

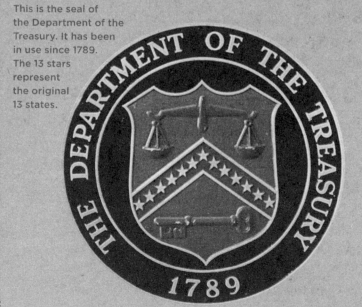

Index

Glossary

counterfeiter *(KOWN-tur-fit-ur)* someone who makes a copy or imitation of something in order to cheat people *(page 13)*

crash *(KRASH)* a sudden ruin or failure in business *(page 19)*

currency *(KUR-uhn-see)* the money used in a country *(page 15)*

debt *(DET)* something that is owed to another *(page 5)*

denomination *(di-nom-uh-NAY-shuhn)* one kind of unit in a system; here, the different coins and bills used in American money *(page 12)*

executive branch *(eg-ZEK-yuh-tiv BRANCH)* the branch of government that manages the affairs of a nation and sees that the laws are carried out *(page 4)*

federal *(FED-uhr-uhl)* having to do with the central government of the United States, thought of as separate from the government of each state *(page 3)*

finances *(FIGH-nan-sez)* money matters for people, businesses, or governments *(page 3)*

foreign aid *(FAWR-uhn AYD)* money given to other countries to help them *(page 18)*

Internal Revenue Service (IRS) *(in-TUR-nuhl REV-uh-new SUR-vis)* the organization that runs the tax system of the federal government *(page 3)*

mint *(MINT)* to make coins *(page 3)*

private enterprise *(PRIGH-vit EN-tur-prighz)* a system in which people are free to own businesses and property *(page 21)*

ratify *(RAT-uh-figh)* to agree to officially *(page 4)*

22

© 2007 Macmillan/McGraw-Hill

Behind the Scenes at the Treasury

What does the Department of the Treasury do? In a nutshell, the Treasury Department takes care of the money in the United States. It prints paper bills. It **mints**, or makes, coins. And it guards our money supply to be sure it is safe. The Treasury Department watches over the banks in the United States and makes sure that the banks follow the laws. It is also home to the **Internal Revenue Service (IRS)**. The IRS runs the **federal** tax system. It makes sure that people pay their taxes. (And most people do. No one wants a visit from the IRS.) The Treasury Department also manages the **finances**, or money matters, of the United States government. It makes sure that all laws that deal with money are followed.

3

ALL ABOUT THE TREASURY DEPARTMENT

The Department of the Treasury has been part of the government from the very beginning. Alexander Hamilton was the first Secretary of the Treasury. He was an important leader in the United States when it was first formed. He was an aide to General George Washington during the American Revolution. He worked hard to see that the U.S. Constitution was passed, or **ratified**.

The Executive Branch

The U.S. Constitution set up our government with three branches: the executive, the legislative, and the judicial. The **executive branch** is headed by the President. The President has 15 departments that help him. The Treasury Department was one of the first four departments created.

President Washington named his good friend Alexander Hamilton the first Secretary of the Treasury in 1789.

The health of our country depends on money.

The United States runs on a system of **private enterprise**. That means that in our country people are free to own and start businesses. Almost all wealth in our country is held by individuals and companies. But the government has a big role in making sure that the whole system treats its citizens fairly.

The Treasury Department prints and distributes bills and coins. It collects taxes. It manages the very large business affairs of the United States government. It pays the government's debts. It makes sure the banking system works well and honestly. And finally it fights financial crime, such as money laundering. The Treasury Department rarely makes headlines in the news. But it is a very important part of the United States government.

CONCLUSION

We don't think about our bones very much. But the skeleton is a very important part of the human body. In the same way, our health as a country and our way of life depend on the financial skeleton of society. Everything we do depends on money. Yet we often can't see what's going on with our country's finances. The Department of the Treasury plays a very large role in making sure that our country is financially healthy.

Washington, D.C.

. . . .

George Washington chose the exact spot for the new capital. Workers began to build the White House in 1792. Congress held its first session in Washington in 1800, moving there from Philadelphia. Thomas Jefferson was the first President to be inaugurated in the new capital.

The White House

Hamilton quickly took action to get the new nation's finances in order. Both the federal government and the states had large **debts** because of the high cost of the recent war.

Hamilton wanted the federal government to pay off the debts of the states. That was his plan. Jefferson was against this plan. He was afraid it would give the federal government too much power. Could these two powerful men ever agree?

Jefferson wanted to move the new capital from Philadelphia to what is now Washington, D.C. Jefferson needed Hamilton's support. In 1790 the two men made a deal. Jefferson accepted Hamilton's plan on how to pay the debts. Hamilton accepted Jefferson's plan to move the capital. That is how the capital of the United States came to be in Washington, D.C.

THE TREASURY BUILDING

A Treasury Building was put up in the new capital. But fires burned down the original building. The first fire was in 1801. Then the British burned the building down during the War of 1812. The building burned down again in 1833. The current building was put up in 1842. This time it was built to be fireproof!

A statue of Alexander Hamilton stands in front of the south wing of the Treasury Building. This wing was completed in September of 1861.

6

HEALTHY BANKS

In 1929 the U.S. stock market **crashed**, or collapsed, starting the Great Depression. Millions of people lost their jobs. When people rushed to the banks to take out their savings, the banks did not have enough money. They had made bad loans to failing businesses. Hundreds of banks simply closed their doors. People lost all their savings.

Congress passed laws to make sure that this never happened again. Today, the Treasury Department has put rules in place to make sure that banks are run well.

The Great Depression

The Great Depression was a terrible event. It began when the stock market lost much of its value. Then banks closed, and then factories closed. By 1932 about 25 percent, or one worker in four, were out of work. Thousands of people were homeless. President Franklin D. Roosevelt took office in 1933. He helped millions of Americans. But the country did not really recover until World War II started in 1941.

19

American foreign aid has helped millions of people around the world.

FOREIGN AID

The United States is the richest country in the world. It trades with other countries. It often helps smaller, poorer countries by giving them **foreign aid**. The Treasury Department is the branch of the government that works with other countries. It also works to help make trade between countries easier.

The Treasury Department works with the World Bank and the International Monetary Fund. These are two government agencies that give aid to foreign countries in need.

Salmon P. Chase

In 1861 Abraham Lincoln named Salmon P. Chase Secretary of the Treasury. Chase had the hard job of raising money for the Union to fight the Civil War. In 1862 the Treasury Department issued the first paper money to help pay for the war. The money was called Greenbacks, because it was green!

For about two months in 1865, the Treasury Building served as the office of the President. Abraham Lincoln had just been assassinated, making Andrew Johnson President. President Lincoln's wife was very upset. She didn't want to move out of the White House right away. Johnson offered to set up an office elsewhere. The Secretary of the Treasury offered his office. So, for about two months Johnson ran the government out of the Treasury Building.

The Treasury Department quickly outgrew its building. New wings were added to make room for the growing number of workers. Today over 100,000 people work at the Treasury Department. They are lawyers, accountants, and economists. They are also law enforcement officers. Only about 1,000 of its employees still work in the Treasury Building itself.

The Treasury Building is considered one of the great buildings of the United States government. Many say it is as important as the White House and the Capitol Building.

The Secretary of the Treasury

The Secretary of the Treasury has two very important jobs. He or she (no woman has ever held the job) is the main financial adviser to the President. He is appointed to his job by the President. He is also the Chief Financial Officer of the government. He is responsible for how well the American economy works. The Treasurer of the United States works for him.

Vice President Cheney congratulates Secretary of Treasury John Snow.

Today the Department of the Treasury is divided into more than 20 different units. The largest unit is the IRS, the Internal Revenue Service. Its job is to collect taxes from taxpayers. The Secretary of the Treasury is in charge of all the different units.

The government of the United States sometimes changes how it is organized. In 2002 Congress created the Department of Homeland Security. Each executive department including the Treasury Department gave up some of its jobs to the new department.

Chronology of the Income Tax

The federal income tax is less than 100 years old. It was started by the Sixteenth Amendment to the U.S. Constitution, which was passed in 1913. The first income tax only had to be paid by people making more than $3,000 a year. That was a lot of money in those days. Today, people have to file tax returns if they have earned $750 or more in a year.

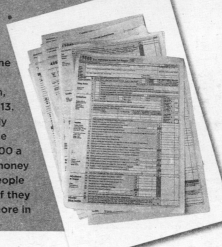

One of the biggest challenges for the IRS is explaining the tax laws to people. The IRS also must persuade every taxpayer to obey the law and pay his or her taxes. Taxpayers must understand why it is important to pay taxes. Taxes pay for the defense of our country, education, building roads, maintaining our national parks, and many other things.

Everyone has to file, or send in, a tax return. Taxes are due to be paid by April 15 every year. Filling out a tax return can take a long time. In 2003 the IRS helped 97 million taxpayers over the phone or in person.

Chapter 3

MANAGING OUR MONEY

The Internal Revenue Service is the largest branch of the Treasury Department. It runs the tax system of the federal government. Every taxpayer and business has to file a tax return with the IRS. In 2003 the IRS handled more than 222 million tax returns. It collected nearly $2 trillion from taxpayers.

Collecting taxes is a complex business. There are different tax laws for individuals and for businesses. There are thousands of special rules. To make things even harder, the tax laws change often.

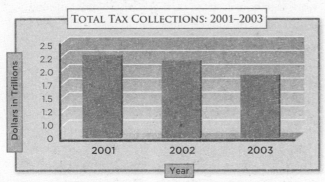

TOTAL TAX COLLECTIONS: 2001–2003

Dollars in Trillions		
2.5		
2.2		
2.0		
1.7		
1.5		
1.2		
1.0		
0		
2001	2002	2003

Year

Tax collections in 2002 and 2003 dropped from 2001. Tax collections go down when businesses make less money.

16

THE TREASURER OF THE UNITED STATES

The Treasurer of the United States heads two important Treasury units. One is the U.S. Mint. The other is the Bureau of Engraving and Printing. The U.S. Mint makes all the coins in the United States. The Bureau of Engraving and Printing prints all the paper money.

Have you ever looked at our money? There are two signatures on every bill. One is that of the Treasurer of the United States. The other signature is that of the Secretary of the Treasury.

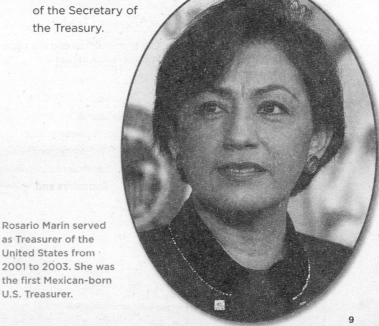

Rosario Marin served as Treasurer of the United States from 2001 to 2003. She was the first Mexican-born U.S. Treasurer.

9

Chapter 2

MAKING MONEY

The United States Mint is a branch of the Treasury Department. It produces coins. It was created in 1792. It has been producing coins ever since. The first Mint was in Philadelphia. It was the first federal building built when the American government was new.

Today the Mint is a huge operation. There are actually five branches of the Mint. Four branches produce coins. They are located in Philadelphia (PA), West Point (NY), Denver (CO), and San Francisco (CA). The fifth branch is located at Fort Knox (KY). The United States government stores its gold at Fort Knox. Soldiers guard it. No outside visitors are allowed in Fort Knox. This keeps the gold safe.

Fort Knox is famous. Have you ever heard the saying, "I wouldn't do that for all the gold in Fort Knox"?

10

Protecting Money

The Secret Service might be best known for protecting the President and Vice President. But the Secret Service was created as a division of the Treasury Department for another reason. It was founded in 1865 to protect the nation's **currency** from counterfeiters. These are people who try to cheat others by using imitation money. After the assassination of President William McKinley in 1901, the Secret Service was also given the job of protecting the President. Today the Secret Service works within the Department of Homeland Security.

The Treasury Department has taken action against money laundering. One of the first things they do is work with banks. After all, that's where most money is. It used to be that criminals could take their cash to a bank and deposit it into their account. Once the money was in the bank, it was "laundered." No one knew how the money was made or where it came from. So, laws were made that limited how much cash could be deposited into a bank account.

The Financial Crimes Enforcement Network (FINCEN) is the branch of the Treasury Department that deals with money laundering and other financial crimes. The work of FINCEN is very important. FINCEN's work helps put criminals out of business.

15

FINANCIAL CRIMES

Countries all over the world are having problems with a crime called money laundering. Criminals make money in ways that are against the law. But they don't want anyone to know that. They want their money to look as though it came from honest work, just like everybody else's. Some criminals want to invest their money in businesses or stocks and bonds. To do that, they must find a way to make their money look like it came through honest work.

This cartoon shows money being "laundered" on its way out of an American bank vault.

50 State Quarters

A recent project of the U.S. Mint is designing 50 different quarters. The front of each quarter will show George Washington's head. But there will be 50 different designs on the coin's back, one for each state. The Mint is in the process of issuing five new quarters every year. The first one made its debut in 1999. The last ones will appear in 2008.

The gold in Fort Knox is in the form of gold bars. The bars are seven inches long. Gold is measured by the ounce. The value of gold changes every day. But usually it is over $400 an ounce.

Fort Knox is such a safe place that during wartime it has been used to store national treasures. During World War II, the original copies of the Declaration of Independence, the United States Constitution, and Lincoln's Gettysburg Address were stored there along with other valuable documents.

PRINTING PAPER MONEY

The Bureau of Engraving and Printing (BEP) prints all paper money in the United States. The BEP was founded in 1862 during the Civil War. Until that time, the federal government did not issue paper money. Today it prints trillions of dollars in bills every year. Most of the money that the BEP prints will replace bills that are worn or torn. Paper money is very strong. But even so, dollar bills wear out in two years. Others last longer, depending on their amount. The continuous folding and handling of money wears the bills out.

The BEP prints bills in the following **denominations**: $1, $5, $10, $20, $50, and $100. Bills are printed at different plants. One is in Washington, D.C., and the other is in Fort Worth, Texas. Every day the two plants turn out about 37 million bills with a value of almost $700 million!

The Bureau of Engraving and Printing sells uncut sheets of bank bills.

Behind the Scenes at the Treasury

THE NEW $20

Security Thread: a strip with the type US Twenty embedded in paper

Watermark, or faint image, appears on bill

Microprinting, or tiny print, appears along bottom

Ink that changes colors in the light

The new $20 bills contain many new security features. It has been carefully designed to prevent **counterfeiters** from making fake money.

The BEP takes special care in printing bills. The bills need to last as long as possible. The BEP uses special paper and inks to make the bills strong. The paper and ink are also hard for outsiders to copy. All through history, criminals have printed counterfeit money.

Periodically, the BEP changes the design of its bills. In 2003 the BEP's new bills have been made more colorful. The colored ink makes it harder for counterfeiters to match the bills.

Word Workout

WORDS TO KNOW

auction	decrease	instinctively	shakily
decades	dilapidated	rafters	swiveled

One Word at a Time Make up a definition for a word. Say your definition one word at a time. How many words do I need to hear before I can guess the word?

SPELLING WORDS

terrible	considerable	audible	changeable
admirable	impossible	available	predictable
reliable	dependable	valuable	horrible
remarkable	acceptable	profitable	noticeable
believable	reversible	probable	lovable

Ible and Able I'll give you a word. Before you spell it for me, tell me if it ends in **ible** or **able**.

(fold here)

Home-School Connection

Dear Family Member:

We make decisions every day. Some of them are no big deal, like whether to wear a blue shirt or a red one. Other decisions are important and sometimes tough. This week we're reading *Honus and Me*, a story about a boy who makes an exciting discovery. In fact, his discovery is so exciting that he is tempted to make a quick decision—but is it the right thing to do? As we read, we're making our own judgments about characters' actions and choices. This skill helps us connect what we read to our own decisions and solutions.

This Week's Skills

Comprehension: make judgments

Vocabulary: thesaurus/dictionary

Spelling/Phonics: Suffixes **able and ible**

Name _____

What Would You Do?

Thinking about strange or difficult situations can help us focus on our values and judgments. How would we react in each of these situations? Let's talk about them and the possible actions you might take. Why would we eliminate choices? Are there other solutions we think are better?

What would you do if you found a wallet with $500 on the street?

- Finders keepers! I'd put the money in my pocket before someone comes looking for it.
- I'd look for I.D. with the owner's name and contact him or her. If there was no name, I would keep the money.
- I'd return the wallet to the police and hope that there would be a reward.

What would you do if you found out your best friend cheated on a quiz at school?

- Tell the teacher right away.
- Try to talk my friend out of cheating in the future.
- Stay out of it—it's none of my business.

What would you do if you woke up one morning to find that the only copy of your book report was accidentally taken out with the garbage?

- Explain what happened to my teacher and say I will turn in the report later.
- Skip breakfast and rewrite the report as quickly as possible so I can hand it in on time.
- Tell my teacher "I guess my report was garbage!" and laugh it off.

What would you do if your dog trampled your neighbors' garden?

- Tell the neighbors what happened and say you're sorry.
- Pretend you have nothing to do with it.
- Tell the neighbors what happened and that you will fix their garden.

Ejercicio de palabras

PALABRAS DE VOCABULARIO

auction   decrease   instinctively   shakily

decades   dilapidated   rafters   swiveled

Palabra por palabra Dame la definición de una de las palabras. Dímela palabra por palabra. ¿Cuántas palabras necesito escuchar antes de adivinar de qué palabra se trata?

PALABRAS DE ORTOGRAFÍA

terrible   considerable   audible   changeable

admirable   impossible   available   predictable

reliable   dependable   valuable   horrible

remarkable   acceptable   profitable   noticeable

believable   reversible   probable   lovable

¿Cómo termina? Te voy a decir una palabra. Antes de deletrearla dime si termina en **ible** o **able**.

······· (fold here) ·······

Conexión con el hogar

Queridos familiares:

Tomamos decisiones todos los días. Algunas son muy simples, como qué ponerse, ¿una camisa azul o una roja? Otras son más importantes, y a veces difíciles. Esta semana estamos leyendo *Honus and Me*, un relato sobre un niño que realiza un descubrimiento emocionante. De hecho, su descubrimiento es tan emocionante que él se siente tentado a tomar una rápida decisión..., pero, ¿es lo que corresponde? Al leer hacemos nuestros propios juicios sobre las acciones y las elecciones de los personajes. Esta destreza nos ayuda a relacionar lo que leemos con nuestras propias decisiones y soluciones.

Destrezas de la semana

Comprensión: hacer juicios

Vocabulario: enciclopedia/diccionario

Ortografía/Fonética: sufijos **able** e **ible**

Nombre_____

¿Qué harías tú?

Pensar en situaciones difíciles o extrañas nos puede ayudar a enfocarnos en nuestros propios valores y juicios. ¿Cómo reaccionaríamos en cada una de estas situaciones? Vamos a hablar acerca de ellas y sobre las posibles acciones que tú emprenderías. ¿Por qué eliminaríamos algunas opciones? ¿Hay otras soluciones que nos parezcan mejor?

What would you do if you found a wallet with $500 on the street?

- Finders keepers! I'd put the money in my pocket before someone comes looking for it.
- I'd look for I.D. with the owner's name and contact him or her. If there was no name, I would keep the money.
- I'd return the wallet to the police and hope that there would be a reward.

What would you do if you found out your best friend cheated on a quiz at school?

- Tell the teacher right away.
- Try to talk my friend out of cheating in the future.
- Stay out of it—it's none of my business.

What would you do if you woke up one morning to find that the only copy of your book report was accidentally taken out with the garbage?

- Explain what happened to my teacher and say I will turn in the report later.
- Skip breakfast and rewrite the report as quickly as possible so I can hand it in on time.
- Tell my teacher "I guess my report was garbage!" and laugh it off.

What would you do if your dog trampled your neighbors' garden?

- Tell the neighbors what happened and say you're sorry.
- Pretend you have nothing to do with it.
- Tell the neighbors what happened and that you will fix their garden.

Comprehension Check

Summarize

Use the Make Judgments Chart to help you decide why baseball is such an important part of American history. Do you think the sport is worthy of a museum? Why do you think it was a good sport to play in a rural place?

Action	Judgment

Think and Compare

1. Why do you think Jackie Robinson was subject to racial insults by baseball fans and other players? Do you think this would happen today? Why or why not? *(Make Judgments)*

2. If you had to create a Hall of Fame museum for a sport, what sport would you pick? Who would be your first Hall of Fame member? *(Analyze)*

3. Explain why many people think that baseball and America are closely tied. *(Synthesize)*

The Baseball Hall of Fame

by Daniel Rosen

Table of Contents

Introduction

"Whoever wants to know the heart and mind of America had better learn baseball."

A famous historian wrote those words in the 1950s when baseball had been America's favorite sport for almost 100 years. People played it in small towns all across the country. In the 1870s many people lived in small towns. Most worked on farms. Baseball was the perfect pastime for them. Baseball was a **rural** game. It slowly became a favorite American sport.

People loved baseball for many reasons. Until the last thirty or forty years, mostly boys played sports. And most American boys grew up playing baseball. They played it all summer long. They played in schoolyards, on farm fields, and in parks. Wherever you could put out four bases, you were likely to find kids playing baseball.

The first professional game of paid players took place in 1869 in Cincinnati, Ohio. In 1876 the National **League** was formed. At the time no other organized sports were played. Professional baseball just made sense to people. It had clear rules. And people enjoyed different things in the game. Some loved memorizing the statistics of individual players. Others admired favorite pitchers or hitters. Still others cheered for their hometown teams. For many years, baseball was the most popular sport in America. It was called America's pastime.

The Cy Young Award is awarded each year ➲ to the best pitcher in honor of Cy Young.

Index

Glossary

artifact *(AHR-ti-fakt)* tool, weapon, or other thing made by people in the past *(page 11)*

commission *(kuh-MISH-uhn)* a group of people chosen to do a special job *(page 5)*

exhibition *(ek-suh-BISH-uhn)* a public show *(page 14)*

golden age *(GOHL-duhn AYJ)* the best years for something *(page 16)*

induction *(in-DUK-shun)* a ceremony of welcoming or including into a group *(page 14)*

integrate *(IN-ti-grayt)* to make open to people of all races *(page 18)*

league *(LEEG)* a number of people or groups joined together for a common purpose *(page 2)*

pennant *(PEN-uhnt)* a flag that stands for the championship in baseball *(page 19)*

plaque *(PLAK)* a flat, decorated piece of metal or wood that is hung on the wall *(page 12)*

rural *(ROOR-uhl)* in the country *(page 2)*

segregation *(seg-ri-GAY-shuhn)* the practice of setting one racial group apart from another *(page 18)*

switch-hitting *(SWICH-HIT-ing)* a player who can bat either right-handed or left-handed *(page 17)*

22

3

Chapter 1
Why Cooperstown?

The small, pretty village of Cooperstown sits about 75 miles southwest of New York's capital, Albany. It is rich with history. It was home to James Fenimore Cooper, a famous American writer. He wrote the book *The Last of the Mohicans*. Cooper's adventure tale was very popular in the 1800s. His father founded the village.

Cooperstown is most famous for the National Baseball Hall of Fame. The Hall of Fame is the museum of baseball. This is where you can learn about the greatest players in baseball. Baseball fans from all over the world visit.

This is the "Field of Dreams" ball field in Cooperstown, NY.

© 2007 Macmillan/McGraw-Hill

The Baseball Hall of Fame

Baseball has been a game of numbers, of dreams, and of heroes. The best of that has been collected by the Hall of Fame. Professional baseball players have been grateful to be able to play the game they love. Today, for some, that job pays millions of dollars a year. The greatest of these players are honored in Cooperstown.

Generations of American children have grown up playing and following baseball. Today most people still watch baseball's most exciting events like the World Series. They cheer for their home team. Just as in decades past, baseball brings people together. The Baseball Hall of Fame and the game it documents continue to be a very important part of America.

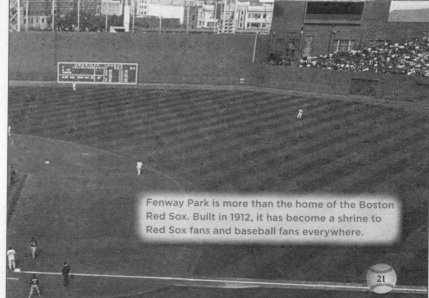

Fenway Park is more than the home of the Boston Red Sox. Built in 1912, it has become a shrine to Red Sox fans and baseball fans everywhere.

Conclusion

Many think that baseball and America go together. In 2002 the Baseball Hall of Fame put together a special show to prove that point. The show, *Baseball as America*, tells about the long history and close connection that baseball has to our country. And for the first time, the show toured the country. It went to many different museums. Most shows only appear at the Hall of Fame in Cooperstown. But this show was so special that the people at the Hall of Fame wanted everyone in the country to have a chance to see it.

© 2007 Macmillan/McGraw-Hill

How did the Hall of Fame come to be located in this little village in the middle of nowhere? There is a very interesting but shakily supported story that gives the reason.

In 1905 a **commission** was appointed to find out how baseball began. Important people sat on the commission. They were mainly politicians and businessmen.

The group studied the issue for three years. In 1908 the commission made an announcement. They claimed that a man named Abner Doubleday had invented baseball. Guess where he did that? You're right. He invented baseball in the village of Cooperstown, New York, in 1839. They said Doubleday had created the game from an old game called Town Ball.

So who was this man? Doubleday had gained fame as an officer in the Civil War. The man who claimed that Doubleday was the inventor of baseball had been a schoolmate of Doubleday's in the 1830s.

Abner Doubleday ⟳
is considered the
inventor of baseball.

5

A Baseball Museum

Baseball officials were delighted with the news that Abner Doubleday had invented baseball. Cheers filled the rafters of the buildings in Cooperstown. Soon people began making plans to start a Baseball Museum there. Someone found an old baseball in a dilapidated barn nearby. People thought that discovery proved that the story was true. In 1939 the National Baseball Hall of Fame and Museum opened in Cooperstown, New York.

◊ Thousands of visitors come to the Hall of Fame every year.

But Branch Rickey signed Jackie Robinson for two reasons. He knew Robinson was strong enough to handle the abuse. And he also knew that Robinson was a great player. Sure enough, Jackie Robinson led the Dodgers to the National League **pennant** with his exciting base-running and timely hitting.

Robinson was a baseball pioneer. But racial discrimination in baseball did not end after Robinson. In 1974 Hank Aaron, an African American slugger for the Atlanta Braves, was poised to break Babe Ruth's career record for homeruns. Aaron received hate mail, even death threats, but went on to set the all-time record for home runs. Jackie Robinson was elected to the Hall of Fame in 1962. Hank Aaron was elected in 1982.

◊ Thousands of fans came to see Negro League games in Major League stadiums. After African American players began to play in the Major Leagues, decreasing attendance meant an end to the Negro League.

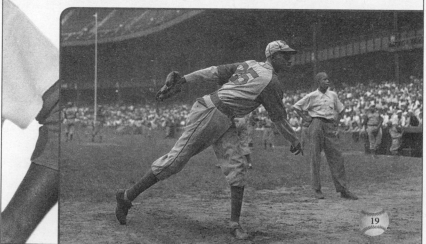

Baseball Gets It Right

The Hall of Fame does more than celebrate great figures in baseball. It also highlights important moments in baseball's history. One of the most important was in 1947 when Jackie Robinson became the first African American player to join a big-league team.

Until the 1940s African Americans were not allowed to play Major League baseball. In much of the American South, **segregation** was the law. That meant separate facilities for whites and blacks. African American players played in their own Negro League. Then in 1947 the Brooklyn Dodgers signed Jackie Robinson. Branch Rickey ran the Dodgers. He warned Robinson that he would be the object of insults and hate.

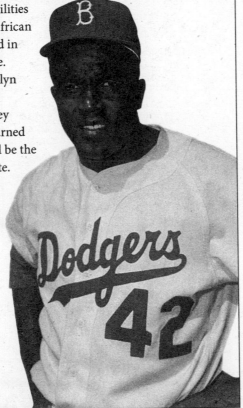

Jackie Robinson was a ↻ great baseball player and the man who **integrated** major league baseball.

Town Ball

The game of Town Ball was played in Massachusetts long before Abner Doubleday is supposed to have invented baseball. The bases were sixty feet apart. They were laid out in a square, not a diamond shape. The batter or "striker" did not stand at the home base but midway between bases. Also, there was no limit to the number of people in the field.

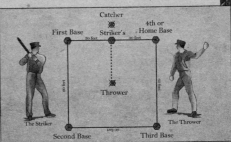

The Baseball Hall of Fame is a wonderful place. And Cooperstown is a wonderful town. But what you just read is not true. Abner Doubleday did not invent baseball. The whole story is a myth!

So, what is the real story? No one knows. Historians do know that baseball developed from several sources. It was based on two English games, cricket and rounders, along with Town Ball and other games. They know it was already being played in the early 1800s. People played it in small towns all across the northeastern United States. Most of the rules of baseball as we know them were set down by Alexander Cartwright in New York City in the 1840s. Abner Doubleday's schoolmate on the commission was wrong.

Chapter 2
The Hall of Fame

In 1939 the Baseball Hall of Fame opened its doors. There are three main parts to the National Baseball Hall of Fame: the Hall of Fame members, the baseball museum, and the research library. The first members were elected to the Hall of Fame in 1936. The Baseball Writers' Association of America was invited to select the first players to be honored. They chose five playing greats to be elected to the Baseball Hall of Fame. They were Babe Ruth, Ty Cobb, Walter Johnson, Christy Mathewson, and Honus Wagner. Who were they?

Babe Ruth might be the best baseball player ever. He is famous for being the first home run slugger who hit more home runs in a season than entire teams did.

Ty Cobb still holds the record for highest batting average in history. Cobb was also a great base stealer. He held the record for hits and stolen bases for many years.

Babe Ruth hit 714 home runs in his career, a record that stood for 38 years.

8

Some people think baseball's best years were the 1950s. At least that is the view of people who lived in and around New York City then. New York City had three teams: the Yankees, the New York Giants, and the Brooklyn Dodgers. Each team had a great centerfielder who was voted into the Hall of Fame.

Many baseball experts consider the Giants' Willie Mays the greatest all-around player ever to play baseball. The Yankees' Mickey Mantle was a **switch-hitting** slugger who led the Yankees to many championships. The Dodgers' Duke Snider was a slugger who was also a great fielder. New York fans loved arguing which centerfielder was the best. Today, many fans still argue about it!

Willie Mays instinctively swiveled and turned at the crack of the bat and outran the ball to make this amazing catch.

17

The Golden Age of Baseball

Before television, fans gathered around radios or telegraph offices to get the latest baseball scores. People went to games whenever they could. Big-league baseball players were everybody's heroes. Those were the sport's finest days. Who were some of the great players elected to the Hall of Fame from this **golden age** of baseball?

Dizzy Dean was one of the greatest pitchers of all time. He pitched for the St Louis Cardinals in the 1930s. Dean won 150 games in a career shortened by an arm injury.

Yogi Berra was a clutch-hitting catcher for the New York Yankees in the 1950s. Berra's "Yogisms" have become part of American folklore.

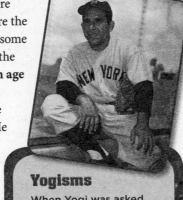

Yogisms

When Yogi was asked if he were going to a popular restaurant, he said: "Nobody goes there. It's too crowded." When he was asked what he thinks about when he is hitting, he said, "Think? Who can think and hit at the same time?" And here's another one: "If you come to a fork in the road, take it."

Walter Johnson pitched many years for the Washington Senators in the American League. Christy Mathewson was a great pitcher for the New York Giants in the National League. They had very similar careers of striking out hitters and winning hundreds of games.

Honus Wagner was a great shortstop and right-handed hitter for the Pittsburgh Pirates in the early 1900s. Wagner won several batting championships. He stole more than 700 bases! And by all accounts, he was the greatest shortstop ever to play the game.

WAGNER, PITTSBURG

⊙ This 1910 baseball card of Honus Wagner was sold at an auction for $640,000.

The Big Train

Walter Johnson was one of the greatest pitchers of all time. Nicknamed "The Big Train," he won 417 games pitching for the Washington Senators from 1907–1927. A hard-throwing right-hand pitcher, Johnson dared batters to hit his fastball. Few could. He set a record for career strikeouts that stood for many years.

The Library and Museum

The research library at the Hall of Fame is a center for fans, writers, and students of baseball alike. It houses all kinds of written information about the game. It has box scores, newspaper accounts, magazine articles, and books. Almost anything you need to know about baseball is there.

Every year the library holds a conference for people who study baseball. Professors from many universities attend to give talks.

The Hall of Fame ⟳ displayed Ichiro Suzuki's bat, spikes, batting gloves, and elbow guard after he broke the 84-year-old record for hits in a season.

Special Elections

Players can not be elected into the Hall of Fame until five years after their last season. But when baseball legend Roberto Clemente died in 1972, the Hall of Fame made a change. Clemente died in a plane crash on his way to help victims of an earthquake. The Hall of Fame held a special election. Clemente received 93 percent of the votes and was inducted into the Hall of Fame in 1973. Clemente made over 3,000 hits during his career and led the National League in batting for four years.

A player must be named on three fourths of the ballots to be accepted into the Hall of Fame. There are other ways to consider nonplayers and players from long ago. A veterans' committee of Hall of Fame members nominates and elects players who did not receive enough votes when they were on the regular ballot. Other committees consider umpires and baseball officials.

The exhibition game at Doubleday Field is a highlight of this special weekend. It's a journey into baseball's past. The field has room for about 9,000 fans. It is much like the baseball fields found in small towns all across America in baseball's early days.

Chapter 3
The People

The highlight of the year at the Hall of Fame is **Induction** Weekend. That is when the newly elected players are made members of the Hall of Fame. Hall of Fame members and thousands of fans attend this celebration. Each new member gives a speech. Then two major league teams play an **exhibition** game at Doubleday Field, located just down the street from the Hall of Fame.

How are members elected? It works this way. Only players who have played ten seasons or more are eligible for consideration. Players do not appear on the ballot until five years after their last season. Then their name goes on the Hall of Fame ballot. A committee of baseball writers and experts votes every year. They can vote for up to ten candidates.

↻ As shown from left to right: Tony Perez, Carlton Fisk, and George "Sparky" Anderson were elected to the Hall of Fame.

14

An 86-Year Wait

The Boston Red Sox won the World Series in 2004 for the first time since 1918. The Red Sox had been close a number of times before but always seemed to find a way to lose. In their previous World Series appearance in 1986, they had a two-run lead with two outs in the ninth inning and lost. Their victory in 2004 was greeted with glee by their fans.

Johnny Damon, centerfield ⊃ for the championship Boston Red Sox, hits a home run.

The baseball museum is home to all the **artifacts**, or objects, of the game. The Hall of Fame has so many artifacts that it constantly changes what is on display. Whenever a player sets a record, the Hall of Fame is there. In 2004, Ichiro Suzuki broke an 84-year-old record for the number of hits in a season. The Hall of Fame requested the bat Suzuki used to get the record hit. The day after the Boston Red Sox won the World Series for the first time in 86 years in 2004, the Hall of Fame asked for and received items from players who had played an important role in the Red Sox victory.

11

 Every member of the Hall of Fame is honored with a bronze plaque.

Would you like to visit the Hall of Fame? Well, you can almost any day of the year. The Hall of Fame is a place that wants visitors. It's open 362 days a year. The Hall is shut down for only three holidays: Thanksgiving, Christmas Day, and New Year's Day.

The main focus of the museum is the Hall of Fame gallery. There each member of the Hall of Fame is celebrated with an individual bronze **plaque**. Each plaque contains a likeness of the player and important facts from his career. Some members of the Hall of Fame were not major league baseball players. Baseball executives, umpires, sportswriters, and broadcasters have also been voted into the Hall of Fame.

12

Upstairs are special displays. Most people want to see the baseball cards from different times. Older fans appreciate finding the cards of players from their youth. Younger fans find today's heroes. Interesting displays are often put together from the many artifacts gathered over the years by the Hall of Fame. Some recent ones have been on baseball in its early days and on women in baseball.

During World War II, many ball players left to fight in the war. But people still wanted to go to baseball games. So, a league of women ball players was started in the Midwest. The museum has a special display telling about the women ballplayers. The women became popular players, but they stopped playing when the men came home.

Baseball Cards

Why are some baseball cards more valuable than others? The cards showing popular players are in greatest demand. Card companies usually make fewer of the most popular cards so that their value goes up.

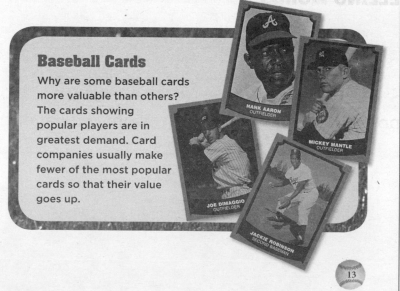

13

Word Workout

WORDS TO KNOW

convictions   evident   oppression   remedies

defiance   momentum   persistent   resonated

Tell Me More Let's talk about fighting for equal rights.
Try to use each vocabulary word in a sentence about
challenges and accomplishments.

SPELLING WORDS

experience   defiance   president   fragrance

occurrence   evident   constant   incident

acquaintance   nuisance   persistent   violence

important   conference   observant   intelligent

permanent   excellent   disappearance

hesitant

This Is the End I'll say a word. Tell me how the word
ends, and then spell it for me.

© Macmillan/McGraw-Hill ·······(fold here)·······

Home-School Connection

Dear Family Member:

Reading biographies helps us learn about the
lives of people who really make a difference. That
is certainly true in *Let It Shine*, a biography about
Rosa Parks. Her brave decision to fight the unfair
rules of segregation gave the civil rights movement
an important focus. We are
learning that many details in
her life prepared her to take
this decisive action. I am
practicing summarizing what
I read. I make sure that my
summaries include the most
important ideas.

This Week's Skills

Comprehension:
summarize

Vocabulary: context
clues

Spelling/Phonics: words ending with **ant, ent, ance,**
and **ence**

Name _____

Which One and Why?

We can find summaries in many places, including TV listings and book catalogs. Reading summaries helps us decide what to watch or read.

- Read these summaries of four documentaries. Which documentary would you like to watch? Why?
- Which one do you think would be best for your class at school? Why?

Sojourner Truth: Ain't I a Woman?

This 30-minute documentary describes the life of Sojourner Truth (c. 1797–1883), a former slave who traveled throughout the United States to gain support for the anti-slavery movement. The story of how she was abused, sold, and exploited helped to convince many people to join this growing movement.

Eyes on the Prize: America's Civil Rights Years

A seven-part documentary explores the key events in the civil rights movement from 1954 to the mid 1980s. Each two-hour episode includes archival footage as well as interviews with experts and people involved in these tumultuous times.

Ida B. Wells: A Passion for Justice

Watch this 54-minute film to learn more about the fascinating life of Ida B. Wells (1862–1931). An early activist for African-American rights, Wells protested many forms of injustice toward black Americans, such as lynching and the unfair treatment of black soldiers.

Nelson Mandela: The Long Walk to Freedom

This excellent 28-minute film brings you an overview of Mandela's life. Jailed in South Africa for his opposition to that country's unfair racial laws, Mandela was eventually released and has helped lead the country to establish a more just government. The film includes rare footage of major events, including several of Mandela's stirring speeches.

Ejercicio de palabras

PALABRAS DE VOCABULARIO

convictions evident   oppression remedies

defiance   momentum persistent resonated

Ampliación Vamos a hablar sobre la lucha por la igualdad de derechos. Trata de usar cada una de las palabras de vocabulario en una oración sobre desafíos y logros.

PALABRAS DE ORTOGRAFÍA

experience   defiance   president   fragrance

occurrence   evident   constant   incident

acquaintance   nuisance   persistent   violence

important   conference   observant   intelligent

permanent   excellent   disappearance

hesitant

Así termina Te voy a decir una palabra. Dime cómo termina y luego deletréala.

(fold here)

© Macmillan/McGraw-Hill

Conexión con el hogar

Queridos familiares:

Leer biografías es bueno para aprender sobre la vida de personas que han hecho algo significativo. Ese sin duda es el caso de *Let It Shine*, una biografía de Rosa Parks. Su valerosa decisión de luchar contra las injustas reglas de la segregación constituyó un importante foco para el movimiento por los derechos civiles. Estamos viendo cómo muchos detalles de su vida la fueron preparando para tomar esta acción decisiva. También estoy practicando resumir lo que leo. Debo asegurarme de que mis resúmenes incluyan las ideas más importantes.

Destrezas de la semana

Comprensión: resumir

Vocabulario: claves de contexto

Ortografía/Fonética: palabras terminadas en **ant, ent, ance** y **ence**

Nombre _____

¿Cuál y por qué?

En las listas de los programas de televisión y en los catálogos de libros hay ejemplos de resumenes. Leerlos nos ayuda a decidir qué mirar o leer.

Lee estos resúmenes de cuatro documentales. ¿Cuál de ellos te gustaría ver? ¿Por qué?
¿Cuál crees que sería mejor para tu clase? ¿Por qué?

Sojourner Truth: Ain't I a Woman?

This 30-minute documentary describes the life of Sojourner Truth (c. 1797–1883), a former slave who traveled throughout the United States to gain support for the anti-slavery movement. The story of how she was abused, sold, and exploited helped to convince many people to join this growing movement.

Eyes on the Prize: America's Civil Rights Years

A seven-part documentary explores the key events in the civil rights movement from 1954 to the mid 1980s. Each two-hour episode includes archival footage as well as interviews with experts and people involved in these tumultuous times.

Ida B. Wells: A Passion for Justice

Watch this 54-minute film to learn more about the fascinating life of Ida B. Wells (1862–1931). An early activist for African-American rights, Wells protested many forms of injustice toward black Americans, such as lynching and the unfair treatment of black soldiers.

Nelson Mandela: The Long Walk to Freedom

This excellent 28-minute film brings you an overview of Mandela's life. Jailed in South Africa for his opposition to that country's unfair racial laws, Mandela was eventually released and has helped lead the country to establish a more just government. The film includes rare footage of major events, including several of Mandela's stirring speeches.

Comprehension Check

Summarize

Use the Summary Chart to outline the chapters and main ideas in *César Chávez*. With the help of your chart, write a short summary of César Chávez's life and work.

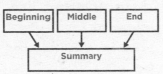

Think and Compare

1. Choose one chapter from the book. Write a short summary of it. Be sure to include details from the chapter. *(Summarize)*

2. Would you want to become a leader like César Chávez? Explain the reasons behind your answer. *(Analyze)*

3. What other people do you know who have made a difference in people's lives? *(Synthesize)*

César Chávez

by Johanna Ehrmann

Table of Contents

CHAPTER ONE

The Early Years

"We can choose to use our lives for others to bring about a better and more just world for our children."
—César Chávez

César Chávez was one of the great labor leaders of our time. Some people are driven to improve the lives of those around them. César Chávez was that kind of person.

When Chávez was young, he and his family were **migrant** workers. They traveled from field to field picking crops. This meant that the Chávez children changed schools often. It also meant that the Chávez family remained poor and had no permanent home.

César's life was filled with hardship, yet he never gave in. He spent his life fighting to improve the lives of migrant workers. Because of Chávez, the lives of **campesinos** (kam-puh-SEE-nohs), or farm workers, are much better today.

Césario Estrada Chávez was born on March 31, 1927, near Yuma, Arizona. He was the second child of Librado and Juana Chávez. César was named for his grandfather, which was telling. To escape **oppression** by the harsh government, his grandfather had fled Mexico in the 1880s. He claimed land in Arizona and started a farm. César was influenced by his grandfather's love of farming and his desire for a better life.

2

Index

23

Glossary

boycott *(BOY-kot)* a refusal to buy something as an expression of protest or as part of a negotiation *(page 14)*

bracero *(brah-SER-oh)* literally "a pair of arms"; Mexican worker admitted to the United States for seasonal agricultural work *(page 10)*

campesino *(kam-pe-SEE-noh)* Latin American farm worker *(page 2)*

Chicano *(chi-KAH-noh)* Mexican American *(page 8)*

collective bargaining *(kuh-LEK-tiv BAR-guhn-ing)* negotiation between an employer and a union *(page 11)*

grievance *(GREE-vuhn(t)s)* complaint, like one a farm worker might bring to an employer about conditions in the fields *(page 10)*

lobby *(LOB-ee)* to work for the passage of a law *(page 18)*

migrant *(MIGH-gruhnt)* a person who moves regularly to find work *(page 2)*

oppression *(uh-PRE-shuhn)* unjust use of power *(page 2)*

picket line *(PIK-it LIGHN)* people posted by a union at a workplace hit by a strike *(page 12)*

scab *(SKAB)* a worker who accepts work during a strike *(page 12)*

strike *(STRIGHK)* a work stoppage *(page 6)*

union *(YEWN-yuhn)* an organization of workers *(page 6)*

César Chávez

As a young boy, César often visited his grandfather's farm. He played in the fields and in secret places on the farm with his brothers and sisters. César worked hard, too, by helping to raise crops and to care for the animals.

César's mother, Juana, was a woman of strong convictions. She taught her son to care for poor people. Although the Chávez family didn't have much money, she never turned a hungry person away. Juana also taught César that fighting wasn't the best way to end a conflict. She always had a *dicho* (DEE-choh), a saying, to explain how one should behave.

⊕ César Chávez's grandfather had a farm like this one in Arizona.

John Steinbeck and *The Grapes of Wrath*

John Steinbeck was a writer who lived in California. He witnessed the migrant workers' awful living and working conditions and wrote about them in a series of newspaper articles. In 1939 Steinbeck published *The Grapes of Wrath*, a novel about the struggles of a family who leaves home in Oklahoma to work in the fields of California. The novel, and the movie based on it, brought public attention to the hard lives of migrant workers.

John Steinbeck ⮂

In 1929 the United States entered the Great Depression. Many people lost their jobs. Then they weren't able to make enough money to feed and clothe their families. At the time the Chávez family owned three businesses. They lost the businesses when customers couldn't pay their bills. The family moved to César's grandparents' farm. Unfortunately the grandparents lost their farm because they couldn't pay the taxes on it. Like hundreds of thousands of others, the Chávez family went to California to find work on farms. To earn money they moved from field to field and picked crops. The hours were long and the work was hard. They earned little money. César was 10 years old.

© 2007 Macmillan/McGraw-Hill

César Chávez

The work didn't end with César Chávez's death. Recently the UFW has helped enact new laws. These laws improve contract negotiation for farm workers. They punish labor contractors who cheat. The UFW continues to work for more laws that will improve conditions for farm workers.

⮂ Today Chávez is an honored leader.

César Chávez was remembered ⮂ with a postage stamp.

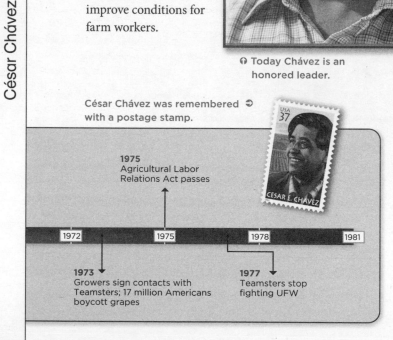

1975
Agricultural Labor Relations Act passes

1972   1975   1978   1981

1973
Growers sign contacts with Teamsters; 17 million Americans boycott grapes

1977
Teamsters stop fighting UFW

Conclusion

"In the end we will overcome."
—César Chávez

César Chávez was a man of humble beginnings. But he spent his life improving conditions for the poorest, most powerless people in the country. He lived by some basic principles. He worked for unity among groups of farm workers and with other unions. He believed in nonviolence. He refused to give in to racism or corruption. These principles made Chávez's efforts successful. People all around the world still admire his example.

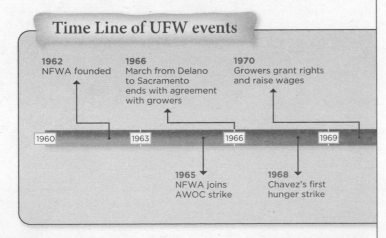

Time Line of UFW events

1962 NFWA founded

1966 March from Delano to Sacramento ends with agreement with growers

1970 Growers grant rights and raise wages

1960   1963   1966   1969

1965 NFWA joins AWOC strike

1968 Chavez's first hunger strike

César Chávez

Over the next years, the Chávez family drove from town to town. They picked strawberries, apricots, lettuce, cotton, or whatever crop was ready to harvest. As workers they had to bend over for hours at a time. There were few if any breaks.

César may have attended as many as 65 schools. César hated school. Teachers often treated migrant children harshly. The migrant students were forbidden to speak Spanish. They were made fun of because of their clothes and their lack of education. César left school after finishing eighth grade. It was time to earn more money to help his family.

In the fields Chávez saw how badly the farm workers were treated. The conditions were unsafe. People were sprayed with pesticides. Once César saw a small girl killed by a tractor.

↻ The Chávez family lived in immigrant housing like this.

ⓘ Signs like this were common in the United States in the mid-twentieth century.

The Chávez family didn't accept the harsh conditions. In hopes of improving conditions, Librado joined several **unions**. If a **strike**, or work stoppage, was called, the Chávez family were the first to leave the fields. César called his family the "strikingest family." Many workers were afraid to protest. They were afraid they would lose their jobs if they said anything.

In 1943 César met Helen Fabela. He was 16 years old and she was 15. Helen, like César, had done farm work from an early age. They became good friends. At the age of 17, César joined the U.S. Navy. He was tired of farm work and wanted to do something different.

In those days many public places separated people by race. One day César went to the movies in Delano, California. In an act of defiance, he sat in the whites-only section. César was taken to jail. He wasn't charged with a crime and was released shortly. The experience of standing up for equal rights stayed with Chávez.

In 1991 César received the *Aguila Azteca* (Aztec Eagle). The award is Mexico's highest honor. Two years later, his fight ended. He died in his sleep on April 22, 1993, at the age of 66. The years of hard work, fasting, and putting others' concerns ahead of his own had taken their toll.

It was evident that a great labor leader was gone. Tens of thousands of people marched behind his coffin. After his death, Chávez was awarded the Presidential Medal of Freedom. Today his son-in-law and others carry on the work of the UFW.

ⓘ Chávez became a powerful speaker.

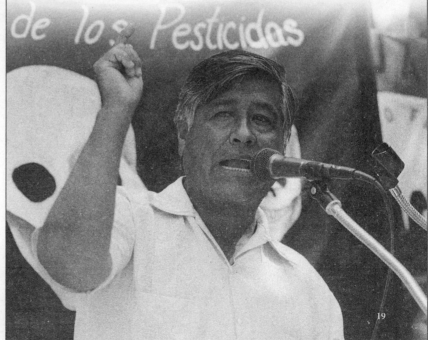

César Chávez

CHAPTER FOUR

The Fight Continues

"We draw our strength from the very despair in which we have been forced to live. We shall endure."
—César Chávez

But by 1975, about 17 million Americans were boycotting grapes. César felt that more was needed. One thing that became clear to him was that labor laws needed to cover farm workers. If they didn't, farm workers would never have a lasting victory. Each time a contract expired, growers tried to replace it with one that cost them less—and that was less fair to farm workers.

César began to fight for a state law that would protect California farm workers. In June 1975, the California Agricultural Labor Relations Act was signed. The act gave farm workers the right to bargain collectively and to vote for unions. In 1977 the Teamsters finally agreed to let only the United Farm Workers of America (UFW) represent farm workers. In the early 1980s, UFW membership peaked at close to 100,000 members.

Through the 1970s and 1980s, César fought for the rights of farm workers. He turned to **lobbying** to make lasting changes. Despite problems within the UFW, he always remembered what the real struggle was. César returned to boycotting to ban pesticide use in 1984.

A Day in the Life of a Migrant Worker

Rita Chávez Medina, César's sister, wrote this story about a migrant worker's typical day.

My mother and I used to tie carrots in the field. We would leave about 3:00 in the morning in order to get a space to go to work. We would start work with headlights from cars and tractors.

It gets hot very early—well over a hundred degrees—and we couldn't work when it was hot, but we stayed in the fields in the shade until it got cool, and then we would start working again until we couldn't see at night.

In those days they had raffia, that grasslike string, to tie the carrots with, and we had to buy it by the pound. It was so expensive we'd soak it, then split it into four strands so that it would go much farther. Later they let that go, and we used wire.

We tied bunches by the dozen, and then we crated them; I think we got about five cents a dozen. My mother and I made about three dollars a day, and we had to pay three dollars a week to the person that gave us the ride there, plus our lunch. After we got home, about 6:00, we would cook, clean the house, and do all the chores.

CHAPTER TWO

Organizing the Workers

*"It is my deepest belief that only by
giving our lives do we find life."*
—César Chávez

In 1946 César left the Navy. He returned to the
California fields. He and Helen Fabela were married.
Then César had an encounter that changed his life. He
met Fred Ross of the Community Service Organization
(CSO). The CSO fought for fair treatment for **Chicanos**
(chi-KAH-nohs), or Mexican Americans.

At first César didn't believe a white person could
understand the problems of the Chicano people. After
hearing Ross speak, Chávez changed his mind. Fred
Ross's words resonated inside César like a song he'd
heard long ago. This was a person who understood.
This was a person who was making a difference. This
was someone César could learn from.

8

The growers still were not ready to work with the
farmworkers' union. Once again César drew attention
to the cause. He sent people across the country to
convince shoppers to stop buying grapes. At the end of
July 1970, the growers finally agreed to allow the union
in. The union, now known as the United Farm Workers
Organizing Committee (UFWOC), won in many places.
New contracts were more favorable to the farm workers.
They promised better pay and limited the use of some
pesticides. This was perhaps Chávez's biggest victory.

Unfortunately the new contracts weren't lasting
remedies. They expired in three years. In 1973 the
growers signed new contracts with the Teamsters. These
new contracts were not as favorable to the farm workers.
Violence rose in the fields. Several people were killed.

César decided to end the fight once
and for all. He declared a
worldwide boycott of grapes.
Consumers responded and
many Americans refused
to buy grapes. As the
momentum of the boycott
grew, so did the violence
between the Teamsters and
striking farm workers.

Union members and ↺
ordinary people walked
in picket lines.

17

Gandhi and Nonviolence

Mohandas K. Gandhi (1869–1948) was the man who helped free India from British rule. He pioneered the tactic of nonviolent resistance that César Chávez followed. Gandhi spent years resisting the British with simple yet powerful acts. He wove his own cloth so he wouldn't have to buy British goods. He led a march to the sea to get salt, because the government controlled the salt industry. He fasted to stop violence. India won independence in 1948, largely through Gandhi's efforts.

Growers weren't the only group unhappy with the NFWA's growing power. Another union, called the Teamsters, wanted to organize farm workers, too. The Teamsters was a national organization with millions of members. Chávez and others didn't think the Teamsters understood the problems of farm workers.

The Teamsters continued to oppose the NFWA. The two unions fought. Chávez believed that nonviolent resistance was the right path. César decided to fast until union members agreed not to fight back if attacked. He stopped eating for 25 days. César lost weight and grew weak. His fast didn't end until union members agreed to nonviolence.

Fred Ross

Fred Ross, like César Chávez, was a man who worked hard to end injustice. He spent his life helping ordinary people improve their lives. During the Depression he managed migrant-labor camps. After the war he started the Community Service Organization (CSO). Ross realized the importance of voter registration. He was a firm believer in making changes one person at a time.

By day César worked in the fields. At night he worked for the CSO, registering voters. By voting, workers could try to make their voices heard. He also helped people deal with immigration, welfare, and the police. César was an unlikely leader. He was only 5 feet 6 inches tall—and very shy. Because of his shyness, he found it hard to speak in front of groups of people. At his first meeting, César stood still for a long time without saying anything.

But César was persistent and didn't give up. He was very successful in registering voters. In a few years, he became head of the CSO. Because of his own experiences, César wanted the CSO to help organize a union for farm workers. The CSO refused to back this effort. As a result Chávez left the CSO. He started organizing farm workers on his own.

◔ Fred Ross speaks to a group at a CSO meeting.

The challenge of starting a union both frightened and excited César Chávez. His family was growing. He worried about supporting them.

César helped organize the National Farm Workers Association (NFWA). His goal was to improve the lives of the farm workers who were still working under harsh conditions. The growers ignored the workers' **grievances**, or complaints. The growers brought in *braceros* (brah-SER-ohs), guest workers from Mexico, to work their fields. By law local workers had to be hired first, but the growers used Mexican workers anyway. They could pay *braceros* less.

César and the NFWA began organizing farm workers. They left postcards where farm workers would see them. On one side of the card, the worker wrote his or her name and address. On the other side, the worker wrote what he or she would like to change about working conditions. In 1962 the new organization held its first gathering.

At the first meeting of the NFWA, its new flag with the union eagle was displayed prominently. ↻

10

César Chávez

15

CHAPTER THREE

The Grape Boycott

"When a man or woman, young or old, takes a place on the picket line even for a day or two, he will never be the same."
—César Chávez

Despite the strike, the grape grower would still not make a deal with the union. So César started a **boycott**. He asked people not to buy the company's products.

To gain more publicity, Chávez decided on a march. Sixty-five people began to march on March 17, 1966, in Delano. Along the way more people stepped in. At times the line of marchers stretched for two miles. As they marched, they sang and chanted slogans like *Viva la Causa* (Long Live the Cause). The march ended in Sacramento. There, on April 10, 1966, Chávez made an announcement. The company had agreed to a contract with the union.

The victory was a partial one. Other grape growers refused to work with the union. To get their grapes past the boycott, some growers switched labels on boxes. Customers thought they were buying grapes that weren't being boycotted. In 1968 the confusion convinced Chávez to extend the boycott to all California grapes.

Chávez speaks to a crowd ➲
about the boycott.

14

Labor Unions

Labor unions are based on the idea that a group of people has more power than an individual. In the nineteenth century, workers started forming unions to use **collective bargaining**. One or more workers would meet with the employer to try to agree on wages, working conditions, and hours. Workers could threaten to go on strike if their conditions weren't met.

Unions were slow to take root in California's migrant farm worker community. This was partly because of racism. The labor movement wanted nothing to do with unions whose members weren't white. Many of the early farm workers were Chinese or Japanese.

A migrant work force moved around a lot. Many workers didn't share a common language. The different ethnic groups were often suspicious of one another. All of these things kept the workers separated and powerless. César Chávez was about to change all that.

11

Members of the NFWA continued to meet with workers. By 1965 the union represented 1,700 families. In September, Filipino (a group of people from the Philippines) workers went on strike. To fight for better pay, they refused to pick ripe grapes on the vines.

The NFWA voted to strike with them. Most of the NFWA members were Chicanos, which created a diverse group. It was unusual to have different ethnic groups working together for a common goal. To bring down wages, growers often set groups against each other.

Growers didn't want to negotiate with the strikers. They brought in 5,000 **scabs**—workers who were willing to cross **picket lines** to work. The Great Delano Grape Strike was on.

An NFWA organizer stands on the roof of a car. *Huelga* is the Spanish word for "strike."

El Malcriado
(The Voice of the Farm Worker)

One reason for the success of Chávez and the NFWA was *El Malcriado*, the newspaper of the movement. It reported what was happening in the union, and it was written in a humorous tone. Because not all farm workers could read, the newspaper included cartoons to get its point across.

To increase the strike's impact, Chávez decided to focus on one big company that owned the farms where the grapes were grown. Farm workers picketed the docks in Los Angeles and San Francisco. Longshoremen load and unload cargo on boats. They honored the picket line. They refused to load grapes picked by scabs onto boats.

↻ Workers stand in a picket line.

12

13

Word Workout

WORDS TO KNOW

commissioned	envisioned	philosopher
recommend	elaborate	miniature
proportion	renaissance	

What Would You Build Let's use words to describe a statue you would like to create for our local park.

SPELLING WORDS

co-worker	cooperate	submit
submarine	combine	commission
intersection	interrupt	postwar
interfere	transformation	profession
postpone	transform	transfer
proportion	transparent	companion
suburb	copilot	

Word Families Let's see how many words we can define by understanding the prefix and base word.

(fold here)

Home-School Connection

Dear Family Member:

A project can take a long time, but the story of Leonardo's horse stretches more than five hundred years! Leonardo da Vinci dreamed of creating a huge bronze horse. Although he accomplished many remarkable feats during his lifetime, he died without fulfilling this dream. We are reading "Leonardo's Horse," the true story of two artists who decided to make Leonardo's dream a reality. While I read this article, I am also making generalizations about art, hard work, and dedication.

This Week's Skills

Comprehension: make generalizations

Vocabulary: word parts

Spelling/Phonics: Greek and Latin prefixes

Name _____

Make It True

These generalizations are just plain false. How many ways can we reword each one to make the sentence true. For example, you might change *All cats can fly* to *No cats can fly* or *All eagles can fly*. Be creative in your statements.

All apples are blue.

All paintings are beautiful.

No students study hard.

All horses can talk.

Ejercicio de palabras

PALABRAS DE VOCABULARIO

commissioned	envisioned	philosopher
recommend	elaborate	miniature
proportion	renaissance	

¿Qué construirías? Vamos a usar las palabras para describir una estatua que podrías construir para el parque de tu vecindad.

PALABRAS DE ORTOGRAFÍA

co-worker	cooperate	submit
submarine	combine	commission
intersection	interrupt	postwar
interfere	transformation	profession
postpone	transform	transfer
proportion	transparent	companion
suburb	copilot	

Definiciones Vamos a ver cuántas palabras podemos definir a partir del prefijo y la palabra base.

Conexión con el hogar

Queridos familiares:

Está bien que un proyecto puede tomar mucho tiempo, pero la historia del caballo de Leonardo dura más de quinientos años. Leonardo Da Vinci soñaba con construir un enorme caballo de bronce. Aunque realizó hazañas admirables durante su vida, el artista murió sin cumplir con ese sueño. Estamos leyendo *Leonardo's Horse*, la verdadera historia de dos artistas que decidieron convertir en realidad el sueño de Leonardo. Mientras leo este artículo hago generalizaciones sobre el arte, el empeño y la dedicación.

Destrezas de la semana

Comprensión: hacer generalizaciones

Vocabulario: partes de una palabra

Ortografía/Fonética: prefijos del griego y del latín

Nombre _____

Vuélvelo verdadero

Estas generalizaciones son todas falsas. ¿De cuántas maneras podemos cambiarlas para convertirlas en verdaderas? Por ejemplo, se puede cambiar *Todos los gatos pueden volar* a *Ningún gato puede volar* o a *Todas las águilas pueden volar.*

All paintings are beautiful.

All horses can talk.

All apples are blue.

No students study hard.

Comprehension Check

Summarize

Use the Generalization Chart to help you summarize each chapter of *Stories on the Ceiling*. What did the choices Michelangelo made say about him?

Important Information	Generalization

Think and Compare

1. Look back at the description on page 19 of how Michelangelo painted the Sistine Chapel ceiling. Why do you think he worked so hard on this project even though he nearly ruined his health? *(Make Generalizations)*

2. Would you want to become an apprentice as Michelangelo did when he was only 13? What do you think were some of the good things about being an artist's apprentice? What were some of the bad things? *(Analyze)*

3. During the Renaissance, art was very important. Do you think it is still as important today? Why or why not? *(Evaluate)*

Stories
on the
Ceiling

by George Capaccio

Table of Contents

Introduction

Would you like to create a painting on a ceiling? Well, one artist did. Many think that he is one of the greatest artists who ever lived. Who was he? He was an Italian named Michelangelo Buonarroti (migh-kuhl-AN-juh-loh bwawn-uh-RAW-tee). But Michelangelo did more than paint. He was also a poet, a **sculptor**, and an architect.

Michelangelo was born during a period of time called the **Renaissance** (REN-uh-sahns). The word *Renaissance* is French. It means "rebirth." The Renaissance took place in Europe. This "rebirth" of art and learning began in the 1300s. It lasted about 200 years.

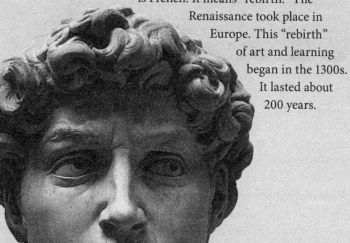

↫ This is the head of *David*, one of Michelangelo's most famous sculptures.

2

23

Glossary

apprentice *(uh-PREN-tis)* a person who works for a skilled worker in order to learn a trade or art *(page 7)*

bronze *(BRONZ)* a reddish brown metal made by melting together copper and tin *(page 15)*

commission *(kuh-MISH-uhn)* a thing that a person or persons are asked and trusted to do *(page 12)*

fresco *(FRES-koh)* the art of painting on fresh, moist plaster *(page 10)*

master *(MAS-tuhr)* a person who has great skill or knowledge about something *(page 8)*

pollution *(puh-LEW-shuhn)* harmful materials such as certain gases, chemicals, and wastes that pollute the air, water, or soil *(page 21)*

proportion *(pruh-POR-shuhn)* the relation of one thing to another with regard to size, number, or amount *(page 18)*

Renaissance *(REN-uh-sahns)* the revival in learning, art, and literature that began in Italy in the 1300s *(page 2)*

restorer *(ri-STAW-uhr)* a person who brings back something to its former or original condition *(page 21)*

sculptor *(SKULP-tuhr)* a person who makes or carves figures in stone, wood, marble, metal, or any other material *(page 2)*

vaulted *(VAWLT-id)* arched *(page 17)*

🎧 This is a portrait of Michelangelo painted by another artist.

The Renaissance was a special time for artists. Painters and sculptors created many great works of art. Artists were much admired in this period. Rich families helped to support them.

Today museums around the world display the finest of these works of art, which we still admire. But Michelangelo's works stand out in modern times even more than they did during his life. Every year, people come from around the world to see one of his most famous works, the Sistine Chapel.

Michelangelo: Budding Genius

Michelangelo's family had deep roots in the city of Florence. His mother, Francesca, was related to a very powerful man. He was Lorenzo de Medici (MED-uh-chee), who ruled the city. Michelangelo's father, Lodovico (loh-doh-VEE-koh), came from a long line of government officials. But at the time Michelangelo was born, the family wasn't doing well. Money was scarce. Yet Lodovico refused to get a regular job. He thought of himself as a gentleman. In those days, gentlemen didn't work, at least not with their hands.

The family was saved when Lodovico became mayor of a small village called Caprese (kah-PRAY-zay). Lodovico and his family moved into a simple stone house and began a new life.

⌒ The photo on top shows the fresco before cleaning and the photo on the bottom shows it after.

In 1979 an art **restorer** used a new cleaning solution on a small section of one of the frescoes. It did not harm the paint. So for the next 10 years, a team completely cleaned and restoredall of the frescoes on the ceiling.

Since the restoration, special air filters have been installed. They reduce **pollution** and will help to keep the colors fresh for years to come.

Today, people from around the world come to see the Michelangelo's masterpiece. His greatest work will last forever.

Conclusion

Michelangelo is considered on of the greatest artisits who ever lived. And the Sistine Chapel is considered a masterpiece.

But 500 years later, candle soot, dust, oil, and grease had damaged the ceiling of the Sistine Chapel. The gorgeous colors of Michelangelo's frescos had darkened. Could the ceiling be preserved?

↻ Restorers used computer technology to help in their work.

Early in the morning of March 6, 1475, Francesca gave birth to her second child. They named him Michelangelo.

While Michelangelo was still a baby, his father lost his job. The family decided to return to Florence. His mother was very ill at the time. She could not care for her infant son. So she left him with a stonecutter and his wife. The couple lived in a nearby village. Most of the men in this village were also stonecutters.

Later, his father sent for Michelangelo. But when the boy was only six, his mother died. After that, his father sent him back to the stonecutter and his wife. Michelangelo was happy to go because he loved living with them.

The Craft of Stonecutting

Stonecutters were highly skilled workers. They cut and finished stone. In Michelangelo's time, stonecutters carved the decorative parts of frames and moldings. They were artists who worked in stone.

☜ The house in Caprese where Michelangelo was born is still standing.

6

🎧 When Michelangelo finished, he had filled the enormous ceiling of the Sistine Chapel with paintings of stories and portraits of people. The paintings above and to the right are two small sections of the ceiling.

19

Michelangelo then began working out the details of the design he envisioned. At the same time, he built a platform from which he would work.

Because he would be working in fresco, he had to make exact drawings of all the important scenes and figures. These would later be transferred to wet plaster on the ceiling. Michelangelo hired models to pose for him. He made hundreds of sketches of each one. Because he loved sculpting so much, he also used miniature clay or wax models for his drawings. He did this to get a sense of **proportion**.

In July 1508, Michelangelo climbed up to the platform. He had five helpers on hand, but they were poor painters. Michelangelo soon sent them home.

From then on, he worked alone. He spent most of each day standing on his platform some 60 feet in the air. His back was bent like a bow. He wrote, "My paintbrush all the day doth drop . . . on my face."

Often he ate nothing but a chunk of bread. At night he would fall into bed with his boots and clothes still on. For four long years, Michelangelo lived and worked this way.

Pope Julius kept pestering him to finish. He threatened to have Michelangelo thrown from his platform if he didn't stop painting. Michelangelo got the message. He completed his work. On October 31, 1512, the Sistine Chapel was opened to the public.

© 2007 Macmillan/McGraw-Hill

Stories on the Ceiling

Four years later, Lodovico remarried. He brought his 10-year-old son back to Florence a second time. He enrolled him in grammar school. Michelangelo had to study penmanship, reading, Latin, and Greek. His father hoped he would grow up to become a gentleman.

But young Michelangelo soon grew bored with school. He had dreams of his own. Even as a child, he wanted only one thing—to become an artist.

Michelangelo became close friends with an older boy named Francesco. Francesco worked as an **apprentice**, or person learning to be an artist. His master was Domenico Ghirlandaio (doh-MEHN-ee-koh geer-lahn-DIGH-oh), a famous Florentine painter. Michelangelo showed his drawings to Francesco. His friend knew right away that Michelangelo had talent   lots of it. Francesco gave Michelangelo drawings to study and copy. Michelangelo so impressed his friend that Francesco brought him to meet Ghirlandaio.

Michelangelo spent a lot of time hanging around the studio. When he was 13, he decided that he wanted to become an apprentice to an artist. To do so, he would have to quit school. He asked his father for permission. His father got very angry. He thought artists were no better than shoemakers. They were not gentlemen.

But Michelangelo did not give up. Finally in April 1488 Michelangelo began a three-year apprenticeship at Ghirlandaio's studio.

↩ This sketch is Michelangelo's earliest known drawing. He was a teenager when he drew it.

CHAPTER 2

Becoming an Artist

Ghirlandaio and his brother were **master** artists. They taught Michelangelo and the other apprentices everything about painting and drawing. Most apprentices paid for their lessons. But the masters saw how talented Michelangelo was. They felt honored to train him. So, they paid him!

Michelangelo had a lot to learn. He had to know how to mix paints and make brushes. He had to spend long hours copying the work of older artists. He had to learn to draw. He had to learn how to use different tools, such as pen and ink, charcoal, and paints.

Apprentices learned to paint in workshops. These workshops were like painting factories. Artists were businessmen. They had to sell their art to make money. Ghirlandaio had one of the most successful workshops in Florence. The people who bought his drawings and paintings could afford to pay high prices. They were among the city's wealthiest citizens.

Michelangelo did this ⟳
charcoal drawing.

© 2007 Macmillan/McGraw-Hill

Stories on the Ceiling

The Pope was very pleased with his statue. So he commissioned Michelangelo to paint the ceiling of the Sistine Chapel in Vatican City. The Chapel was named after its founder, Pope Sixtus IV. It is a rectangular brick building with a **vaulted**, or arched, ceiling. The Chapel is where church leaders meet to elect a new pope.

The ceiling was painted blue and decorated with gold stars. Pope Julius wanted Michelangelo to paint frescoes over the old ceiling. The artist didn't like painting. He especially didn't like painting in fresco.

How do you paint a ceiling that is about the size of two tennis courts? Michelangelo searched for a good design. Finally, he came up with an idea. He would paint frescoes that would tell stories from the Bible.

Michelangelo ⟳
painted nine stories
in the center of the
ceiling, surrounded
by smaller portraits
on the sides.

Making a Bronze Statue

Bronze is a blend of two metals—copper and tin. During the Renaissance, artists made statues out of bronze. They used a method called the lost wax process. This process is one of the oldest ways of making art. Here's how you do it:

Step 1 Make a sculpture out of clay. Be sure every detail you want in the final bronze statue is in your original.

Step 2 Create a plaster mold around your sculpture.

Step 3 When the mold is dry, remove the original sculpture. Clean the inside of the mold.

Step 4 Pour hot wax into the mold. After the wax hardens, remove the mold. What's left is a wax version of your original sculpture.

Step 5 Now create a new plaster mold around the wax sculpture.

Step 6 When this mold is dry, put it in an oven to melt the wax from inside. You will be left with a hollow mold.

Step 7 Pour liquid bronze into the empty mold.

Step 8 Let the bronze cool and harden. Then, cut away the outer plaster mold. Now you have it—a bronze version of your original clay sculpture.

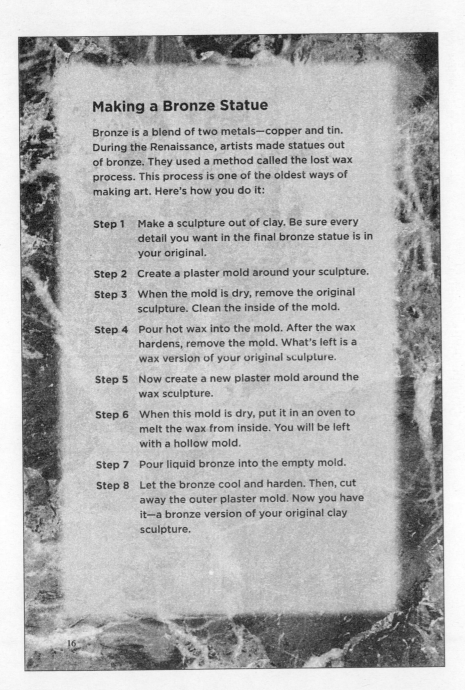

16

Stories on the Ceiling

9

Ghirlandaio taught the young Michelangelo how to draw with pen and ink. The master also taught him the art of **fresco** (FRES-koh) painting. Ghirlandaio was famous for his fresco paintings. *Fresco* is an Italian word that means "fresh." Painters apply water-based paint to a layer of wet plaster. During drying, the paint chemically bonds with the plaster. For this reason, the colors resist fading, even after hundreds of years.

The artists must work fast. This is because the plaster dries in about 6–12 hours, depending on the weather. Artists painted in sections. Each section had to be small enough to finish in one day. If they made a mistake or wanted to change something, they waited until the plaster had dried. Then they painted in their changes. But there was a problem with this method. The paints that were applied after the plaster had dried didn't last.

Artists also had to learn how to work together when painting in fresco. It was a team effort. The master painted the main figures. Then his best apprentices painted in the other figures. Finally, helpers added the background and details, such as trees, flowers, or birds. Ghirlandaio probably put Michelangelo to work on frescoes as a way to train him.

CHAPTER 4

Painting the Ceiling of the Sistine Chapel

Michelangelo wanted to devote himself to sculpture. It was the art form he loved the most. When he was 23 years old, he left his father's home and settled in Rome. Here he created many beautiful statues.

Over the next 10 years, Michelangelo became the most famous artist in Italy. He was so respected that Pope Julius II, head of the Catholic Church, commissioned Michelangelo to work on several very important projects. Pope Julius was used to getting his way. He demanded a giant **bronze** statue of himself. Michelangelo agreed although he hated working in bronze.

This is a portrait ⮑
of Pope Julius.

⊙ Michelangelo often practiced drawing the human form.

Almost overnight, Michelangelo found himself living in an elaborate palace. He wore elegant clothes. He went to school with Lorenzo's three boys. Evenings at the palace were special. He would often have dinner with Lorenzo's friends. They included some of the most famous philosophers in Europe.

Three years later, Lorenzo de Medici suddenly died. Michelangelo's life changed again. With a heavy heart, the 17-year-old artist moved back to his father's house in Florence. He was no longer an apprentice. He was an artist doing his best to take care of his family.

Painting in Fresco

Steps:

1. Make a full-size drawing, called a cartoon.

2. Poke tiny holes along the outlines of the drawing.

3. Have your apprentices apply a layer of wet plaster to the wall.

4. Have them transfer your drawing to the wet plaster.

5. Tell them to rub charcoal dust through the holes along the outlines and then remove the cartoon.

6. Now pick up your brush and begin to paint.

7. Be sure to do the most important parts yourself. Leave the rest to your apprentices and helpers.

CHAPTER 3

Adopted by the Medicis

Michelangelo worked to improve his drawing. He also worked on sculptures. He was happy. But Michelangelo was to stay with his teacher for only one year. He received an invitation that he couldn't refuse.

Lorenzo de Medici, the wealthy and powerful ruler of Florence, kept many ancient Greek and Roman statues in his private garden. One day he decided to start a school to train young sculptors. He hoped that in time he could **commission**, or pay, them to create statues as beautiful as the ones in his garden.

Lorenzo met with Ghirlandaio. He asked him to recommend two of his own apprentices. The painter chose Francesco and his good friend Michelangelo, who was now about 14 years old.

Michelangelo would need his father's permission, of course. But this time, Lodovico didn't put up a fight.

↳ Lorenzo de Medici was also known as Lorenzo the Magnificent because of his wealth.

© 2007 Macmillan/McGraw-Hill

Stories on the Ceiling

Pietro Torrigiano (tohr-ee-JAHN-oh) was the boy who punched Michelangelo in the nose. He grew up to become a sculptor. This is what he said happened:

Buonarroti had the bad habit of making fun of anyone else who was drawing there, and one day he provoked me so much that I lost my temper more than usual, and, clenching my fist, gave him such a punch on the nose that I felt the bone and cartilage crush like a biscuit. So that fellow will carry my signature until he dies.

So Michelangelo began to study sculpture in Lorenzo's garden. He kept to himself much of the time. He did not make friends easily. One day he insulted a fellow apprentice. The boy lost his temper. He hit Michelangelo, breaking his nose.

Lorenzo wanted to help Michelangelo. He asked Lodovico for permission to adopt Michelangelo. He promised to raise him like his own son. He even promised to find a job for Lodovico. Lodovico agreed.

Michelangelo ↳ painted this portrait of himself.

Word Workout

WORDS TO KNOW

destination	formally	honorable	tinkering
fidget	glumly	immigrated	unsteady

One Word? Choose one of the words above. Give me a one- or two-word clue to help me guess your word.

SPELLING WORDS

immigrate	arrive	illuminate
suffix	illegal	impatiently
collect	accommodate	illogical
support	accompany	arrest
collaborate	immigration	correspond
announce	irregular	immature
suppress	assembly	

Beginning to Sound the Same I'll ask you to spell one of the words. Then I'll ask you to give and spell the other words that begin with the same sound.

(fold here)

© Macmillan/McGraw-Hill

Home-School Connection

Dear Family Member:

One of the great things about science fiction stories is that anything can happen! This week, we're reading a fun story called *LAFF*. It's about a genius kid who invents a time travel machine and the clever way another student uses this discovery. When traveling back and forth from the future, it's very important to keep track of what happens when. A lot happens, so I need to pay attention to the sequence of events.

This Week's Skills

Comprehension: sequence

Vocabulary: thesaurus/dictionary

Spelling/Phonics: suffixes

Name _____

It's About Time

The events here and on the opposite page tell about Marcia, a student who wants to make a great display for her upcoming school projects fair. We see Marcia's efforts both in the past and the future. Put the events in order from 1 to 10. Then we can read the story aloud together.

_____ Then, Marcia gets a great idea.

_____ When she returns, Marcia makes a display for the school history fair about the 1939 World's Fair. The key chain is the centerpiece.

_____ At the Projects Fair, Marcia's display is a big hit. Everyone says that the 2039 key chain shows Marcia's great imagination. She just smiles.

_____ Marcia invents a time machine. She keeps it a secret.

_____ At the fair, she buys a key chain as a souvenir.

_____ Marcia replaces the key chain from the past with the one from the future to her display.

_____ She decides to use the time machine to travel forward in time to 2039.

_____ She goes to the World's Fair that takes place in 2039. She gets a key chain souvenir and returns home.

_____ She uses the machine to travel back to the 1939 World's Fair in New York City.

_____ However, Marcia is not satisfied with her display. She thinks it is missing something.

Ejercicio de palabras

PALABRAS DE VOCABULARIO

destination	formally	honorable	tinkering
fidget	glumly	immigrated	unsteady

Pocas palabras bastan Escoge una de las palabras de la lista. Dame una pista de una o dos palabras para que yo pueda adivinar de qué palabra se trata.

PALABRAS DE ORTOGRAFÍA

immigrate	arrive	illuminate
suffix	illegal	impatiently
collect	accommodate	illogical
support	accompany	arrest
collaborate	immigration	correspond
announce	irregular	immature
suppress	assembly	

Un comienzo parecido Te voy a pedir que deletrees una palabra. Luego te pediré que me digas el resto de las palabras que comienzan con el mismo sonido y que las deletrees.

(fold here)

© Macmillan/McGraw-Hill

Conexión con el hogar

Queridos familiares:

¡Una de las cosas que más me gusta de la ciencia ficción es que puede pasar cualquier cosa! Esta semana estamos leyendo un divertido relato que se llama *LAFF*. Trata de un niño genio que inventa una máquina de viajar en el tiempo, y del ingenioso uso que le da otro estudiante a este descubrimiento. Cuando se va y se vuelve del futuro, es muy importante seguir la pista de lo que pasa y cuándo. Como pasan muchas cosas hay que prestar atención al orden.

Destrezas de la semana

Comprensión: orden de los sucesos

Vocabulario: enciclopedia/diccionario

Ortografía/ Fonética: sufijos

Nombre_____

El momento indicado

Los sucesos narrados en esta página y la siguiente se refieren a Marcia, una estudiante que planea hacer una gran exhibición para la próxima feria de proyectos de la escuela. Se describen las acciones de Marcia tanto en el pasado como en el futuro. Pon los sucesos en orden de 1 a 10. Después, podemos leer juntos el relato en voz alta.

_____ Then, Marcia gets a great idea.

_____ When she returns, Marcia makes a display for the school history fair about the 1939 World's Fair. The key chain is the centerpiece.

_____ At the Projects Fair, Marcia's display is a big hit. Everyone says that the 2039 key chain shows Marcia's great imagination. She just smiles.

_____ Marcia invents a time machine. She keeps it a secret.

_____ At the fair, she buys a key chain as a souvenir.

_____ Marcia replaces the key chain from the past with the one from the future to her display.

_____ She decides to use the time machine to travel forward in time to 2039.

_____ She goes to the World's Fair that takes place in 2039. She gets a key chain souvenir and returns home.

_____ She uses the machine to travel back to the 1939 World's Fair in New York City.

_____ However, Marcia is not satisfied with her display. She thinks it is missing something.

Comprehension Check

Summarize

What happens to Oliver McBride as he tries to find his brother? How does one event lead to another? Use a Sequence Chart to summarize the plot.

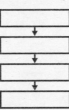

Think and Compare

1. Where does scientific curiosity lead Carter and Jessica? What actions do they take? What events happen as a result? *(Identify Sequence of Events)*

2. Suppose you could travel anywhere in time—back to the past, or forward to the future. Where would you go, and why? Explain what you hope to discover about this era. What might you discover about yourself? *(Analyze)*

3. What if, one day, scientists discover how to time travel? Should people journey to the past and future? What benefits might time travel give today's society? What problems might time travel pose for the present? *(Evaluate)*

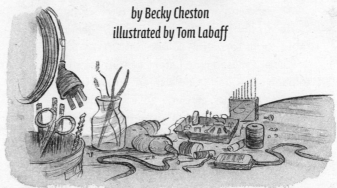

Speed Dial

by Becky Cheston
illustrated by Tom Labaff

Table of Contents

Chapter One
Special Effect

"Can we turn up the heat? My hands are like ice!" Thirteen-year-old Oliver McBride rubbed his hands over his cup of cocoa.

"Try moving around," said his older brother Carter from behind the sports page. "Clearing the table ought to warm you right up."

Oliver ignored him. Lately, everything they said to each other had to be a smart remark.

"Oh," said Mrs. McBride. "Are you cold, Ollie dear? Hudson, would you mind turning up the heat?" Oliver's dad rose to check the thermostat.

"The pwin-cess is ve-wy, ve-wy cold," Bailey chirped. "It's 'cause her castle is made-a snow. See, Owie?" Oliver looked down at his three-year-old sister, who sat cross-legged under the table. He pretended to be interested and smiled.

"So," said Mr. McBride. "What have you boys got planned for today?"

Carter peeked over the top of the newspaper. "I'm meeting some guys at the basketball courts in a little while."

"Isn't it kind of cold for basketball?" said Oliver.

Epilogue

"Warm enough now, Ollie?" Safely back in the Gadgetorium, Carter joked about the coating of perspiration, brought on by their shared sense of fear. "But seriously, though. That took courage to come after me, little bro. It was an amazingly honorable thing to do."

When they had returned, the boys called to check in with their parents. But first, Carter and Jessica had disconnected all the time-travel devices. What they had tapped into was too dangerous for them to explore alone—at least for now.

"It's a shame," said Carter. "I mean, just think of all the stuff we could learn."

Oliver smiled to himself, suddenly remembering the set of symbols he'd seen scratched into Rockin' Rock: "J. 'G.' B. + C. McB. 2008 Tru Luv." Finally, Oliver possessed a bit of knowledge that his older brother had no clue about. At least, not at the present time.

"Look! Someone from Dad's class carved this." Carter traced one hand over a section of rock face that read, HOMECOMING 1982. Barely visible now, it sat next to a freshly carved slogan: HOMECOMING 2118. And now, Oliver discovered a set of symbols that made his jaw drop. Should he show Carter and Jessica?

Suddenly, another *whoosh* made the three of them turn their attention back to the road. A C.P. vehicle slammed to a hovering halt.

"We have to get out of here!" Jessica whispered. "Listen, I've figured out the series of numbers. . . . At least I think it'll get us back."

"Help me, Carter!" she whispered. The lab partners hurriedly punched in the numbers. Oliver glanced through the bushes toward the road. A whole squad of agents had emerged from the car. Jessica handed him back his phone. The C.P. agents were fanning out around the trees.

Jessica grabbed Carter's hand, then Oliver's. "On the count of three, press CALL. One, two, three!"

© 2007 Macmillan/McGraw-Hill

Speed Dial

"Some of us just have thick skin, I guess," Carter replied sarcastically.

Oliver resented how Carter acted so superior, using every available chance to emphasize how he was smarter, more athletic, and more adventurous than his younger brother. "Hey—I can shoot hoops. It's just that Joey and I might go to the movies. . . ."

From somewhere, a cell phone rang. Carter rummaged around for it on the table.

"Where did you put your phone, dear?" asked Mrs. McBride. Carter knocked over an empty juice glass as he looked under napkins and plates.

"Ring, ring, ring," said Bailey.

Carter dropped to the floor. "Give me that, little missy." He snatched his cell phone from Bailey's hand. Then he stood, turned, walked toward the living room, and. . . .

Oliver replayed the next few seconds in his mind so many times, he could almost convince himself it hadn't happened. "Talk to me," Carter said as he answered his cell phone. As he spoke, Carter began to disappear.

First, Oliver noticed he could see through his brother's head. Next, Carter's whole body thinned until he was just patches of tiny pixels. Finally, he shimmered and winked out, like a special effect.

Oliver gasped. "Did you see that?" He turned to his parents.

"What, dear?" asked his mom. But Oliver knew she wasn't paying attention.

"Carter . . . he. . . ."

Mrs. McBride picked up a stack of dishes and walked into the kitchen and commented that Carter could have cleaned up after himself before he left.

His heart racing, Oliver began to fidget with his napkin. *I did not just see that,* he thought. *The cold must have frozen my brain.* His little sister crawled out from under the table and toddled over. Her eyes were wide as she asked Oliver to disappear, too. Oliver thought that maybe he had misheard her, so he asked what she was talking about. Bailey smiled, yelled, "Poof!" and clapped her hands.

© 2007 Macmillan/McGraw-Hill

Speed Dial

Furthermore, Carter knew where the three of them had landed. "Look closely at that dome," he said. "And the field." Oliver and Jessica peered across the street. Immediately, Jessica spotted their high school emblem, looking like an ancient artifact on the ultra-modern doors. Then Oliver pointed out the high school gate, carved with the team logo that was preserved in the silvery fence.

"And something else!" Oliver whispered. "Look behind you, at this rock." A huge boulder, taller than a high ceiling, peeked out from the stand of trees.

"Rockin' Rock?" said Jessica. In their own "present," it stood across from the high school, at the edge of a second, smaller field. "But it can't be. I mean, look at all these new trees . . . , which obviously have had many years to grow. I just wonder how many."

Jessica pointed. "The skateboard of the future?" Oliver smiled as he watched two kids head for the dome on skateboard-style platforms that skimmed and hovered, just like the vehicle, without touching the ground.

"Where do you think—" Oliver's words were cut off as something grabbed him and Jessica from behind. He turned to find—Carter!

"What are you guys doing here?" he whispered.

"We came to find you!" said Jessica. "Why are we whispering, by the way?"

"I think some guys are after me—well, after us now, I guess."

Carter explained that a government agency called the Chronological Police was after him. Investigating signals they'd received from the past—probably when he and Jessica had made their test "jump"—they had deliberately dialed into Carter's cell. Luckily, he had spotted the squad and had taken cover. Apparently, there was strict monitoring of who—and how many people—immigrated to various times.

16

Chapter Two
Not Your Ordinary Cell Phone

It took Oliver almost 30 minutes to end up on Jessica Blue's doorstep. A tall woman—probably Jessica's mother—stood in the entryway, adjusting a pair of half-moon glasses on her long, regal nose.

"Um, is Jessica here?" Oliver stammered.

"And whom shall I say is calling?" Jessica's mother spoke quite formally.

"Ollie—I mean Oliver McBride. Carter's brother?"

Earlier, after he had seen Carter vanish, Oliver had grabbed his own cell phone and wallet. Struggling into his jacket, he yelled to his parents, "Good-bye! I'm going to Joey's now!" Then he ran for the door.

Bailey lay in his path, wrapped in a shawl of paper towels. Her eyes were closed.

"One kiss fwom the prince, and Sweeping Beauty will awaken hewself," she whispered. Oliver swooped her up and gave her a wet smack on the cheek and quickly put her down.

5

Oliver headed straight for the basketball courts behind the high school. His brother had to be there. After all, people don't just vanish into thin air. Two boys, juniors like Carter, were playing a game of one-on-one.

They continued their game, but shouted to Oliver and asked him where Carter was. Oliver muttered that he had thought Carter would be there. One of the boys, Jonah, laughed and asked Oliver if he saw Carter anywhere on the court. Oliver desperately looked around one more time and then shook his head.

"So, you haven't seen him?" Oliver's breath twirled white in the air.

Jonah shook his head and focused on the game. Then he abruptly stopped and told Oliver to try Gadget's house. She and Carter were working on a project for the technology fair. Oliver remembered that *Gadget* was the nickname kids gave Jessica Blue, Carter's lab partner. What else would you call someone who took apart her first appliance when she was only four?

© 2007 Macmillan/McGraw-Hill

Speed Dial

Chapter Four
"We Have to Get Out of Here!"

Oliver's first sensation was an all-over tingling, as if the dentist had given him a huge shot of novocaine. Then the feeling subsided, and slowly, Oliver became aware of a pain in his left hand, as if someone were crunching his bones. It was Jessica. At least they had arrived together.

They were standing in front of a row of small trees. In front of them lay a road. Beyond that, a long, low dome stood next to a fenced-in field. Farther down, some of the tallest buildings Oliver had ever seen stretched into the sky, which was hazy pink. Sunset in the middle of the day.

"Pollution effect," Jessica pointed out, shaking her head sadly.

Then came a sudden *whooshing* noise. Something fast zipped down the road. The vehicle was a half sphere that skimmed about two feet above the road. It stopped and hovered in front of the dome. People emerged and entered through a pair of gigantic sliding doors.

Dial

"Way to go, Ollie! Now, we're in business." Jessica grabbed a second phone and tossed it to Oliver. "Ready?"

Oliver gulped. "R-ready for what?"

"We have to go after him, and you know it!" Jessica exclaimed. "Your brother could be in deep trouble."

"Yeah, but even if you *could* travel to the future, I have no idea what to do!"

"This part of it's easy, Ollie. You punch in a number and. . . ." She entered the number in both refurbished phones and held out Oliver's for him to take. He recoiled, his unsteady feet causing him to trip over a chair. Jessica yanked him up. "I'll be right next to you the whole way," she said in a softer tone. Oliver took the phone.

"Okay," said Jessica. "On the count of three, press CALL. One, two, three!"

© 2007 Macmillan/McGraw-Hill

Speed Dial

So, as he stood glumly on Jessica's doorstep, Oliver realized that he should have been smart enough to figure it out and come here first. Never mind—he was here now. Jessica Blue came clumping down the stairs in clogs and denim overalls and looked at Oliver oddly. Oliver took a deep breath and wondered how on earth he was going to talk to Gadget about his brother's disappearance.

First, Oliver calmly asked Gadget if she had seen Carter. She calmly answered that she hadn't and continued to stare at Oliver. So, Oliver told Jessica (it was too serious a situation to be calling her Gadget) exactly what had happened. *Okay, wait for it,* he thought. But Jessica didn't laugh. Instead, she grabbed his arm and asked him if he was absolutely positive about what he had seen. Oliver nodded.

Jessica, still holding his arm, dragged him toward the back of the house. She opened the cellar door and switched on the light. Then she pulled Oliver down a rickety flight of stairs and opened a door that was covered in signs: PROJECT BLUE . . . GENIUS AT WORK . . . DO NOT DISTURB THE GADGET.

So this was Jessica Blue's infamous laboratory. Carter had raved about her setup. Apparently, everything a technological, engineering-minded kid could possibly dream of was here in the Gadgetorium.

"Wow," said Oliver, his mouth agape. Shelves stocked with books, jars, and other paraphernalia, covered one large wall. Someone had fashioned two desks from old doors laid flat over file cabinets. On one was a desktop computer with a large, flat-screen monitor. On the other sat a laptop. A round worktable held CD players, cell phones, and other electronic gadgets, most cracked open, with their innards spilling out. A couple of beanbag chairs rounded out the furnishings.

Jessica plunked Oliver in one of the desk chairs. "All right," she said, pacing. "I think I know what might have happened. I just can't believe he'd be careless enough to go it alone! I mean we specifically said—"

"What?"

"Never mind." Jessica stopped pacing. "Now, think, Ollie. Who did Carter call right before he disappeared?"

"No one! He—"

"I thought you said he was on his cell phone!"

© 2007 Macmillan/McGraw-Hill

Speed Dial

Jessica explained that, because light has to travel such long distances from space to Earth, we in the present can watch events *as they happen* in the past. Oliver's head ached. It still didn't make sense. But they had to find Carter.

"This device works." Jessica held up a cell phone. "We've been there—to the future." A few days ago, they had tested the devices—just for a few minutes. First, Carter had dialed a predetermined number that pinpointed a specific time and place. Then, the special GPS chip, interacting with the cell phone's signal, did the rest. Jessica stayed behind to monitor Carter on the computers. Then they had switched roles.

"But then, Carter got that call, and now he's gone," said Jessica. "That means either someone— from the future, obviously—accidentally dialed him. Or, someone did it deliberately, to bring him there. We have to figure out where that call came from!"

"I know a way!" Oliver swiveled to face the computer. The McBrides belonged to a family wireless plan. All he had to do was pull up the records.

"There it is!" Oliver pointed to the last incoming call. He scribbled down the odd-looking number.

They wanted to experiment with adapting it to function in a cell phone. Oliver knew that some expensive cell phones already had certain "locator" capabilities. They had maps and even a tracking device, so someone else could pinpoint your location. According to Jessica, she and Carter had been able to customize their basic cell phones with GPS features. Then their curiosity took them further.

"We thought, instead of plotting out a physical destination, what if you could program a GPS chip to locate a chronological one?" said Jessica.

"Chronological?" Oliver wrinkled his eyebrows. "That means 'time.' Wait a minute—time travel? That's nuts! I mean, how is that possible?"

"Well, our theory is based on the science of matter and the laws of motion." Jessica scribbled something on a pad of paper. "And the belief that other points in time—like past and future—don't necessarily exist in sequence, one after the other, but in a kind of parallel space. Here, this equation shows. . . ." She looked at Oliver's clueless face.

9

"He was," Oliver explained, "but he didn't call anyone. Someone else called him!" Jessica immediately stopped her pacing and looked at Oliver. Then, in a quiet voice that was barely audible, she croaked, "That's impossible."

Oliver was beginning to lose his temper. Oliver repeated to Jessica that his brother Carter had gotten a call. There was nothing weird or impossible about that situation. But Jessica just stood there frozen and shook her head.

"Look, Oliver, that is no ordinary cell phone." Oliver waited for her to continue, but instead she just absentmindedly resumed pacing. Finally, she scooted the other desk chair close to Oliver. "I'm going to tell you something. But you have to swear not to repeat it."

"Well, I don't know. . . ."

"You've got to promise, Ollie!" Jessica grabbed both his wrists.

"All right. If you promise to stop touching me!"

"Deal."

© 2007 Macmillan/McGraw-Hill

Speed Dial

Chapter Three
Chronological Destination

After witnessing his brother vanish into thin air, Oliver thought he was ready for anything. But, the story Jessica began telling him was even more unbelievable. . . .

She and Carter had been working on an entry for the annual technology fair. Though it was a high school event, the two had participated since the sixth grade. One year, they refitted a portable CD player with a transceiver that could seek out unassigned FM bands and broadcast music on nearby radios. Oliver could remember the uproar this caused before they ironed out all the bugs. Imagine the reaction from 73-year-old Mrs. Stetson down the street when rock music suddenly blasted from her stereo. Now multiply that problem about 20 times.

Oliver could imagine the pair of them tinkering with just about anything. Today's mystery actually began when Carter and Jessica had taken apart a handheld Global Positioning System (GPS) to inspect its computer chip.

Word Workout

WORDS TO KNOW

anthropologists   nuisance   presumably

immense   portable

A Wordy Paragraph Let's see if we can write one paragraph that includes all five vocabulary words.

SPELLING WORDS

democrat	telepathy	pianist	apology
technician	democracy	sympathy	geologist
politician	novelist	physician	technology
musician	tourist	archaeology	zoology
biologist	ecology	heroism	specialist

People and Things I'll ask you to spell a word and tell me whether it is a person (such as a physician) or a thing. Remember that some nouns name abstract things, such as zoology, that you cannot see or touch.

© Macmillan/McGraw-Hill

(fold here)

Home-School Connection

Dear Family Member:

This week we're reading "Keeping in Touch," an article about messages people left on rocks very long ago. These early examples of communication can be found in Europe, Africa, and Australia. It's amazing to think that people made some of these cave drawings more than 20,000 years ago! However, just because they lasted that long, doesn't mean they will last forever. Once they were discovered, they were in danger. Tourists and other people might treat them carelessly. I'm reading to learn more about this problem as well as possible solutions.

This Week's Skills

Comprehension: problem and solution

Vocabulary: word parts

Spelling/Phonics: prefixes

Name _____

What's the Problem?

Thinking about solutions can help you determine what problems brought them about. Can we figure out what problems these kids are trying to solve?

I'll make a list of everything I have to do. I'll put the things in order, from most important to least important. I might even cross some things off if they aren't important at all. I'll have it done by Tuesday.

Instead of every kid creating a project, we can work together as a class. We'll make one super-terrific project that is sure to make our school proud.

We should have two wastebaskets in every classroom. One is for things that can be recycled. The other is for trash. Then we need a recycling center. There, students can sort the recyclables into baskets for glass, plastic, metal, and paper.

I'll help Joshua by introducing him to some of my friends. We'll make sure to include him in games and special events. I'll also suggest that he join our softball team. I'll help him practice, too.

Ejercicio de palabras

PALABRAS DE VOCABULARIO

anthropologists   nuisance   presumably

immense   portable

Un párrafo denso Vamos a ver si podemos escribir un párrafo que incluya las cinco palabras del vocabulario.

PALABRAS DE ORTOGRAFÍA

democrat	telepathy	pianist	apology
technician	democracy	sympathy	geologist
politician	novelist	physician	technology
musician	tourist	archaeology	zoology
biologist	ecology	heroism	specialist

Personas y cosas Te voy a pedir que deletrees una palabra y me digas si es una persona (como *physician*) o una cosa. Recuerda que algunos sustantivos se refieren a cosas abstractas, como *zoology*, que no puedes ni ver ni tocar.

(fold here)

Conexión con el hogar

Queridos familiares:

Esta semana estamos leyendo *Keeping in Touch*, un artículo sobre mensajes que fueron grabados en rocas mucho tiempo atrás. Estos ejemplos de comunicación temprana pueden hallarse en Europa, África y Australia. ¡Es asombroso pensar que estos dibujos de las cavernas tienen más de 20,000 años de antigüedad! Sin embargo, el hecho de que hayan durado tanto tiempo no significa que durarán para siempre. Su sólo descubrimiento ya los puso en peligro. Los turistas y otras personas pueden tratarlos descuidadamente. Estoy leyendo para aprender más de este problema y de su posible solución.

Destrezas de la semana

Comprensión: problema y solución

Vocabulario: partes de una palabra

Ortografía/Fonética: prefijos

Nombre_____

¿Qué problema hay?

El pensar en las soluciones puede ayudarte a determinar cuáles fueron los problemas que las originaron. ¿Puedes darte cuenta cuáles son los problemas que estos chicos están tratando de resolver?

I'll make a list of everything I have to do. I'll put the things in order, from most important to least important. I might even cross some things off if they aren't important at all. I'll have it done by Tuesday.

How will I ever solve this?

YIKES!

We should have two wastebaskets in every classroom. One is for things that can be recycled. The other is for trash. Then we need a recycling center. There, students can sort the recyclables into baskets for glass, plastic, metal, and paper.

I've got a PROBLEM!

Instead of every kid creating a project, we can work together as a class. We'll make one super-terrific project that is sure to make our school proud.

I'll help Joshua by introducing him to some of my friends. We'll make sure to include him in games and special events. I'll also suggest that he join our softball team. I'll help him practice, too.

Comprehension Check

Summarize

What are the Nazca lines, and what are two theories about them?

Think and Compare

1. Choose one theory and tell what problems must be solved before the theory can be proved or disproved. *(Identify Problem and Solution)*

2. Which theory in this book interests you the most? Explain your answer? *(Analyze)*

3. How does science help people solve mysteries like the Nazca lines? Give at least two examples. *(Synthesize)*

TALKING PICTURES
A MYSTERY IN PERU

by Elizabeth West

Table of Contents

INTRODUCTION

In the 1900s, airplanes crossing the deserts of Peru made an amazing discovery. Passengers looked out of the windows and saw immense drawings scratched into the earth. These drawings showed birds, mammals, bugs, and patterns.

People on the ground did not know that these drawings existed. Yes, they knew that lines were scratched into the ground. They could see them clearly. However, until people saw the lines from the sky, they had no idea that the lines formed pictures.

Most people believe that the drawings were made by the Nazca people. They lived in that area around 200 B.C.E. They lived in Pampa Colorado, which means Red Plain. The surface there is flat and stony. The surface pebbles are reddish. Only the surface is red, though, while the soil below is much lighter. The lines were made by removing topsoil so that the lighter soil showed through.

Scientists have studied these images for years. The images raise many questions. How were these lines created and by whom? What was the purpose of these drawings? So far, there have been no solid answers. But scientists do have some **theories**.

Index

Glossary

anthropologist *(an-thruh-POL-uh-jist)* scientist who studies human beings *(page 7)*

aqueduct *(AK-wi-dukt)* a channel that carries water *(page 13)*

astronomical *(as-truh-NOM-i-kuhl)* having to do with astronomy, which is the study of the planets and other objects in space *(page 15)*

constellation *(kon-stuh-LAY-shuhn)* a group of stars that form a particular pattern *(page 15)*

culture *(KUL-chur)* the beliefs, customs, and art of a certain group of people *(page 7)*

eclipse *(i-KLIPS)* a darkening or hiding of the sun, a planet, or a moon by another heavenly body *(page 19)*

fault *(FAWLT)* a crack in the earth's crust *(page 12)*

galaxy *(GAL-uhk-see)* a huge group of stars that form one system *(page 8)*

glyph *(GLIF)* a symbol or character that transmits information *(page 7)*

irrigation *(ir-i-GAY-shuhn)* a system that supplies water to an area *(page 10)*

observatory *(uhb-ZUR-vuh-tawr-ee)* a building designed to look at objects in the sky, such as stars and planets *(page 16)*

theory *(THEE-uh-ree)* an explanation that is based on observation and reason *(page 2)*

trapezoid *(TRAP-uh-zoid)* a four-sided figure, in which two are parallel and two are not parallel *(page 12)*

22

From the ground, these lines in the desert don't look like anything. From the sky, people can see drawings of animals, plants, and geometric figures.

3

CHAPTER ONE

HIDDEN IN PLAIN SIGHT

The Nazca drawings are located in the Peruvian desert. The Peruvian desert hugs the Pacific Ocean. It runs for more than a thousand miles at the base of the Andes Mountains. The geography and climate may be the reason why these figures have lasted for so long.

Rain seldom falls in the deserts of Peru. It is one of the driest places on Earth, so the lines were not washed away. Because the soil is dark, it is warmer than the upper air. A blanket of warm air may protect the soil from the wind.

↻ The Nazca drawings lie about 200 miles south of Lima, the capital of Peru. The drawings cover hundreds of square miles.

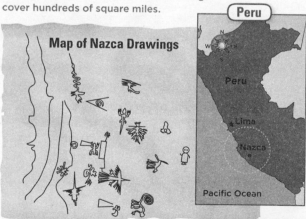

Map of Nazca Drawings

Peru

Peru

Lima

Nazca

Pacific Ocean

CONCLUSION

For centuries, the Nazca drawings have decorated the desert of Peru. Evidence points to their importance. Yet despite almost a century of experimenting, no one has solved the riddle of why they are there.

Many theories exist. So far no evidence has been strong enough to identify the function of these lines. Yet scientists and non-scientists continue to work on the question. They think they know how the figures were built. However, they still do not know who built them or why. One day the mystery of the Nazca drawings may be solved.

↻ Many drawings have no lines that cross, including this hummingbird. Some people have suggested that the lines form paths of a maze or racetrack.

21

Many people have asked another question. Why would ancient Nazcans create images that could be viewed only from the sky? Could they ever see the pictures? That idea prompted scientists to ask if the Nazcans could fly. Did the technology exist at the time to make a hot air balloon?

Two men decided to find out. Jim Woodman and Julian Nott built a balloon. They used cloth that was similar to that made by ancient Nazca people. They made a basket, or gondola, that hung below this. The basket was made from local reeds. Reeds are light and portable. They could have been carried over long distances. The hot air inside the balloon was made by a smoky fire.

The plan worked. As watchers cheered, the balloon ascended into the sky. Then it floated over the Nazca desert. Not only did it prove that such flight was possible, but it also increased interest in the lines.

⋔ The balloon was named *Condor*, and it proved that ancient Nazca people could have soared above the earth to see their creations.

Ancient Builders

Throughout history, people have built huge structures of earth or stone. This Serpent Mound was probably made by the Adena people of Ohio between 800 B.C.E. and A.D. 100. This coiling snake is nearly a quarter mile long.

The Peruvian desert is not a sandy desert. The surface is made mainly of red stones. To create the drawings, people moved the stones to expose the lighter-colored soil beneath.

Researchers divide the drawings into two types, called *biomorphs* and *geoglyphs*. Biomorphs show living creatures, such as plants and animals. There are about 70 plant or animal figures. Geoglyphs are geometric forms. These include lines, triangles, and spirals. There are about 900 geometric figures.

Scientists solve mysteries like the Nazca drawings by looking at pieces of evidence. One piece of evidence is the sheer size of these drawings. Moving that many stones would have been a massive job. It would have taken time and effort. This suggests that the drawings were not the work of one person or even one small group. They must have been the result of many people working many years. The drawings are similar to the building of the Egyptian pyramids. Both took many people many years to build.

☝ This monkey was drawn by people who clearly knew what monkeys looked like. Other biomorphic drawings show llamas, birds, spiders, lizards, and flowers.

☝ The black shadow of the moon surrounded by the white corona of sunrays does look a bit like a huge eye.

Scientists continue to work on pieces of this puzzle. Here are some other theories.

Many cultures have written about a huge flood. Some researchers have thought that the lines might be a memorial for creatures killed during a flood.

Perhaps the drawings were meant to be seen by gods. Several solar **eclipses** happened around the time that the drawings were made. The Nazcans knew about eclipses. They showed some on their artwork. During a solar eclipse, some people felt that the darkened sun was the eye of a god.

CHAPTER FIVE

OTHER THEORIES

Once people learned about the Nazca drawings, interest grew. Here was a problem for science to solve. Who made these drawings? Why were they made? How can this be proved? Most evidence points to the Nazca people. Still, no one is completely sure that they made the drawings.

There are reasons to believe that they did. For instance, drawings found on other Nazca artwork look like the drawings in the earth. Also, scientists have found Nazcan items that were left at the lines. But this only proves that the Nazcans were there. It does not prove that they made the lines.

☙ Some drawings show spirals, seashells, zigzags, and trapezoids. Others show clear images of specific animals, such as this huge spider.

18

The Mayan Codex

The ancient Mayan people left thousands of drawings in the jungles of Central America. Many were carved in stone, but some were written in manuscripts. Only four of these books have been found. Each book, or codex, had many pages. Each page was divided into sections. A **glyph**, or symbolic character, was drawn in each section. Scholars think that the codices dealt with astronomy, religion, and agriculture.

Jobs this big suggest that they were important to the **culture** that built them. The Nazca lines have been compared to the pyramids of Egypt and Mexico. Yet we know why those were built. **Anthropologists** do not know why these lines were made.

The Nazca people did live in the area, but no one is sure they made the drawings. The drawings do look like those found in Nazca art. Still, similar drawings have also been found in other parts of Peru.

The similarity between Nazca art and the desert drawings is not proof that the lines were created by the same people. People have always drawn animals and figures. For example, the people of ancient Egypt and the Anasazi of North America did this often. So, what do scientists think about these drawings?

7

CHAPTER TWO

THE ALIEN THEORY

One well-known theory about the Nazca lines is also the least scientific. It was developed by a European writer named Erich von Daniken. Von Daniken was not a scientist. He did not even finish school but instead went to work in hotels.

Von Daniken thought that space travelers from far-off **galaxies** visited Earth in the past. He published his ideas in his first book, called *Chariots of the Gods*. Until this book came out in the 1960s, few people had heard of Nazca.

In his book, von Daniken offers evidence to support his theory. For instance, he points to details from many myths and religions. One common theme tells of visitors from the sky. As further proof, Daniken points to drawings found around the world. Many ancient ones show figures who seem to be in modern clothes. Presumably, these pictures show visitors from space.

⊙ Scientists study rock carvings, like these Mayan glyphs, to learn about previous cultures.

Taking Pictures A Mystery in Peru

Reiche also noticed that some lines pointed to spots where the sun rose and set during the solstice. The winter and summer solstice are times when the seasons change. These would have been important to an agricultural society. The seasons affect planting and crop growth.

This theory is hard to prove. One problem is the age of the drawings. Over the centuries, the stars and planets have moved in relationship to each other. Scientists must estimate where they were when the pictures were made. To do this, they use computers. The computers calculate where stars once were.

Many scientists have tested Reiche's theories. At one point, the National Geographic Society looked at the lines. They saw that some lines did line up with the positions of the sun and moon, but most did not.

In the 1970s, scientists used computers to try to match the lines with the stars and planets. Once again, they matched up only some of the time. Do you think Reiche's theory was correct?

Scientists now believe that many ancient people, including the Mayans, studied astronomy carefully. These buildings at Chichen Itza, on the Yucatan Peninsula, are believed to be astronomical **observatories**. ↻

↻ Nicknamed "Spaceman," drawings like this one have been used by some people as evidence of visits by aliens from outer space.

Von Daniken believed that visitors from outer space once landed in Nazca. He thought the lines in the desert were part of a huge airfield. However, the visitors did not stay, and people on Earth wanted them to return. The lines were an attempt to lure back the visitors.

Other people also have theories about aliens. Many were popular because some people found it hard to believe that ancient people could have made such complex drawings. However, other ancient projects, such as the Egyptian pyramids, are also complex, so this idea is false.

Scientists have argued against the alien theory by pointing out that such a huge airfield would have been very busy. The soil would have shown signs of aircraft landings, but no such signs exist. What do you think?

CHAPTER THREE

THE WATER THEORY

Recently, scientists have begun to test another theory. Several scientists believe that the Nazca lines have something to do with water sources. Water is very important in a desert region. Finding enough for crops and humans is always a huge problem.

Some anthropologists think that the lines might be related to **irrigation**. Others think that the lines were used in religious ceremonies about water. Right now, scientists are testing yet another idea. They wonder if the figures show the location of groundwater, or water that is stored underground.

⟡ Most of Earth's fresh water lies under the ground. People can reach this water after it surfaces at springs. They can also dig wells down into it.

10

Water Symbols

A symbol is a mark that stands for something else. These marks are all symbols for water. In some cases, water itself may be a symbol for something else, such as life.

Chinese	水
Sumerian	≈
Native American	ᾝᾝᾝ
Water Drop	🌢
Chemical Symbol	H_2O

Once the lines were famous, many visitors would stop to look at them. Reiche could be a nuisance to people who were careless with the lines. She would chase them off, so the lines would not be ruined.

Reiche developed a theory that the lines were a type of calendar. This calendar described **astronomical** events. She thought that some drawings, such as the monkey, might match **constellations**, such as the Big Dipper. The Big Dipper was a symbol for water. Reiche also noted zigzag marks. She said that they looked like a water symbol. Both North American Indians and ancient Egyptians had symbols like that.

15

© 2007 Macmillan/McGraw-Hill

Taking Pictures A Mystery in Peru

CHAPTER FOUR

THE CALENDAR THEORY

The best-known researcher of the Nazca lines was Maria Reiche, a German mathematician. She first learned about the lines in the 1940s. She was working in Peru for a man named Kosok, who was studying the lines. He believed that they might be irrigation ditches.

Kosok later dropped that theory, but by then Reiche had become interested in the lines. She became so interested that she spent the rest of her life with them. She studied the Nazca lines and also worked hard to preserve them.

Reiche spent half a century living on the Nazca plains, trying to solve the mystery of the lines. "What compelled me on this quest was my curiosity," she said. "I wanted to know!"

Earth's Water Cycle

Water is always moving and changing. This is called the water cycle. Groundwater is one part of this cycle. Here is how it works.

- **Evaporation:** Water in the ocean evaporates, or changes from a liquid to a gas called water vapor.
- **Condensation:** The water vapor in the air condenses, or changes from gas to liquid. Water vapor forms clouds when it condenses.
- **Precipitation:** The water falls from the sky as precipitation, which can be rain or snow.
- **Runoff:** Some of the precipitation flows into streams and rivers and eventually back into the ocean.
- **Groundwater:** Some of the precipitation is absorbed into the soil. This becomes groundwater.
- **Aquifers:** Some groundwater seeps deep into the ground and is held in an area called an aquifer. Aquifers hold a large amount of usable water.

⊙ A fault is a crack in the earth's crust. This shows the San Andreas Fault, which runs for hundreds of miles in California.

One researcher, David Johnson, began mapping the location of ancient and modern wells in one area. He noticed that ancient wells were often very close to modern ones. The old wells probably had water all year round. They would have been vital in a desert.

Then Johnson noticed something else. Some shapes in the Nazca drawings seemed to correspond to underground features. For example, he saw zigzag patterns over dry areas. He noticed that **trapezoids** often appeared above **faults**. Faults are cracks in the land's surface. The width of the trapezoid showed the width of the fault below it.

A major new theory began to develop. Now researchers believed that the patterns might be related to the water below the ground.

Johnson noted that five factors often occurred together. These factors were faults, old ruins, underground water, a good source of fresh water, and the drawn figures. He began to think that perhaps faults were paths for water. Water often flows along faults. Perhaps the faults carried water to certain spots, where it pooled. If people knew where these spots were, they could dig wells there. Then they would always have a supply of fresh water.

Scientists are now trying to prove this theory. First, they will chart the underground water in the Nazca area. Then they will learn if the drawings map that water. The plan now is to look at five different places and study the relationship between the water and the drawings. What do you think of the water theory?

⊙ Scientists are looking not only at the drawings but also at structures, such as this **aqueduct**.

Word Workout

WORDS TO KNOW

alloy	established	obstacles	privileged
guilds	manuscripts	penniless	scribes

Good Question Ask me a question that includes one of the words. For example: *Where might I go to look at some real manuscripts from the Middle Ages?* I'll answer the question to show that I understand what the word means.

SPELLING WORDS

iris	solar	romance	psychology
tantalize	nectar	geography	geometry
phobia	hygiene	cosmetics	mania
helicopter	terrain	mercury	chaos
titanic	nocturnal	amnesia	marathon

Spelling Syllables I'll give you the first syllable of a word and you can take over from there.

© Macmillan/McGraw-Hill

·······(fold here)·······

Home-School Connection

Dear Family Member:

We see printed words everywhere nowadays, but once books were all made by hand. This week, we're reading *Breaking Into Print*, about the history of printing. The story begins long ago and passes through China and Korea to Germany. There a man named Johannes Gutenberg invented a printing press and moveable type that revolutionized the world. The author describes in detail the press and type Gutenberg created. His descriptions, along with the illustrator's pictures, make it possible to truly see what happened when words were printed on paper long ago.

This Week's Skills

Comprehension: description

Vocabulary: word parts

Spelling/Phonics: words from mythology

Name _____

Two Times Different

Want to create two houses? By adding different descriptive words to the story, we can make two different houses.

This house is _____ and _____. The first thing that you notice from the outside is the _____.

When you walk inside, the _____ will make you feel _____. Open the attic door and the smell of _____ will drift down to your nose.

The basement is filled with _____ and _____. The walls are _____, and the floor is _____.

However, the room that really sums up this house is the _____. In this room you will discover _____.

An advertisement to sell the house would say: _____.

This house is _____ and _____. The first thing that you notice from the outside is the _____.

When you walk inside, the _____ will make you feel _____. Open the attic door and the smell of _____ will drift down to your nose.

The basement is filled with _____ and _____. The walls are _____, and the floor is _____.

However, the room that really sums up this house is the _____. In this room you will discover _____.

An advertisement to sell the house would say: _____.

Ejercicio de palabras

PALABRAS DE VOCABULARIO

alloy	established	obstacles	privileged
guilds	manuscripts	penniless	scribes

Preguntas y respuestas Hazme una pregunta donde esté una de las palabras de la lista. Por ejemplo: *Where might I go to look at some real manuscripts from the Middle Ages?* Te daré una respuesta que demuestre que entiendo lo que significa la palabra.

PALABRAS DE ORTOGRAFÍA

iris	solar	romance	psychology
tantalize	nectar	geography	geometry
phobia	hygiene	cosmetics	mania
helicopter	terrain	mercury	chaos
titanic	nocturnal	amnesia	marathon

Sílabas iniciales Te daré la primera sílaba de una palabra, tú tendrás que terminar de deletrear la palabra a partir de esa sílaba.

(fold here)

© Macmillan/McGraw-Hill

Conexión con el hogar

Queridos familiares:

Hoy en día vemos palabras impresas en todas partes, pero en un tiempo los libros estaban hechos a mano. Esta semana estamos leyendo *Breaking into Print*, sobre la historia de la imprenta. Esa historia comienza hace mucho tiempo, y va de China y Corea hasta Alemania. Allí, un hombre llamado Johannes Gutenberg inventó una impresora con tipos móviles que revolucionó el mundo. El autor describe en detalle la imprenta y los tipos que creó Gutenberg. Sus descripciones, junto con las imágenes del ilustrador hacen posible que veamos lo que pasó cuando las palabras se imprimieron en papel por primera vez.

Destrezas de la semana

Comprensión: descripción

Vocabulario: partes de una palabra

Ortografía/Fonética: palabras de la mitología

Nombre _____

Perspectivas diferentes

¿Quieres crear dos casas? Si agregamos palabras descriptivas diferentes al mismo relato, podemos crear dos casas distintas.

This house is _____ and _____. The first thing that you notice from the outside is the _____.

When you walk inside, the _____ will make you feel _____. Open the attic door and the smell of _____ will drift down to your nose.

The basement is filled with _____ and _____. The walls are _____, and the floor is _____.

However, the room that really sums up this house is the _____. In this room you will discover _____.

An advertisement to sell the house would say: _____.

This house is _____ and _____. The first thing that you notice from the outside is the _____.

When you walk inside, the _____ will make you feel _____. Open the attic door and the smell of _____ will drift down to your nose.

The basement is filled with _____ and _____. The walls are _____, and the floor is _____.

However, the room that really sums up this house is the _____. In this room you will discover _____.

An advertisement to sell the house would say: _____.

438

Comprehension Check

Summarize

Choose the method of publishing that you like best. Then use the Description Chart to summarize the different steps involved in that method.

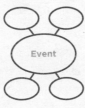

Event

Think and Compare

1. Look back at Chapter 1. How does the author describe each format? What details does she give that help you understand each format? *(Analyze Text Structure)*

2. What skills and abilities do you have that would help you become a publisher? What additional skills would you need to learn? *(Apply)*

3. Do we need publishers? What do they contribute to our lives? How would our lives be different today if there were no publishers? *(Evaluate)*

Spread the Word

Become a Publisher

by Barbara Burt

Table of Contents

Introduction

When I was in sixth grade, my friends were doing amazing things. Ann wrote beautifu poems. Ray drew funny cartoons. Donna was a sports nut. She p ayed soccer and basketball, and was a star on the swim team. Heather went to every new movie and had strong feelings about each one

I fe t privileged to have such interesting friends. I was so proud of them that I wanted to tell the wor d. So I started a newspaper. Every month I collected interesting stories and articles by and about the other sixth-grade kids at Humiston Schoo

I named the newspaper the *Scribe*. It was printed on a photocopy machine. I so d each copy for five cents, and every issue so d out. I knew that I oved working on the *Scribe*, and I knew that my friends liked reading it. What I didn't know was that I was a publisher.

© 2007 Macmillan/McGraw-Hill

Spread the Word Become a Publisher

Index

Glossary

audio *(AW-dee-oh)* having to do with sound or how sound is recorded, sent, or received *(page 4)*

bind *(BIGHND)* to fasten together between covers *(page 8)*

blog *(BLOG)* a kind of online diary that's usually updated every day *(page 11)*

download *(DOUN-lohd)* to transfer information from one computer to another *(page 9)*

dummy *(DUM-ee)* model pages with type and illustrations pasted into place as a plan for a book, magazine, newspaper, or other publication *(page 15)*

guild *(GILD)* a group of people who share a common skill and come together to work for better pay or working conditions *(page 8)*

layout *(LAY-owt)* page design *(page 8)*

manuscript *(MAN-yuh-skript)* pieces of writing that are meant to be published but aren't in their final format *(page 3)*

marketing *(MAHR-kit-ing)* selling *(page 20)*

producer *(pruh-DEW-suhr)* a person or company that makes or creates something, such as a film *(page 10)*

scribe *(SKRIGHB)* a person whose job is to write things down; in ancient times, a person who hand-copied important documents and books *(page 2)*

video *(VID-ee-oh)* the picture part of television; a videotape, or a videocassette *(page 4)*

Web *(WEB)* a shortened way of describing the World Wide Web, which is a system of Internet computers *(page 4)*

The publisher is the person who takes a writer's **manuscript** and turns it into a book or an article for a magazine or newspaper. Sometimes you read something you like. You're curious about the writer. But you probably don't wonder about the publisher. That's because the publisher's work happens behind the scenes. But even if you aren't aware of the publisher's job, it's still important.

Often a publisher works with a team of people. If it is a big project, like a monthly magazine or a hardcover book, many people are involved. Writers, editors, and perhaps illustrators or photographers work on the project. Designers decide how the pages will look. Salespeople make sure that every copy finds a reader

Sometimes one person does every task. Whether it's a team of one or a team of 100, the publisher is the person who makes sure that the end result is a book, a newspaper, or a magazine.

CHAPTER 1

Choose Your Format

A good publisher is an expert on her audience. You can create a well-established print publication, like a newspaper, magazine, or book. Or you can use an e ectronic format, like **video**, **audio**, or **Web**. Here are a few questions to he p you make a decision

First, how does your audience like to get their reading materia ? Do they read books? Do they have computers? Second, what kinds of techno ogy can you or your team use? How many copies do you want to make? Third, how much money do you have to spend? Even if you're not penniless, don't spend more money than necessary

A reader enjoys the finished product.

Well, your publication is out in the wor d. It's time to ce ebrate. Be sure to invite all the peop e who he ped you. Even if you did all the work a one, this is your chance to tell peop e about it. Readers who share the same interest will want to earn more about your project.

By publishing your project, you've added to the wor d's enjoyment and understanding of your topic. Be proud of your work!

21

Get the Word Out

You're done at ast. Now you need to tell peop e about it. This is called **marketing**. Think about where your readers (or listeners or viewers) can find other publications like yours. Your schoo library is a p ace to start. Ta k to librarians and bookstore owners. Are there any clubs that wou d be interested? If you're publishing a magazine about minera s and alloys, a geo ogy club wou d be a great p ace to find interested readers. Be sure to tell all your friends and re atives. Word-of-mouth advertising is free.

You might send out a press re ease. This is a notice to a news organization that you have something to offer that you think other peop e wou d be interested In. Follow the format in the examp e be ow

FOR IMMEDIATE RELEASE
April 12, 2005
For more information, contact:
Jeremy Stern at jstern@abc.com
or 555-555-5555

Student at Bethune Middle School Publishes Book about Video Games

Jeremy Stern, 11, has announced the publication of his book, *Everything You Need to Know to Win,* a book with hints about playing and winning the most popular video games. Stern's paperback book is available at local bookstores for $5.00.

20

Extra!
The first newspaper published in the United States was *Publick Occurrences, Both Foreign and Domestick.* It was first published on September 25, 1690. Today there are more than 1,456 daily newspapers in the United States.

Newspapers

So you're thinking about creating a print publication. But what kind? There are many choices

Publishing a newspaper can be a fun project. A newspaper is a way to communicate with a arge group of peop e. It's exciting to have peop e waiting eagerly to read the atest issue.

When I was publishing my newspaper, the *Scribe,* I found severa challenges. Newspaper readers expect to see a new issue on a regu ar schedu e. Once you set that schedu e, you have to stick with it. Just when you've finished one issue, it's time to start another.

Peop e who read newspapers are ooking for information. A newspaper needs reporters to research and write articles. But newspapers have other features, too. Photographs add variety. Comic strips are popu ar with readers. Puzz es are fun, too. Including these things will make your newspaper more interesting

Knowing the format your audience wants will help you sell your materials.

5

Books

   Maybe you don't want to publish something on a regular schedule. Then consider publishing a book. A book is a big project, but you only do it once. No one is waiting impatiently for you to deliver the latest issue.

   Putting together a book takes a writer, an editor, a book designer, and salespeople. The biggest obstacle to publishing a book is finding or writing a good manuscript.

   A book can be a collection of poems or short stories. It can be a novel or a work of nonfiction. It can have pictures or photographs or no illustrations at all. The one thing it must have is the reader's interest

The Six Steps to Publication

1. Choose the format (newspaper, book, or magazine).

2. Write the material.

3. Illustrate it.

CHAPTER 4

Spending Money, Making Money

As you have seen, there are many parts to a publishing project. Choosing your format, finding good writers, putting your publication together . . . and one more thing. As the publisher, you need to know how much things cost. You a so have to find the money to pay your costs. Imagine that you're publishing a newspaper. You p an to charge $.25 a copy. If you sell 100 copies, you'll have $25. Suppose that the paper and printing cost $.20 per copy, or $20 in tota . Your $25 from sa es will cover the $20 in costs, and you'll have $5 eft over

The money you take in from sa es is called *income*. The money that you spend on costs is called *expenses*. Your goa as the publisher is to have more income than expenses. Whatever income is eft over is called the *profit*. If your expenses are arger than your income, the difference is called the *loss*

© 2007 Macmillan/McGraw-Hill

Spread the Word Become a Publisher

Many magazines deal with a specific topic or are for a particular age group.

Magazines

Somewhere between a book and a newspaper is a magazine. A magazine is published on a regu ar schedu e like a newspaper, but not as often. Unlike a newspaper, the articles in a magazine are often linked by a common topic. Think of a sports magazine or a fashion magazine. Newspapers rarely have poetry or fiction, but magazines often do.

4. Design the way it will look.   **5. Get it printed.**   **6. Sell and/or hand out copies.**

The First Books

Imagine writing an entire book by hand. In the Middle Ages, that's what **scribes** would do. Every book was hand written by a scribe. Often scribes would belong to a **guild**. Guilds were groups of people who shared a common skill and would work together for better pay.

Print It!

By now you may have decided to publish in a print format. You still have other choices to make. If you're publishing a book, how will you print and **bind** it? If you're publishing a newspaper or magazine, how many copies do you need to print? Can you print it from a computer printer and run copies on a photocopier?

If you want your publication to ook more professiona , a computer can he p. You can use many programs to he p you publish a book, magazine, or newspaper. Or you can simply type the text into a word processing program. Then cut and paste it into the **layout**, or page design, that you want

Newspapers are usually printed on arge sheets of paper that are fo ded. If your book or magazine has more than a few pages, it needs to be bound. Stapling is probably the easiest way to do that

8

© 2007 Macmillan/McGraw-Hill

Spread the Word Become a Publisher

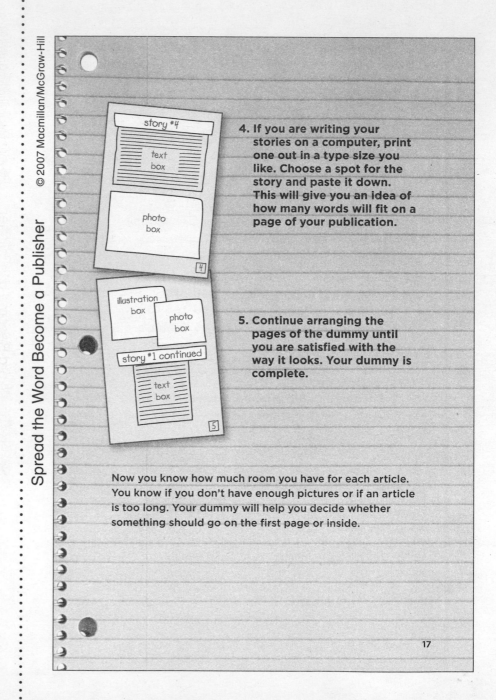

story #4

text box

photo box

4

illustration box

photo box

story #1 continued

text box

5

4. If you are writing your stories on a computer, print one out in a type size you like. Choose a spot for the story and paste it down. This will give you an idea of how many words will fit on a page of your publication.

5. Continue arranging the pages of the dummy until you are satisfied with the way it looks. Your dummy is complete.

Now you know how much room you have for each article. You know if you don't have enough pictures or if an article is too long. Your dummy will help you decide whether something should go on the first page or inside.

17

Making a Dummy

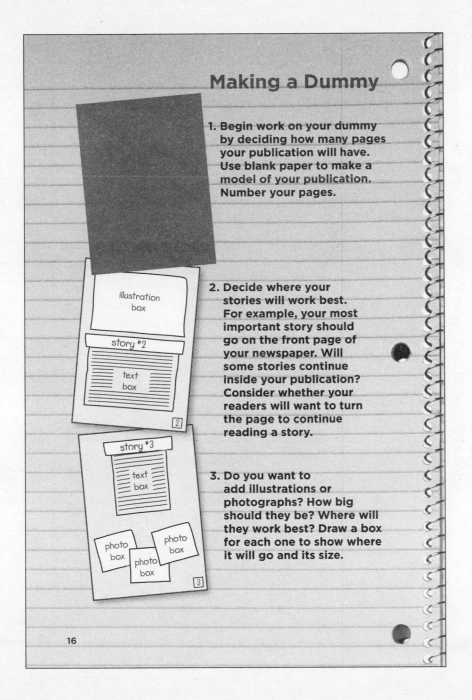

1. **Begin work on your dummy by deciding how many pages your publication will have. Use blank paper to make a model of your publication. Number your pages.**

illustration box

story #2

text box

2

2. **Decide where your stories will work best. For example, your most important story should go on the front page of your newspaper. Will some stories continue inside your publication? Consider whether your readers will want to turn the page to continue reading a story.**

story #3

text box

photo box

photo box

photo box

3

3. **Do you want to add illustrations or photographs? How big should they be? Where will they work best? Draw a box for each one to show where it will go and its size.**

16

CHAPTER 2

Publishing Electronically

The newest way to publish is e ectronically. Once again you have severa options

Consider publishing your work in an audio format. You don't have to worry about how the publication ooks. You don't have to worry about the printing costs. You don't even need to worry about spelling!

You will need a microphone and a recording machine to make a high-quality recording. Be sure to use readers who have p easing voices and can read clearly. You need to be able to make copies of audiotapes. If possible, p ace your recording on the Web. Then anyone who wants to listen to it can **download** it

Borrow a book on tape from the library or listen to a news show on the radio to get a sense of what an audio format would be like.

9

Modern video cameras are not difficult to use.

It may not seem like a big jump to go from making an audiotape to a videotape. But it's a lot harder. You still have to worry about how things sound. But now you also have to worry about how they look. You'll need camera operators and a set. You need to be able to edit film. You'll need people who are appealing on camera to appear in your video

The people who produce videos are not usually called publishers. Instead they're called **producers**. They still have to begin with good writing, or a script, as it's called in the film world.

Designing Your Publication

So you have good material at last. You are ready to put it all together into your final publication. You need to make sure that the design fits the content and writing style of your publication

One way to come up with design ideas is to take a trip to the bookstore, the library, or even a newsstand. Look at as many examples as you can. Do they have illustrations? How are the pages organized? Which examples look most appealing?

Now it's time to put everything together and see how it looks. The way to do that is to make a **dummy** of your publication. This is a model with type and illustrations pasted into place. The steps to take are on the following pages

This girl is reviewing books to find a format.

This editor is a fact-checker. She is making sure that the facts in a nonfiction article are correct by looking them up.

Who will be your editor? Here's some advice: never be both the writer and the editor on the same project. You need a new set of eyes to look over your manuscript and get it ready for publication. You'd be amazed at all the mistakes even the best writers make.

Are you an excellent speller and a good writer? You might be able to edit someone else's work. If not, search hard to find a good editor. There's nothing worse than hearing a reader say, "Oh, I found a typo on page 1."

14

Web publishing can contain all of the elements of print, audio, and video publishing. But it can do all these things at a lower cost. You don't need to make copies. Text and pictures can simply be put on your Web site. Video and audio clips can be part of a Web-based publication.

For a Web publication, you need a computer with Internet access. Many easy programs now exist that help you get a Web site. One of the exciting things about a Web publication is that you can set up a **blog**, a kind of online diary that is usually updated every day. And it's easy to reach your readers. You just have to give them your Web address

This boy is putting together a Web publication. Good writing is still very important.

11

Finding Good Material

Apublication is only as good as its writing. Your job as publisher is to get the best writers you know.

What makes a good writer? You need someone with great ideas who can write clearly. But you a so need a writer who will turn in assignments on time. If the article is nonfiction, your writer must be accurate. If the writing is fiction or poetry, the writer must be origina and exciting

How do you find good writers? You can advertise. Make some posters. Ask your friends for ideas. Teachers can be a big he p, too

Editors don't change the style or message of the writing. They try to make the writing as good as it can be.

© 2007 Macmillan/McGraw-Hill

Spread the Word Become a Publisher

Proofreader's Marks

Editors use a set of symbols when they are making corrections or proofreading a manuscript. Here are some of them.

- ℓ   Delete
- #   Add space
- ∧   Insert
- ¶   Begin new paragraph

Editors

A publisher's job doesn't end when she finds good writers. Your writers will need an editor to review and proofread their work

There are severa kinds of editors. In a newspaper or magazine, a managing editor is the person who decides which stories will be covered. A copy editor carefully reads a manuscript. He checks to make sure that the story makes sense. A proofreading editor makes sure that the spelling and the grammar are correct

Word Workout

WORDS TO KNOW

agonized   drowsy   lounge   revived

ambitious   dwelling   pondering vapors

No Talking! Try to act out a word using only your hands, facial expressions, and actions. Can I guess the word you are showing? Then we'll switch places and I'll try to guess your word.

SPELLING WORDS

bazaar	denim	pizza	pajamas	balcony
bronco	gong	barbecue	plateau	yacht
sombrero	plaza	canoe	poodle	cruise
caribou	igloo	chocolate	apricot	ballet

Around the World in 20 Words I'll give you a clue to a spelling word. Spell the word, then see if you can tell me where the word originated. If we don't know the origin, we can talk about the word and guess the origin.

© Macmillan/McGraw-Hill

(fold here)

Home-School Connection

Dear Family Member:

Sometimes writers are inspired by things they see. This week, we're reading *The Dog of Pompeii*, a story set in that ancient city. The writer got the idea for this story when he saw a plaster cast of a dog that died when Vesuvius erupted in 79 A.D. He decided to write a short story about a boy and his dog who lived together at that time. The details of the plot, setting, and character combine to reveal the story's theme. So far, the theme seems to be the bond between humans and animals.

This Week's Skills

Comprehension: theme

Vocabulary: dictionary

Spelling/Phonics: words from around the world

Name _____

Theme Them!

Let's think of a book, conversation, TV show, or newspaper article we think have themes. We can talk about them and jot down notes on these pages.

TV Show

Book

Newspaper Article

Conversation

Ejercicio de palabras

PALABRAS DE VOCABULARIO

agonized	drowsy	lounge	revived
ambitious	dwelling	pondering	vapors

Sin hablar Trata de representar una palabra con tus manos, expresiones faciales y gestos. ¿Puedo adivinar la palabra que representas? Luego, podremos cambiar de papel y yo representaré la palabra.

PALABRAS DE ORTOGRAFÍA

bazaar	denim	pizza	pajamas	balcony
bronco	gong	barbecue	plateau	yacht
sombrero	plaza	canoe	poodle	cruise
caribou	igloo	chocolate	apricot	ballet

Alrededor del mundo en 20 palabras Te voy a dar una pista de una de las palabras de ortografía. Deletréala, luego trata de decirme de dónde proviene la palabra. Si no sabemos su origen, podemos hablar de la palabra y adivinar de dónde viene.

(fold here)

Conexión con el hogar

Queridos familiares:

A veces los escritores se inspiran en cosas que ven. Esta semana estamos leyendo *The Dog of Pompeii*, un cuento que transcurre en esa ciudad de la antigüedad. Al autor se le ocurrió la idea del relato cuando vio un antiguo molde de yeso de un perro que murió en la erupción del volcán Vesuvio en el año 79 d.C. Fue entonces que decidió escribir un cuento sobre un niño que vivía junto con su perro en esa época. Los detalles del argumento, ambiente y personajes se combinan para revelar el tema del cuento. Hasta ahora, el tema parece ser el lazo que existe entre los seres humanos y los animales.

Destrezas de la semana

Comprensión: tema

Vocabulario: diccionario

Ortografía/Fonética: palabras de otras partes del mundo

Nombre _____

¡Dales un tema!

Vamos a pensar en un tema, conversación, programa de televisión o artículo de periódico que tengan temas. Hablemos sobre ellos y hagamos algunas anotaciones en estas páginas.

Book

Conversation

TV Show

Newspaper Article

Comprehension Check

Summarize

Use the Theme Chart to summarize *Eruption on the Mountain.*

Setting
What the Characters Wan
Plot Problem
Outcome
Theme

Think and Compare

1. Look back at page 13. What action does Seth take after Sarah's voice revives him? What does Seth realize he must do? *(Retell)*

2. Seth could only stare in horror when he heard Jed's agonized shrieks, yet Sarah took action. How do you think you would react in a similar situation? Explain. *(Apply)*

3. Volcanoes are beautiful, yet very dangerous. Why do you think some scientists take risks to get close to volcanoes that are close to erupting? *(Analyze)*

Eruption on the Mountain

by Ann M. Rossi

illustrated by Michael Jaroszko

Table of Contents

— CHAPTER ONE —

Going Fishing

Today was going to be a perfect day, thought Seth. For starters, dawn was mild and dry. Despite the early hour, he'd been ambitious to get going before Ma changed her mind about sending them fishing. Seth seldom had a chance to spend time alone with his older brother. He and Jed were usually too busy doing chores or minding their younger siblings. Not that going fishing wasn't a chore in its own way. Ma hoped they'd catch enough fish for dinner and have some left over to dry for the winter. Still, spending time alone with Jed was a treat.

"What do you figure Pa'll bring back from his trip?" Seth asked Jed.

"He's bound to bring back news about what's happening in the rest of the world. And you know he'll have a tall tale about his adventures at the trading post," answered Jed, chuckling.

"Do you remember the story about the time the syrup trapped him?" giggled Seth.

Silently, Seth speculated about Mount Saint Helens. Then he asked, "Pa, do you think Mount Saint Helens will erupt again? Do you think it could ever blow apart?"

Pa drew a deep breath and answered slowly, "I don't know, Seth, but I hope that if it does, it doesn't happen in our lifetimes."

Mount Saint Helens Today

Little did Seth and his family know that more than 100 years later, on May 18, 1980, Mount Saint Helens would erupt so violently that the north face of the mountain would collapse. That explosion would kill more than 50 people and cause great destruction.

For eighteen years, from 1986 to 2004, Mount Saint Helens lay dormant. Then on October 1, 2004, Mount Saint Helens, the smoking mountain, began to erupt once again.

Epilogue

Pa came home several days later. By then Mount Saint Helens had stopped rumbling and spewing ash and rocks into the air. The mudslide had swept away hundreds, maybe thousands, of trees, but it hadn't injured any people or livestock as far as they knew.

Jed's scorched eyelids were healing, thanks to Ma's care. Luckily, his eyes were not harmed.

Pa was relieved to find everyone safe. He'd been at the trading post when ash had started falling. A trapper had rushed in and told everyone that Mount Saint Helens was erupting. Right away, Pa had rushed back home, leaving his purchases behind.

"Not to worry, they'll still be there when I go back to get them," proclaimed Pa. "I didn't want to waste time loading up the wagon. I just wanted to get home to make sure you were all safe. As it was, it was slow going with the ash falling and covering everything so I couldn't recognize where I was! If I hadn't known what was happening, I would have thought gray snow was falling from the skies!"

Seth, Sarah, and Jed filled Pa in on their adventures. Jed and Sarah both said that if it hadn't been for Seth, they would never have made it home. Seth blushed from everyone's praise.

© 2007 Macmillan/McGraw-Hill

Eruption on the Mountain

"As I recollect," recounted Jed, "Pa said he'd been doing a fair bit of pondering at the trading post, trying to decide which of the fabrics Ma would like for a new dress and which ones he should buy for the little ones' smocks. He was mighty tired looking at all those bolts of cloth, so he leaned his elbows on the counter, looking left, right, up, and down, over and over, until finally he'd made his decisions. But when he tried to stand up, he couldn't budge! His elbows were stuck in a pool of syrup that he hadn't noticed was on the counter."

"And the syrup had hardened by the time Pa wanted to stand up, so he felt like a beetle trapped in pitch," finished Seth, nearly convulsed with laughter. "Do you remember how Pa showed us what had happened to him?"

Jed joined in Seth's mirth, mimicking Pa's efforts to free himself from the syrup. Seth thought that Jed could tell a story better than anyone else could, except for maybe Pa. With a light heart, Seth thought to himself that this was surely going to be a great day!

Suddenly Seth's good humor vanished as he heard his younger sister Sarah's plaintive cries, "Stop! Wait for me, Jed! Stop, Seth!"

Scowling, Seth barked, "What are you doing here? You're supposed to be at home!"

His harsh words didn't stop Sarah, who trotted up to them, red-cheeked and panting, "You forgot your lunch! Ma told me to bring you your lunch."

"Okay, you've brought it. Now go on back home!" ordered Seth.

"Seth, that's no way to thank Sarah," remarked Jed gently, smiling at his sister and taking the pail she handed him.

Sarah smiled back at Jed, and Seth grudgingly said, "Thanks, Sarah." Then he continued, "Now you'd better go on home."

Sarah replied, "Ma told me I could go with you and pick berries."

Seth's face crumpled. "But Jed and I have work to do! We have to fish!"

"I have work to do, too!" retorted Sarah hotly. "Ma wants me to pick berries while you fish."

Jed intervened in the blossoming dispute, just as he often did when squabbles erupted between his siblings. "I guess none of us will be lazing about today! But just think of the rewards for our labors. We'll have a delicious dinner of pan-fried fish followed by plump berries for dessert. We're honored to have you in our company, aren't we Seth?"

"I guess so," Seth admitted. Berries were one of Seth's favorite desserts.

Eruption on the Mountain

Sarah, still carrying the pail, let out a scream as she began to slide down the slope.

"Drop the pail!" yelled Seth.

"No!" yelled Sarah stubbornly as she tried to scramble up the embankment.

Impulsively, Seth hurled himself down the slope toward Sarah. He grabbed her with one hand and clutched a tree root protruding from the embankment with the other. Seth yanked Sarah up beside him and then pushed her toward Jed's outstretched arms. With Sarah safe, Seth scooted up the slope, barely escaping the bubbling river of mud, trees, and rocks that rushed past.

"Sarah, you should have listened to Seth and dropped that pail! Your life is more important than berries," scolded Jed.

Sarah stammered a tearful apology, and Seth surprised her with his kind reply, "That's okay, Sarah. Sometimes it's hard to know what to do."

An hour later, they reached home. If Seth hadn't known where they were, he'd have thought the ash-covered dwelling belonged to someone else.

Hearing her children's shouts, Ma opened the door and rushed out to greet them. She promptly led Jed into the house and ministered to his eyes while Seth and Sarah blocked the cracks around the door to keep out the ash.

16

"So, Seth, where shall we go fishing? Remember the glen partway up the mountain?" Jed asked. "We picnicked there last summer."

Did Seth remember! Their family had spent a glorious afternoon feasting, swimming, and listening to Pa tell tales. It had been one of the best days ever, and Jed knew Seth thought so.

"If that suits you, let's go there," said Jed. "But it's a long walk, so we'd best move along quickly."

Seth nodded eagerly, his good humor restored. He wished he could be more like Jed, who always knew the right things to say and do. In an effort to be like Jed, Seth refrained from telling Sarah to be obedient and not cause trouble. Maybe the day wouldn't be so bad after all.

5

CHAPTER TWO

The Mountain's Alive!

By midmorning Jed, Seth, and Sarah had reached the site of the previous summer's picnic. To Sarah's delight, they found a clump of blackberry bushes. As she carefully picked and sampled blackberries, her brothers quietly fished.

When Sarah had filled her pail with blackberries, she ambled over to the river to join her brothers. Her fingers were stained purple with blackberry juice, and so were her apron and her mouth.

"Did you save any for us, or did you eat them all?" laughed Jed when he saw his sister's face.

"You're all purple around the mouth," shrieked Seth with laughter. "You look just like a blackberry!"

As Sarah hastily washed her face in the cool river water, Jed noted the sun directly overhead and announced, "It must be about noon or so. We might as well break for lunch."

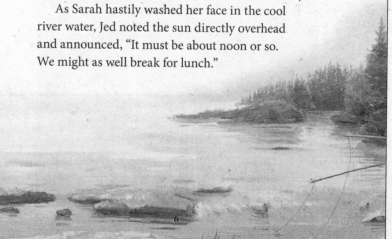

6

CHAPTER FOUR

Danger!

Guiding Jed by the arm, Seth carefully continued toward home along the trail they'd marked on their way to the glen. Their progress was slow, as the ash-filled air made it difficult to see the markings. Seth helped Jed around stones, tree roots, and other obstacles that they'd scrambled over that morning in their haste to reach the glen.

"Are you okay carrying everything, Sarah?" Seth called out. "We can leave things if they're too heavy and come back another day for the pails."

14

"Here, come with me, Jed," said Sarah, and her voice revived Seth, who immediately tried to make himself useful.

Sarah led Jed to a boulder, and Seth helped him sit down. As Sarah soaked her apron in the water, Seth whispered, "Does it hurt really badly, Jed? Can you see?"

With an effort to remain calm, Jed replied, "I think the sparks burned my eyes. They hurt, Seth. I can't open my eyes. I can't see!"

Sarah returned with her soaked apron and said, "Here, Jed. Let me cover your eyes with a wet cloth. Help me, Seth!"

Together Seth and Sarah wrapped Sarah's wet apron around Jed's eyes and the top of his head. If the situation hadn't been so dangerous, Seth would have laughed out loud. Jed looked like a partially wrapped mummy. As it was, Seth felt like crying, but he knew he mustn't. Jed was hurt, but things could have been much different. Thanks to Sarah's quick thinking and actions, Jed was alive.

Now Seth would have to be strong. He would have to do whatever Jed would have done. Seth would have to take care of all of them. It was up to Seth to lead them safely home, but could he do it?

© 2007 Macmillan/McGraw-Hill

Eruption on the Mountain

Jed distributed the lunch his mother had packed, and they ate greedily.

Then, pointing to the nearby mountaintop, Seth exclaimed, "Did you see that? The mountain moved!"

"It did not!" said Sarah.

"Sometimes smoke and fire come out of the top of that mountain," said Seth in a serious, quiet voice. "You see, that mountain's alive. It sleeps for a long time, and then it wakes up."

"It is not alive!" yelled Sarah. "You're just trying to scare me!"

7

"That's enough, Seth," chided Jed. "That mountain is called Mount Saint Helens. It's a volcano. Usually it's quiet, but I've heard that sometimes it's active."

Seeing the surprised look on Sarah's face, Jed explained, "I don't mean that the volcano gets up and moves around. But sometimes there are rumbling noises from deep within the mountain, and smoke and even flames shoot out of the top of Mount Saint Helens. Pa says that some of the Native Americans call it 'smoking mountain.' They have legends about it."

Seeing Sarah's worried face, Jed continued, "But don't you worry, Sarah. Look at how peaceful the mountain is. Just looking at it makes me want to lounge about in the sunshine. Why don't we all have a rest? Then we can get back to work."

The warm sun, their full bellies, and the hum of insects made them feel drowsy, and soon all three were fast asleep. As Sarah slept, she dreamed of the mountain trying to shake itself loose from the earth. Frustrated because it couldn't free itself, it started to rumble in anger and then to belch smoke.

Sarah, disturbed by her dreams, awakened first. She sat up and sleepily rubbed her eyes. Then she stopped, unable to believe her eyes. Was she awake or dreaming? A plume of smoke was rising from the top of Mount Saint Helens!

© 2007 Macmillan/McGraw-Hill

Eruption on the Mountain

"Here, come with me, Jed," said Sarah, and her voice revived Seth, who immediately tried to make himself useful.

Sarah led Jed to a boulder, and Seth helped him sit down. As Sarah soaked her apron in the water, Seth whispered, "Does it hurt really badly, Jed? Can you see?"

With an effort to remain calm, Jed replied, "I think the sparks burned my eyes. They hurt, Seth. I can't open my eyes. I can't see!"

Sarah returned with her soaked apron and said, "Here, Jed. Let me cover your eyes with a wet cloth. Help me, Seth!"

Together Seth and Sarah wrapped Sarah's wet apron around Jed's eyes and the top of his head. If the situation hadn't been so dangerous, Seth would have laughed out loud. Jed looked like a partially wrapped mummy. As it was, Seth felt like crying, but he knew he mustn't. Jed was hurt, but things could have been much different. Thanks to Sarah's quick thinking and actions, Jed was alive.

Now Seth would have to be strong. He would have to do whatever Jed would have done. Seth would have to take care of all of them. It was up to Seth to lead them safely home, but could he do it?

"Soak your handkerchiefs in this pond and tie them around your nose and mouth. You'll breathe better," ordered Jed.

Suddenly, hot rocks and a shower of sparks rained down around them. With an agonized shriek, Jed brought his hands to his eyes, moaning, "My eyes! My eyes!"

Seth stared in horror, unable to move even when sparks landed on Jed's shirt. Instantly, Sarah emptied a bucket of berries and filled it with pond water, dashing it over Jed to douse his smoldering shirt. It was Sarah, his little sister, who saved Jed. Seth felt awful. He, who was four years older than Sarah, should have done something, but all he did was stare.

12

Eruption on the Mountain

Quickly, Sarah scrambled over to where Jed lay sleeping and shook him. Then she grabbed Seth by the arm, shaking him and crying, "Jed, Seth, wake up! The mountain's on fire! It's alive! The mountain's alive! Wake up, wake up!"

Seth, still half asleep, thought that Sarah was playing a prank on him. Certain that she was getting revenge for his trying to scare her, Seth muttered, "Go back to sleep, Sarah!" Sarah in her frustration threw some cold water on her brother. That quickly revived him. Seth sat up. What he saw stunned him. His mouth agape, Seth could only sit and stare at the smoke rising from Mount Saint Helens into the turquoise sky.

9

Eruption

"What's going to happen now, Jed?" asked Sarah in a hushed voice.

"I don't know," answered Jed truthfully. Then, seeing the anxious looks on his siblings' faces, he continued, "I've heard that smoke sometimes puffs up from the mountain for days, and then the mountain goes back to sleep."

Sarah relaxed against her brother's side, and finally Seth spoke, "Do you think Pa knows any of those Native American legends about the volcano? I'd really like to hear one!"

"We'll ask him when he gets home," answered Jed with a smile, "but now I think we'd better start packing up. I think we've stayed longer than we should have. We have a long trek home, remember."

At the mention of going home, both Sarah and Seth begged to stay just a little longer.

"Please, Jed, can't we stay here just a little longer?" wheedled Sarah. "It won't take long to fill the empty pail with berries. I'll bake a blackberry pie just for you, Jed."

Seth had to hand it to Sarah. She sure knew how to cajole people into doing what she wanted. He wasn't at all surprised when Jed said, "All right, but we won't stay long."

10

As Sarah and Seth picked berries, Jed looked worriedly at the summit of Mount Saint Helens, pondering their next move. They really ought to head back. The cloud of smoke was getting bigger.

"Listen. Why aren't the animals making any sounds?" asked Seth.

The eerie stillness made them shiver, and Jed replied, "It's later than we thought. We've got to head home, otherwise we'll be out in the dark!"

As Jed strode over to pull the fish they'd caught from the river, a tremendous boom filled the air, and the earth trembled beneath their feet. Dark clouds and fiery sparks billowed from the mountain.

Ashen-faced and trembling, Sarah and Seth quickly grabbed their belongings as Jed shepherded them toward home. As they stumbled along the trail they'd marked, the air became dark and full of powdery smoke. The smell of rotten eggs filled the air. The vapors from the volcano made their eyes water and itch.

11

Calendar

_____

Monday	Tuesday	Wednesday	Thursday	Friday

Name _____

Calendar

Monday	Tuesday	Wednesday	Thursday	Friday

Name _____

Calendar

Monday	Tuesday	Wednesday	Thursday	Friday

Name _____

Calendar

Monday	Tuesday	Wednesday	Thursday	Friday

Name _____

Calendar

_____

Monday	Tuesday	Wednesday	Thursday	Friday

Name _____

Calendar

_____

Monday	Tuesday	Wednesday	Thursday	Friday

Name _____

Calendar

Monday	Tuesday	Wednesday	Thursday	Friday

Name _____

Calendar

Monday	Tuesday	Wednesday	Thursday	Friday

Name _____

Calendar

Monday	Tuesday	Wednesday	Thursday	Friday

Name _____

Calendar

_____

Monday	Tuesday	Wednesday	Thursday	Friday

Name _____

Credits

Unit 1 Week 3 *On Level From Dragonflies to Helicopters: Learning from Nature*
Cover: (bkgd) Aero Graphics, Inc./CORBIS. 1: (c) George Hall/CORBIS. 2: (bkgd) PhotoDisc/Getty Images. 4: (b) Bettmann/CORBIS. 3: (cr) AGStockUSA, Inc./Alamy Images. 4: (b) Joe McDonald/CORBIS. 5: (tr) Allnari Archives/CORBIS. 6: (t) Stone/Getty Images. 9: (b) Clouds Hill Imaging Ltd./CORBIS. 11: (tl) Kris Mercer/Alamy Images; (br) George Hall/CORBIS. 12: (b) Joe McDonald/CORBIS. 15: (t) Aero Graphics, Inc./CORBIS. 16: (br) Lynda Richardson/CORBIS. 17: (t) Bob Anderson/Masterfile. 18: (t) Anthony Bannister; Gallo Images/CORBIS. 19: (c) Dr. Jeremy Burgess/Photo Researchers, Inc. 21: (c) NASA/Roger Ressmeyer/CORBIS.

Unit 1 Week 4 *On Level Arts of the Navajo*
Cover: (bkgd) Karen Tweedy-Holmes/CORBIS. 1: (tc) Twin Rocks Trading Post. 2-3: (t) Vince Streano/CORBIS. 4: (b) Pete Saloutos/CORBIS. 5: (tc) Royalty-Free/CORBIS. 6: (t) Michael T. Sedam/CORBIS. 6: (c) Wittemann Collection, New York. 17: (tc) Royalty-Free/CORBIS. 6: (b) The Granger Collection, New York. 8: (all) Edward S. Curtis Collection/Library of Congress. 7: (b) The Granger Collection, New York. 9: (tc) Royalty-Free/CORBIS; (tr) Kevin Fleming/CORBIS. 10: (t) The Granger Collection, New York. 11: (c) Royalty-Free/CORBIS; (bc) Josef Muench/Northern Arizona University. 12: (c) Karen Tweedy-Holmes/CORBIS. 13: (c) Marilyn "Angel" Wynn/Nativestock.com. 14-15: (t) Twin Rocks Trading Post. 15: (tr) Twin Rocks Trading Post. 16: (b) The Granger Collection, New York. 17: (tc) #457550 Index Stock Imagery, Inc. 20: (tc) Diebold/CORBIS. 18-19: (tc) George B. Diebold/CORBIS. 20: (tc) George H. H. Huey/CORBIS. 21: (b) George H. H. Huey/CORBIS.

Unit 1 Week 5 *On Level Saving Peregrine Falcons*
Cover: (bkgd) PhotoDisc/Getty Images; (bkgd) Jim Zipp/Photo Researchers, Inc. 1: (t) Peter Arnold, Inc./Alamy Images. 2: (bl) Jim Zipp/Photo Researchers, Inc. (bkgd) Ralph Ginzburg/Peter Arnold, Inc. 4: (t) PhotoLink/Getty Images. 5: (c) Ron Austing/Photo Researchers, Inc. (bkgd) PhotoLink/Getty Images. 6: (bl) Jim Zipp/Photo Researchers, Inc. 9: (t) X. Eichaker/Peter Arnold, Inc. (t) USGS/NASA. (c) Jim Zipp/Photo Researchers, Inc. 10: (t) Frank Lane Picture Agency/CORBIS. (bkgd) PhotoDisc/Getty Images. 10: (b) Bettmann/CORBIS. (t) PhotoLink/Getty Images. 12: (bkgd) PhotoDisc/Getty Images; Howes/Wild Places Photography/Alamy. 8: (br) Peter M. Wilson/Alamy Images. 2: (t) Royalty-Free/CORBIS. (cr) Hemera Technologies/Alamy Images. 13: (b) Kennan Ward/CORBIS. 14: (t) Galen Rowell/Peter Arnold, Inc. 15: (tr) PhotoLink/Getty Images. 16: (b) Kennan Ward/CORBIS. 18: (t) PhotoLink/Getty Images. 20: (b) Galen Rowell/CORBIS. 20: (tr) Jim West/Alamy Images. 21: (t) Peter Arnold, Inc./Alamy Images.

Unit 2 Week 2 *On Level Stargazers: Astronomers in Ancient Times*
Cover: (bkgd) Royalty-Free/CORBIS; (br) Jim Wark/Peter Arnold, Inc. 7: (t) Chris Howes/Wild Places Photography/Alamy. 8: (br) Peter M. Wilson/Alamy Images. 1: (t) Royalty-Free/CORBIS; (cr) Hemera Technologies/Alamy Images. 2: (t) Royalty-Free/CORBIS. 4: (t) Royalty-Free/CORBIS. Hemera Technologies/Alamy Images. 5: (b) John Wong/Getty Images; (c) StockTrek/Getty Images. 6: (br) Jim Wark/Peter Arnold, Inc. 7: (t) Chris Howes/Wild Places Photography/Alamy. 8: (br) Peter M. Wilson/Alamy Images. 9: (t) Felix Stensson/Alamy Images. 10: (bc) Michael Freeman/CORBIS. 12: (b) Stock Connection Distribution/Alamy Images. 13: (t) Janet Wishnetsky/CORBIS. 14: (t) StockTrek/CORBIS; (tr) Bryan & Cherry Alexander Photography/Alamy; (t) Royalty-Free/CORBIS. 15: (t) Photodisc Collection/Getty Images. 16: (c) Bettmann/CORBIS. 17: (tr) FY 1404 Takyuddin and other astronomers at the Galata observatory founded in 1557 by Sultan Suleyman, from the Sehinsahname of Murad III, c.1581 (vellum), Turkish School, (16th century)/University Library, Istanbul, Turkey/www.bridgeman.co.uk. 18: (c) Paul Almasy/CORBIS. 19: (c) StockTrek/CORBIS. 20: (br) Gustavo Tomsich/CORBIS. (t) Royalty-Free/CORBIS. 21: (t) Bettmann/CORBIS. 21: (c) StockTrek/Getty Images.

Unit 2 Week 3 *On Level The Great Flood of 1993*
Cover: (bkgd) Brooks Kraft/CORBIS. 1: (t) FK PHOTO/CORBIS. 3: (c) Fritz Hoffman/The Image Works. 5: (bc) Najlah Feanny-Hicks/CORBIS SABA; (cl) Wally McNamee/CORBIS. 6: (t) AP Photo/Charlie Neibergall. 7: (bc) Brooks Kraft/CORBIS. 8: (b) Fritz Hoffman/The Image Works. 10: (t) FK PHOTO/CORBIS. 12: (bc) Sheffer Jim/CORBIS SYGMA. 13: (c) CORBIS. 15: (t) Fritz Hoffman/The Image Works. 16: (t) Najlah Feanny/CORBIS SABA. 18: (b) Reuters/CORBIS. 20: (tr) Miner Doug/CORBIS SYGMA.

Unit 2 Week 5 *On Level Sled Dog Heroes*
Cover: (bkgd) Paul A. Souders/CORBIS. 1: (c) 2005 Jeff Schultz / AlaskaStock.com. 2: (b) Troy Wayrynen/NewSport/CORBIS. 3: (cr) AGE Fotostock America. 4: (cr) Rob Howard/CORBIS. 6: (tr) Comstock Images/Alamy Images. 6: (t) Michael Mastan Historic Photographs/CORBIS. 8: (b) 2005 Jeff Schultz / AlaskaStock.com. 9: (b) 2005 Jeff Schultz / AlaskaStock.com. 10: (tl) Comstock Images/Alamy Images. 13: (tl) 2005 Jeff Schultz / AlaskaStock.com. 12: (b) 2005 Jeff Schultz / AlaskaStock.com.

Unit 3 Week 3 *On Level Energy: Problems and Solutions*
Cover: (bkgd) Richard Hamilton Smith/CORBIS. 1: (c) Honda Motor/Handout/Reuters/CORBIS. 2: (b) 1996 CORBIS; Original image courtesy of NASA/CORBIS. 3: (cr) Stock Trek/Getty Images. 4: (br) SSPL/The Image Works. 5: (tr) Dr. Marli Miller/Visuals Unlimited. 6: (t) Michael T. Sedam/CORBIS. 7: (tr) Gary Braasch/CORBIS. 8: (t) Robert Landau/CORBIS. 10: (t) Associated Press, World Wildlife Fund. 11: (t) NASA. 12: (cr) Photo Researchers, Inc. 13: (b) Photodisc Red/Getty Images. 14: (ll) Peter Arnold, Inc./Alamy Images. 15: (t) Jeff Greenberg/Photo Edit, Inc. 16: (tr) Photodisc Green/Getty Images. 17: (b) Richard Hamilton Smith/CORBIS. 18: (b) Honda Motor/Handout/Reuters/CORBIS. 19: (tr) Roger Ressmeyer/CORBIS. 20: (b) Michael Newman/Photo Edit, Inc. 21: (t) PhotoLink/Getty Images.

Unit 3 Week 4 *On Level Rock Art from the Stone Age*
Cover: (bkgd) Royalty-Free/CORBIS; (c) Time Life Pictures/Getty Images. 1: (c) Photo Edit, Inc.; (t) Royalty-Free/CORBIS. 3: (c) Réunion des Musées Nationaux/Art Resource, NY; (bkgd) Royalty-Free/CORBIS. 4: (t) CNP/MIN.CULTURE/CORBIS. 17: (bc) The Granger Collection, New York. (t) Royalty-Free/CORBIS. 18: (b) Royalty-Free/CORBIS. (bc) Pierre Vauthey/CORBIS SYGMA. (t) Royalty-Free/CORBIS; (b) Philippe Giraud/Goodlook Pictures/CORBIS. 5: (tr) National Geographic. 6: (b) SuperStock, Inc./SuperStock. 7: (tr) Dmitri Kessel/Time Life Pictures/Getty Images. 8: (b) Royalty-Free/CORBIS. (c) Photo Edit, Inc.; (c) Art Resource, NY. 9: (cr) Time Life Pictures/Getty Images. 10: (t) Royalty-Free/CORBIS. 12: (b) Réunion des Musées Nationaux/Art Resource, NY. 13: (c) Travel Ink/Alamy Images. 15: (b) Royalty-Free/CORBIS. (bc) The Granger Collection, New York. 16: (tr) Inc. 20: (tc) SuperStock, Inc./SuperStock. 21: (b) Pierre Vauthey/CORBIS SYGMA.

Unit 4 Week 1 *On Level Marla Runyan: In It for the Long Run*
Cover: (bkgd) Salloz Photography. 1: (c) David Nardini/Masterfile. 2: (tr) Jeffery Allan Salter/CORBIS. 5: (tr) Jerry Cooke/CORBIS. 7: (b) Stone/Getty Images. 8: (br) Rhoda Sidney/Photo Edit, Inc. 9: (tl) Tony Freeman/Photo Edit, Inc. 10: (r) John Gillmoure/CORBIS. 11: (tr) Jeffery Allan Salter/CORBIS. 12: (b) Richard Cummins/CORBIS. 13: (tl) Tony Duff/All Sport/Getty Images. 14: (c) Salloz Photography. 15: (tr) Bob Daemmrich/CORBIS. 16: (br) Salloz Photography. 17: (t) Jeffery Allan Salter/CORBIS. 18: (b) Reuters/CORBIS. 19: (cr) Comstock Images/Alamy Images. 21: (br) AP Photo/Harry Koundakjian.

Unit 4 Week 2 *On Level Jacques Cousteau*
Cover: (bkgd) Lawson Wood/CORBIS. 1: (c) David Nardini/Masterfile. 2: (bkgd) Image Bank/Getty Images. 3: (br) AFP/Getty Images. 4: (bl) Comstock Images/Alamy Images. 5: (t) Agence Images/Alamy Images. 6: (b) David Lawrence/Panoramic Images. 8: (t) The Mariners' Museum/CORBIS. 9: (tr) The Granger Collection, NY. 10: (t) Lawson Wood/CORBIS. 12: (tr) Colin Paterson/Getty Images. 13: (tl) Jonathan Blair/CORBIS. 16: (b) OAR/National Undersea Research Program (NURP); Univ. of Connecticut. 17: (t) Jeffrey L. Rotman/CORBIS. 18: (b) Georgette Douwma/Getty Images. 19: (b) David Nardini/Masterfile. 20: (b) Tim Davis/CORBIS. 21: (cr) AFP/Getty Images.

Unit 4 Week 3 *On Level Achievements in Business: Amadeo Giannini*
Cover: (t) Florida Photographic Collection/Florida State Archives. 1-2: (c) Florida Photographic Collection/Florida State Archives. 3: (t) AP Photo/Harvey Georges. 4: (b) CORBIS. 5: (t) Florida Photographic Collection/Florida State Archives. 6: (b) Bettmann/CORBIS. 8: (b) Florida Photographic Collection/Florida State Archives. 10: (b) Florida Photographic Collection/Florida State Archives. 11: (b) CORBIS. 13: (b) Florida Photographic Collection/Florida State Archives. 14: (br) Gordon Parks/Library of Congress. 15: (tl) Library of Congress, Prints & Photographs Division, Carl Van Vechten Collection. 17: (b) Bettmann/CORBIS. 18: (all) Bettmann/CORBIS. 21: (cr) North Wind/Nancy Carter/North Wind Picture Archives.

Unit 4 Week 4 *On Level Lance Armstrong: Racing into Bicycling History*
Cover: (bkgd) Duomo/CORBIS. 1: (b) Wolfgang Rattay/Reuters/CORBIS. 2: (b) Duomo/CORBIS. 5: (all) Duomo/CORBIS. 6: (tl) Duomo/CORBIS. (b) Tim De Waele/CORBIS. 8: (t) AP Photo/David Brauchli. 9: (b) Underwood & Underwood/CORBIS. 10: (t) Reuters/CORBIS. 11: (b) Photo/Tim Sheffer. 12: (tl) Reuters/CORBIS. 14: (b) Eric Gaillard/Reuters/CORBIS. 16: (t) Reuters/CORBIS. 19: (all) Tim de Waele/CORBIS.

Unit 3 Week 3 *On Level Energy: Problems and Solutions*
Cover: (bkgd) Jeff Schultz / AlaskaStock.com. 17: (tr) 2005 Jeff Schultz / AlaskaStock.com. 18: (bl) Paul A. Souders/CORBIS. 19: (cr) 2005 Jeff Schultz / AlaskaStock.com; (bkgd) Comstock Images/Alamy Images. 21: (b) Paul A. Souders/CORBIS.

Jeff Schultz / AlaskaStock.com. 15: (t) Comstock Images/Alamy Images; (br) Paul A. Souders/CORBIS. 16: (t) Comstock Images/Alamy Images; (br) 2005 Jeff Schultz / AlaskaStock.com. 17: (tr) 2005 Jeff Schultz / AlaskaStock.com. 18: (bl) Paul A. Souders/CORBIS.

Unit 4 Week 5 *On Level Crafts in Medieval Europe*
Cover: (bkgd) Francis G. Mayer/CORBIS. 1: (t) David Lees/CORBIS. 2: (b) The Granger Collection, New York. 3: (c) imagestopshop/Alamy. 5: (all) Gianni Dagli Orti/CORBIS. 6: (b) imagestopshop/Alamy. 7: (tl) akg-images; (cr) David Lees/CORBIS. 8: (t) imagestopshop/Alamy. 9: (b) Hulton Archive/Getty Images. 10: (b) The Art Archive/Issogne Castle Val d'Aosta/Dagli Orti. 11: (t) imagestopshop/Alamy; (tr) akg-images/Pirozzi. 13: (all) akg-images/British Library. 14: (c) imagestopshop/Alamy. 16: (b) Francis G. Mayer/CORBIS. 17: (tr) Bettmann/CORBIS 18: (all) Lee Snider/Photo Images/CORBIS. 20: (t) Gianni Dagli Orti/CORBIS. 21: (b) Bettmann/CORBIS.

Unit 5 Week 3 *On Level Behind the Scenes at the Treasury*
Cover: (bkgd) Alan Schein Photography/CORBIS. 1: (br) Brand X Pictures/Getty Images. 2: (b) Courtesy of the United States Department of Treasury. 3: (t) John Van Hassell/CORBIS SYGMA. 4: (br) Archivo Iconografico, S.A./CORBIS; (tr) Brand X Pictures/Getty Images. 5: (tr) The Granger Collection, New York. 6: (b) Hisham F. Ibrahim/Getty Images. 8: (cr) Reuters/CORBIS. 9: (b) Mike Theiler/Getty Images. 10: (b) Bettmann/CORBIS; (tr) Brand X Pictures/Getty Images. 11: (cr) United States Mint. 12: (br) John Van Hassel/CORBIS. 13: (tc) AP Photo/Treasury Department. 14: (bc) Mike Mosedale/Cartoon Stock. 15: (tr) Annie Griffiths Belt/CORBIS. 16: (tr) Brand X Pictures/Getty Images. 17: (tr) Comstock Images/Getty Images. 18: (t) J.B. Russell/CORBIS SYGMA. 19: (br) Bettmann/CORBIS. 20: (t) Alan Schein Photography/CORBIS.

Unit 5 Week 4 *On Level The Baseball Hall of Fame*
Cover: (bkgd) AP Photo. 1: (b) Ezra O. Shaw/Allsport/Getty Images. 2: (b)Photodisc/Getty Images. 3: (c) Bettmann/CORBIS. 4: (b) Index Stock Imagery, Inc. 5: (br) National Baseball Hall of Fame Library/MLB Photos via Getty Images. 6: (b) Ezra O. Shaw/Allsport/Getty Images. 7: (t) C. Borland/PhotoLink/Getty Images. 8: (br) Bettmann/CORBIS. 9: (tr) Kit Kittle/CORBIS; (b) C. Borland/PhotoLink/Getty Images. 10: (br) AP Photo/Tom Roske. 11: (tr) Ron Vesely/MLB Photos via Getty Images; (t) C. Borland/PhotoLink/Getty Images. 12: (tr) Ezsra O. Shaw/Allsport/Getty Images. 13: (b) C. Borland/PhotoLink/Getty Images; (br) Guy Motil/CORBIS. 14: (b) Reuters/CORBIS. 15: (t) C. Borland/PhotoLink/Getty Images; (tr) Bettmann/CORBIS. 16: (tr) Bettmann/CORBIS; (br) C. Borland/PhotoLink/Getty Images. 17: (r) AP Photo. 18: (br) AP Photo. 19: (b) AP Photo/Mathy Zimmerman. 20: (b) Kevin Fleming/CORBIS.

Unit 5 Week 5 *On Level Cesar Chavez*
Cover: (bkgd) Najlah Feanny/CORBIS. 1: (c) Bettmann/CORBIS. 3: (b) CORBIS. 4: (cr) Bettmann/CORBIS; (t) Kent Knudson/PhotoLink/Getty Images. 5: (b) Library of Congress. 6: (t)CORBIS. 7: (b) 1976 Bob Fitch/Take Stock; (c) Kent Knudson/PhotoLink/Getty Images. 8: (bc) 1976 Bob Fitch/Take Stock. 9: (t) Kent Knudson/PhotoLink/Getty Images; (tr) Bettmann/CORBIS. 10: (br) 1976 George Ballis/Take Stock. 11: (t) Kent

Knudson/PhotoLink/Getty Images; (c) Bettmann/CORBIS. 12: (br) 1976 George Ballis/Take Stock. 13: (t) Kent Knudson/PhotoLink/Getty Images; (b) Farrell Grehan/CORBIS. 15: (c) Bettmann/CORBIS. 16: (t) Kent Knudson/PhotoLink/Getty Images; (tr) Hulton-Deutsch Collection/CORBIS. 17: (br) Ted Streshinsky/CORBIS. 19: (b) Bettmann/CORBIS. 21: (tr) Najlah Feanny/CORBIS; (cr) AP Photo/U.S. Postal Service Handout.

Unit 6 Week 1 *On Level Stories on the Ceiling*
Cover: (bkgd) Bettmann/CORBIS. 1: (c) The Granger Collection, New York. 2: (bl) Arte & Immigani srl/CORBIS. 3: (r) Scala/Art Resource, NY. 4: (br) Scala/Art Resource. 5: (cr) John Heseltine/CORBIS; (r) Siede Preis/Getty Images. 6: (all) Alinari Archives/CORBIS. 9: (all) Alinari/Art Resource, NY. 11: (t) H. Wiesenhofer/PhotoLink/Getty Images; (b) Joe Ginsberg/Getty Images. 12: (bl) Bettmann/CORBIS; (bl) C Squared Studios/Getty Images. 13: (t) Siede Preis/Getty Images; (br) SuperStock, Inc./SuperStock 3804-397090-D-P27; (br) Glenn Mitsui/Getty Images. 14: (t) Joseph Barnell/SuperStock 2145-436615-1-P52B. 15: (br) The Granger Collection, New York; (br) C Squared Studios/Getty Images. 16: (c) Siede Preis/Getty Images. 17: (b) The Granger Collection, New York. 18: (t) Erich Lessing/Art Resource, NY. 20: (t) Joe Carini/The Image Works. 21: (c) Bettmann/CORBIS; (b) Robert Harding Picture Library Ltd/Alamy.

Unit 6 Week 3 *On Level Talking Pictures: A Mystery in Peru*
Cover: (bkgd) Yann Arthus-Bertrand/CORBIS. 1: (tc) Yann Arthus-Bertrand/CORBIS. 2-3: Wetzel and Company/Janice McDonald. 3: (c) Charles & Josette Lenars/CORBIS; (inset) AP Photo/John Moore. 4: Charles & Josette Lenars/CORBIS. 5: (cr) Richard A. Cooke/CORBIS; (t) Steven P. Lynch. 6: (b) Yann Arthus-Bertrand/CORBIS. 7: (t) Steven P. Lynch. 8: (br) 2005 by Robert Frerck and Odyssey Productions, Inc. 9: (tl) Yann Arthus-Bertrand CORBIS. 10: (bc) Bohemian Nomad Picturemakes/CORBIS. 11: (bkgd) Steven P. Lynch. 12: (t) Craig Aurness/CORBIS. 13: (b) Yoshio Tomii/Superstock. 14: (cr) AP Photo/Alejandro Balaguer. 15: (t) Steven P. Lynch. 17: (c) Danny Lehman/CORBIS. 18: (b) Yann Arthus-Bertrand/CORBIS. 19: (t) Roger Ressmeyer/CORBIS. 20: (cr) Photo by Larry Dale Gordon/Julian Nott. 21: (b) Yann Arthus-Bertrand/CORBIS.

Unit 6 Week 4 *On Level Spread the Word– Become a Publisher*
Cover: (bkgd) Royalty-Free/CORBIS. 1: (t) Felicia Martinez/Photo Edit. 2: (b) PhotoLink/Getty Images; (c) The Image Bank/Getty Images. 4: (b) Royalty-Free/CORBIS. 5: (tr) Image Ideas Royalty Free Photograph; (tl) Photodisc Green/Getty Images. 7: (t) Bob Daemmrich/Photo Edit. 8: (tl) Photodisc Green/Getty Images. 9: (b) Masterfile (Royalty-Free Div.). 10: (t) Jack Hollingsworth/CORBIS. 11: (b) Ariel Skelley/CORBIS. 12: (b) Felicia Martinez/Photo Edit. 13: (tl) Brand X Pictures/Getty Images. 14: (tl) Michael Newman/Photo Edit. 15: (b) Royalty-Free/CORBIS. 16: (all) Brand X Pictures/Getty Images. 17: (all) Brand X Pictures/Getty Images. 19: (t) Lucidio Studio Inc./CORBIS; (all) Brand X Pictures/Getty Images. 21: (t) Royalty-Free/CORBIS.